Separation of
Human Blood and Bone Marrow Cells

Separation of Human Blood and Bone Marrow Cells

Faieza M. K. Ali
Department of Pathology,
Medical College,
University of Baghdad,
Iraq
Formerly
A Postgraduate Candidate,
Department of Haematology,
University of Wales College of Medicine,
Cardiff, United Kingdom

WRIGHT
Bristol
1986

Published under the Wright imprint by
IOP Publishing Limited,
Techno House, Redcliffe Way, Bristol BS1 6NX.

British Library Cataloguing in Publication Data

Ali, Fajeza M. K.
  Separation of human blood and bone marrow cells.
  1. Cell separation   2. Blood cells
  3. Marrow cells
  I. Title
  611'.0181   QH585.C44

ISBN-0-7236-0698-6

Typeset by
Activity Ltd. Salisbury, Wiltshire.

Printed in Great Britain by
Adlard & Son Ltd., Dorking, Surrey

To my family, and especially to my mother and to the memory of my late father.

May God bless them.

There is nothing so capitivating as new knowledge

Peter Mere Latham (1789–1875)
Collected Works, Book 1, Chapter 51.

PREFACE

The field of cell separation continues to grow exponentially due to the ongoing need for efficient and reproducible methods to study the function and properties of different cell types. After several years' experience in cell separation and characterization, the world-wide response to my publications and the valuable contribution the established techniques have made to research projects of colleagues (and their frequent demand to obtain the fine technical details) have prompted me to prepare a detailed manuscript on the separation and identification of blood and bone marrow cells, using physical, immunological and haematological techniques which allow the recovery of viable and metabolically active cells. To broaden the scope of the book, a contributory chapter on cell culture has also been included. Details are given of micromanipulation techniques for cloning and harvesting of pure erythroid cells.

The publication is directed primarily to haematologists, immunologists, oncologists and cell biologists. In addition, I hope that it will be useful to other researchers who intend to apply cell separation in their work.

The book contains a whole range of methods which allow the reader to isolate and identify a particular cell type. The text is presented in a straightforward and logical style, thus enabling both experienced workers in this field and also those in training to carry out cell separation. Furthermore, emphasis is placed on the technical details of the procedure, their reproducibility and pitfalls. The information provided has largely been obtained from personal experience at the laboratory bench. The methods described here can be carried out in any laboratory with standard materials and equipment. In addition they can be used in conjunction with a Fluorescence Activated Cell Sorter (FACS) or an elutriation system.

This book should provide a unique instructive guide for the separation and identification of human blood and bone marrow cells and it should facilitate advancement in the field of clinical and biological research.

Faieza M. K. Ali

ACKNOWLEDGEMENTS

My sincere thanks go to Dr Salim Kaaba, Department of Organ Transplantation, University of Kuwait for his contribution of Chapter 5. Special acknowledgement is made for the editorial assistance of Dr Ann Covell, Department of Internal Medicine, Division of Hematology, College of Health, Science and Hospital, Kansas City, USA.

The bulk of this work formed part of an MSc Thesis submitted to the University of Wales, UK. The thesis was compiled with the help and supervision of Dr A. May and Professor A. Jacobs, Department of Haematology, University of Wales College of Medicine (UWCM). Some of the work in this book has previously been published in the *Journal of Immunological Methods*, **49** (1982) by F. Ali, A. May, G. McLaren and A. Jacobs; *British Journal of Haematology*, **53** (1983) by F. Ali, A. May, B. Jones and A. Jacobs, and *British Journal of Haematology*, **59** (1985) by F. Ali, A. P. Weetman and A. May.

Special thanks are made to the Medical College, University of Baghdad and to the Cultural Department in London for providing the support to make this publication possible.

I am grateful to Dr A. Al-Sumidaie for supplying me with his separation data, and to the members of the Haematology Department, UWCM for applying some of these separation methods and informing me about the results.

My thanks are due to Dr N. Matthews for reviewing part of this book and to Dr Faidyha M. K. Ali, T. Lynes and D. Jones for reading the manuscript.

For typing the draft and for the secretarial assistance, I wish to thank E. Cartwright, Eman and Wissam Mohammed Kamil, Khelod Al-Saffar, M. Doughty, Nedal Al-Debaj and Thekra Al-Dujalea. I wish also to acknowledge the help of the staff of the UWCM Library.

Finally, I am extremely grateful to my family, especially to Nabeel M. K. Ali, for providing the support and encouragement throughout the preparation of this book.

CONTENTS

Chapter 1

The Role of Cell Separation in Science and Medicine

1. THE NEED FOR METHODS OF CELL SEPARATION

The increasing interest in cell separation has been reflected by the many articles which have appeared in the fields of haematology, immunology and cell biology. Separation, identification and characterization of different cell types from mixed cell populations has accompanied and stimulated advances in biological and medical research during the last decade. For instance, during the 1970s researchers reported lymphocyte heterogeneity. The separation and analysis of lymphocyte subpopulations has led us to a much greater understanding of the cellular mechanisms involved in immunology (Kay et al, 1979; Gupta and Good, 1980). In addition, they have enabled more accurate diagnoses of the lymphocytic leukaemias (Gupta and Good, 1980), which is an important factor in therapeutic management. Lymphocyte subsets can be divided even further into different functional groups and therefore the development of cell separation methods will continue to make a significant contribution to this area of knowledge.

Cell separation techniques are required in many areas of medicine. In order to study metabolic derangement and responses to possible therapeutic agents in lymphoproliferative and myeloproliferative disorders, homogeneous cell populations are required. The use of isolated cells in transplantation is another pressing area where great benefits may be obtained. For example, removal of mature T-lymphocytes should alleviate graft versus host disease (GVHD). Separation procedures may be required that not only separate out one particular cell type but which also separate cells at different stages of differentiation. This would be necessary for the investigation of

1

metabolic abnormalities in cells exhibiting different stages of differentiation, such as the bone marrow precursors of peripheral blood cells.

Conventional heterologous antisera to different human cells are usually produced by immunization of an appropriate animal with the relevant cell type. These antisera need extensive absorption before use and it is frequently impractical to prepare large quantities of standardized highly specific antisera. This is, however, not the case with monoclonal antibodies, the production of which is an extremely valuable tool in all areas of biological research (Köhler and Milstein, 1975). This relatively new technique combines conventional immunological methods with somatic cell hybridization and the selection of appropriate hybrids. Hybrids formed by the fusion of myeloma cell lines with B-lymphocytes inherit the ability of the myeloma cells to grow indefinitely in culture (and in serial passage through inbred strains of mice) and also have the ability of B-lymphocytes to synthesize one single antibody with a given immunological specificity. Therefore cell separation methods can facilitate the production of the monoclonal antibody in three ways. Firstly, a highly purified cell population can be used for immunization, secondly the spleen cells exhibiting the required antibody specificity can be separated from the immunized spleen before hybridization, and thirdly the hybridoma with the required specificity can be more easily identified and isolated.

There are other areas where cell separation may be beneficial and some where it is essential. Some examples of the necessity of cell separation for investigation of the biochemistry and metabolism of human erythroblasts are described below.

1.1   GLOBIN SYNTHESIS STUDIES

Although it is only the reticulocytes in peripheral blood that synthesize globin, it is difficult to determine the α/β globin synthesis ratio where contaminating white cells are present. Globin synthesis is studied by the *in vitro* labelling of newly synthesized protein with ^{3}H leucine (Clegg and Naughton, 1965). White cell protein also incorporates this label and separates with β-globin chains on the ion-exchange column, therefore significantly increasing its specific radioactivity (Chalevelakis et al, 1976). Since α/β ratios need to be measured on haematologically normal people with $<1\%$ reticulocytes in order to establish a normal range, a method is required to enrich the percentage of reticulocytes with the concomitant removal of white cells. The problem of non-globin protein contamination is even greater if bone marrow cells are studied. Since most globin synthesis occurs in the erythroblast, this is the best cell for studying

some globin synthesis abnormalities and pure erythroblasts would be
valuable for this purpose.

1.2 RED CELL ENZYMOPATHIES

Some red cell enzymes have a much greater activity in reticulocytes
than in mature erythrocytes. For example, hexokinase is several times
more active in young reticulocytes than it is in the red cells (Valentine
et al, 1967). Diagnosis of some of the red cell enzymopathies therefore
requires comparison of the test sample with age-matched control cells,
whether enzyme activities or intermediates are measured. A method is
therefore required to separate red cells of different ages.

1.3 ERYTHROBLAST IRON METABOLISM

A great deal of work is being directed towards an understanding of
iron metabolism in the developing erythroblast in the hope that some
of the abnormalities, in particular in sideroblastic anaemia, might be
revealed. Previous studies have made use of unfractionated bone
marrow suspensions (May et al, 1982) but the results reflect the total
functional activity of a mixture of cell types. Any contribution from the
non-erythroid cells is therefore ignored. For some studies this
approach will be perfectly valid, but other bone marrow cells take up
iron from transferrin and are able to synthesize haem (Elder, 1980)
and ferritin (Shepp et al, 1972). In order to examine the properties of
the individual enzymes and proteins involved in haem and ferritin
synthesis, pure erythroblasts are required. Ferritin is considered to
play two major roles in iron metabolism: first, to prevent accumulation
of high concentrations of free iron within cells where it can cause
considerable damage, and second, to provide a reserve of iron which is
available for haem synthesis (Harrison et al, 1980). When immature
red cells are incubated with transferrin-bound radioactive iron some of
this iron is incorporated into ferritin (Romslo, 1980). The role of this
ferritin is currently in debate. It may be an obligatory intermediate in
the transfer of iron from transferrin to the mitochondrion for haem
synthesis, as suggested by Speyer and Fielding (1979) and Nunez et al,
(1977, 1980) or it might simply be acting as a store for trapping
intracellular iron in excess of haem synthesis requirements. Since
erythroblasts take up a large amount of iron for haemoglobin synthesis
they require an intracellular pool of ferritin (Mazur and Carleton,
1963; Brown and Theil, 1978; Konijn et al, 1979).

The relationship between globin synthesis and haem is important for
normal erythroid differentiation and this is thought to arise mainly
from a dependence of the initiation of globin synthesis on the presence
of haem, as described by Hunt (1976), although there is some evidence

to the contrary (Rutherford and Harrison, 1979; Peters et al, 1983a). In normal erythroid development this dependency has only been studied in reticulocytes and, since the synthesis of both haem and globin occurs mainly in the erythroblast, these studies should be pursued in pure erythroblasts.

1.4 THE DEVELOPMENT OF PERIPHERAL BLOOD CELLS FROM THEIR BONE MARROW PROGENITOR CELLS

Cell–cell interactions are important in the normal and abnormal differentiation of peripheral blood cells and these are thought to occur at a primitive stage in their development. There are a number of conflicting reports describing the effect of monocytes and T-lymphocytes on the growth of burst forming units-erythroid (BFU-E) from both peripheral blood and bone marrow. Rinehart et al (1978) showed that human monocytes suppressed erythroid colony formation of peripheral blood BFU-E: the number of erythroid colonies was inversely related to the number of monocytes added and more than 20% monocytes in the cells plated suppressed BFU-E activity completely. However, Lipton et al (1980a) found no inhibitory action of fresh viable monocytes on peripheral blood BFU-E formation, and null lymphocyte preparations contaminated with up to 84% monocytes were still able to show BFU-E formation provided that T-lymphocytes or T-lymphocyte conditioned medium was present. Mangan and Desforges (1980) showed that peripheral blood BFU-E proliferation was directly proportional to the T-lymphocyte concentration and inversely proportional to the monocyte concentration in culture. However, Lipton et al (1980b) and Linch et al (1982) have shown that T-lymphocytes are not required for the growth of bone marrow BFU-E. These interactions are likely to be affected by the culture conditions employed. A rational approach to this field would therefore include the development of methods for obtaining pure populations of cells. Purification of the bone marrow progenitors is not yet possible, but they can at least be greatly enriched (Linch et al, 1982). Obtaining purified cells for the study of cell–cell interactions will certainly contribute in demonstrating the role of different cell types in haemopoietic differentiation.

2. HOW TO APPROACH CELL SEPARATION

A knowledge of the properties and functions of cells will help the researcher in choosing or designing separation methods which should yield a particular cell type in a viable and metabolically active form. The characteristics and morphology of different cell types have already been described in great detail in many haematological books (Wintrobe et al., 1974; Thompson, 1979). The identification of cells can be achieved with either conventional or specific stains, as described in Chapter 2. Any cell which is removed from its normal environment is prone to loss of functional integrity. Therefore extreme care is required in choosing a suitable anticoagulant and suspension medium, as well as in regulating other conditions such as temperature, osmolality, and pH. With blood and bone marrow samples clotting should be prevented by the addition of an anticoagulant. Heparin has been the most widely used anticoagulant in cell separation studies. The optimum concentration is about 10–15 units/ml blood. At this concentration the clumping of leucocytes is also prevented. Heparin has been used for the separation of white cells by methods that involve phagocytosis. Oxalate, citrate, or ethylene diamine tetra-acetate (EDTA) are to be avoided because these agents interfere with phagocytosis (Kuper et al, 1961). Inhibition of complement action due to removal of calcium by EDTA has been reported by Thorsby (1967).

Another factor which needs consideration is temperature. Although most of the literature reports the separation of cells being carried out at 37 °C or at room temperature (25 °C) there seems to be little doubt that lower temperatures are preferable. Clumping of leucocytes can be avoided almost completely by cooling the blood and maintaining it between 0 °C and 5 °C. The survival of cells is increased at low temperature and 4 °C is regarded as the optimum. However, when cells are kept at a temperature above 12 °C it is important that the suspending medium contains glucose to support metabolism.

The separation medium must be iso-osmotic throughout the isolation procedure; for human cells the normal range of osmolality is 290–300 mmol/kg H_2O. A higher osmolality causes shrinkage of cells with alteration of their physical properties, such as density. At lower osmolalities the cells will swell and lyse. The pH of the medium or buffer must be maintained at around neutrality. In order to retain the metabolic integrity of the cells, the pH should be between 7·3 and 7·5. At non-optimum pH the metabolism will be adversely affected leading to cell death.

It is preferable to use aseptic conditions throughout the separation procedure. It is of course essential to sterilize all buffers, media and glassware when long-term culture is to be performed. Bacterial endotoxins will affect the viability of the cells. In addition, fungi and bacteria will compete for the nutrients of the media and therefore inhibit growth.

Available methods for cell separation exploit relative differences in physical, biological or chemical properties of cells.

The two main physical properties used to separate subpopulations of cells are density and size. Stokes' Law describes the rate of sedimentation of a spherical particle (cell) of a given diameter in a gravitational field (see Chapter 3 for details). The physical methods of separation offer many distinct advantages with respect to the retention of cell viability, the prevention of cell loss and the duration of the separation procedure. The functional and structural integrity of the purified cells are retained and high recoveries can be obtained. Since physical properties of cells can vary with their environment, separation must be carried out under strictly defined and controlled conditions, such as temperature and duration of centrifugation.

The biological methods of cell separation are more specific since they are based mainly on differentially expressed cell-surface markers. It is therefore essential to have previous knowledge of the specific cell marker to be exploited. One of the most commonly employed biological methods is the depletion of a subpopulation bearing one or more specific markers. This can be achieved by various techniques, for example by treating the heterogeneous suspension with an appropriate antiserum and complement, thereby lysing the unwanted cells. Other biological methods depend on the metabolic properties of cells or on growth and proliferation in specific culture media.

The chemical methods are based on a variety of surface properties, for example surface charge, membrane lipid composition and surface tension. Such characteristics can also be used in membrane research.

Generally, a combination of at least two of the above properties is exploited during the separation of a particular cell population.

3.   A USEFUL METHOD FOR CELL SEPARATION

In order to adopt a method for cell separation it should be analysed for its ability to fulfil certain criteria, and the stringency with which it meets these criteria will depend upon the needs of the investigator. Such criteria should include purity of the required cells, continued viability, metabolism unaltered by the separation procedure, reproducibility and the ability to obtain high yields. Other factors which need important consideration are the time taken to obtain the cells, the instrumentation required, the availability of reagents used and the facility of obtaining cells uncontaminated by bacteria, fungi or endotoxin.

In any method of cell separation, it is important to examine the cells both before and after the purification procedure. A provisional evaluation of their morphological integrity can be achieved by conventional microscopy on stained preparations. This also provides permanent records of the degree of purification that was obtained.

The viability test has been designed to show that the cell membrane of the viable cell is impermeable; the most often applied method is trypan blue exclusion. The best evidence for continued viability of the isolated cells is to show that they can grow and divide in culture. The functional and biological properties of the cells should also be measured. Functional activity of individual cells can be assayed by specific methods such as the ability to fix labelled antibody and rosette formation with red blood cells. Furthermore, various metabolic studies can be performed on the separated cells, such as their ability to synthesize protein.

Finally, it is important that the separation method provides some form of statistical analysis (mean percentage and standard deviation or standard error) of the recovered viable cells and the percentage purity of the wanted cells.

4. THE THEORY OF CELL SEPARATION METHODS AND SELECTED APPLICATIONS ON HUMAN CELLS

In this section the theories of the principal methods of cell separation have been described. It is hoped that this information, together with the technical details included in the following chapters, will help the reader to apply and/or design his own separation procedure. In addition, selected references on purification of human cells are included with each separation method to direct those readers who seek more information to the original sources.

Separation methods of human and non-human cells have been reviewed in many books. These include *Methods of Cell Separation*, Vols 1 and 3 (Ed. Catsimpoolas, 1977 and 1980); *Separation of Cells and Subcellular Elements* (Ed. Peeters, 1979); *Selected Methods in Cellular Immunology* (Eds. Mishell and Shiigi, 1980); and *Cell Separation Methods and Selected Applications*, Vols 1 and 2 (Eds. Pretlow and Pretlow, 1982 and 1983).

For separating a certain cell population numerous approaches have been tried, exploiting differences in cell size and density, membrane properties, and phagocytic or adherence ability. Of these, the most widely used is the density difference between the wanted cells and other cell populations present in the suspension.

4.1 DENSITY GRADIENT CENTRIFUGATION

Density gradient centrifugation is one of the most widely employed techniques for purification of cells and other biological particles. When using this separation method, the sedimentation rate of the particles at a fixed centrifugal force is proportional either to the size of the particles (rate-zonal centrifugation) or to the difference between their density and the density of the suspension medium (isopyknic centrifugation). Stokes' law for the sedimentation of a sphere in a centrifugal field explains the principles of density gradient centrifugation (*see* Chapter 3 for details).

A. Rate-zonal centrifugation

In this technique, the parameter that determines the separation is the size difference between the cells. According to Stokes' law, larger particles sediment proportionally faster through the gradient than small particles. The density range should be chosen so that the density of the cells is greater than the density of the medium at all points during separation. In addition, the centrifugation should be terminated before the separated cell bands mix together or reach the bottom of the tube.

Usually, separation of cells by using the gradient medium Percoll (modified colloidal silica, Chapter 3) is on the basis of density rather than on the basis of size differences. However, Pertoft et al (1979) separated the entire spectrum of blood cells (monocytes, lymphocytes, granulocytes, and erythrocytes) on a preformed Percoll gradient by applying both rate-zonal and isopyknic centrifugation.

B. Isopyknic centrifugation

In this technique, the density difference between the particles forms the basis of the separation, irrespective of size. The particles are sedimented through an increasingly dense medium (continuous or discontinuous density gradients, Chapter 3) during the application of a gravitational force (g) by centrifugation. The cells band in an equilibrium position after reaching a point where their density equals that of the gradient. Cells with a density greater than that of the gradient medium sediment to the bottom of the tube.

The gradient media are formed from materials (high molecular weight polymers with low osmolality and viscosity) which are not going to affect the morphology and functional integrity of the cells after the separation experiment. There are many gradient media which have been employed for the isopyknic centrifugation of cells. Ficoll is one of the most commonly employed gradient media for the separation of blood cells. A rapid separation of blood mononuclear cells and granulocytes by using a discontinuous gradient of Ficoll has been described by Böyum (1968) and by Madyastha et al (1982). The purification of blood eosinophils by sequential centrifugation through Ficoll–Hypaque has also been described (Novato-Silva et al, 1980; Tai and Spry, 1980; and Lee et al, 1982). Albumin gradients (Shortman et al, 1972) have been employed for the separation of lymphocytes and for the removal of cell debris and erythrocytes from the cell suspension. Corash et al (1974 & 1977) used Stractan gradients for the fractionation of blood erythrocytes of different stages of maturation and for the isolation of platelets from whole blood.

Furthermore, the use of the colloid Percoll as a density gradient medium has greatly improved the separation of human cells and other biological particles by centrifugal isolation. This is because Percoll is the only medium which produces gradients that are iso-osmotic throughout, has low viscosity and can separate cells isopyknically under normal conditions for osmolality and ionic strength. Percoll gradients have been used successfully for the separation of human monocytes (Pertoft et al, 1978 and 1980), and for the purification of T-lymphocytes (Ali et al, 1982). In addition, Percoll gradients (continuous and discontinuous) have been used by Gartner (1980) and de Simone et al (1982) to prepare highly enriched eosinophil fractions from normal blood and blood from parasitized patients. Hjorth et al (1981) and Kauffman et al (1983) described the separation of granulocytes and basophils by sedimentation of cells through discontinuous Percoll gradients. The purification of granulocytes and mononuclear cells by using continuous Percoll gradients has been reported by Segal et al (1980). Fractionation of human erythrocytes according to age difference by using step (discontinuous) and linear (continuous) density gradients of Percoll has been demonstrated by Spooner et al (1979) and Rennie et al (1979). Isopyknic centrifugation on a Percoll gradient together with the rosetting technique have been used to separate human natural killer cells (Timonen and Saksela, 1980; and Timonen et al, 1982) from heparinized blood or buffy coat.

Enrichment of normal and abnormal erythroblasts at different stages of maturation by using isopyknic centrifugation has been described by Ali et al (1983).

4.2   SEDIMENTATION RATE

Velocity sedimentation at unit gravity ($1g$) has become a more popular method for separating mammalian cells due to its simplicity and relatively large capacity. When using this technique at ambient gravity, size is the main parameter that determines the rate of sedimentation of cells as explained by Stokes' law (Chapter 3).

Separation at $1g$ is time-consuming, however, and aggregation of cells cannot be neglected. A suitable gradient which allows sedimentation of cells at low temperature ($4\,^{\circ}\text{C}$) will sometimes counteract this unwanted effect. Another problem encountered with the separation of cells by sedimentation velocity is a phenomenon known as 'streaming' which was proved to be due to the unequal viscosity at the interface of the applied cell suspension and the separating gradient. The causes of 'streaming' can be eliminated by adding to the cell suspension a substance with a high intrinsic viscosity, for example polyethylene oxide. The added material is used to increase the viscosity of the cell sample to the value of the viscosity of the gradient.

To achieve separation at 1g, a homogeneous cell suspension (containing up to 10^9 cells) is allowed to sediment for 4–9 h, without centrifugation, in a suitable density gradient medium that is slightly less dense than the cells but fairly viscous (Peterson and Evans, 1967; Miller and Phillips, 1969; Pretlow, 1971). Large cells sediment more rapidly and thus can be separated from the small cells by fractionation of the gradient.

The applications of velocity sedimentation at 1g include the separation of monocytes, lymphocytes, granulocytes, erythrocytes and platelets from human blood (Brubaker and Evans, 1969). Velocity sedimentation of blood cells onto a bovine serum albumin has been described by Catsimpoolas et al (1978). Their technique utilizes commercially available apparatus.

Applying velocity sedimentation onto a Ficoll gradient together with density gradient centrifugation on a Ficoll cushion and hypotonic lysis, Burghouts et al (1978) described the separation of immature myeloid cells from normal human bone marrow cells. In addition, a partial isolation of G_1 (post-mitotic rest phase) and S-phase (DNA synthesis phase) cells in patients with acute myeloid leukaemia was also achieved with this technique.

Haskill (1981) published a full report on the separation of biological particles by velocity sedimentation.

4.3   CENTRIFUGAL ELUTRIATION

Several methods for separating cells on the basis of differences in sedimentation velocity have been developed, for example density gradient centrifugation and velocity sedimentation at unit gravity. Centrifugal elutriation is another technique to be applied in this area. This method is finding a place among other separation procedures as a gentle method for preparing a fraction enriched for one specific cell type.

To apply this technique, a homogeneous cell suspension is injected into the elutriation system. In the chamber of an elutriator, the cells are subjected to two opposite forces resulting from the centrifugal sedimentation velocity and from the streaming velocity of a buffer flowing through the elutriation system in the centripetal direction. The sedimentation velocity is mainly influenced by the size of the cells, while the streaming velocity is independent of cell size. The special design of the separation chamber allows the generation of a gradient of flow rate, decreasing towards the centre of rotation. Specific cell types of a given size can be sequentially washed out of the rotor, mainly according to their size, by increasing the flow rate of the buffer in an incremental pattern or decreasing the centrifugal force. The cells will remain in the chamber if the two forces are equal. Centrifugal elutriation has a very high cell capacity (up to 10^9) and avoids the use of viscous, cytotoxic or hypertonic gradient materials.

Centrifugal elutriation has been applied for separating blood cells, such as monocytes and their subsets (Sanderson et al, 1977; Norris et al, 1979; Weiner and Shah, 1980; Contreras et al, 1980), T- and B-lymphocytes (Griffith, 1978; Berger and Edelson, 1979), granulocytes (Kurtz et al, 1979), and erythrocytes of different stages of maturation (Sanderson et al, 1975). This technique has also been utilized for the enrichment of human bone marrow cells and especially the myeloid cells (Meyskens et al, 1978 and 1979).

A more extensive discussion on the use of centrifugal elutriation in cell separation has been reported by Meistrich (1983).

4.4   CELL ADHERENCE

Most investigators make use of the adherent properties of some cells (e.g. monocytes, granulocytes and some subsets of lymphocytes) to certain materials packed into columns (adherence columns) or to plastic surfaces such as Petri dishes, to separate these cells from the cells that do not adhere firmly. The surface stickness of the cells is not well understood but is very dependent on the conditions used to achieve adherence, for example time, temperature and choice of culture dishes.

Active adherence can be induced by incubating the viable cells at 37 °C for a certain length of time (10–30 min) in the presence of serum as a source of Ca^{2+} and Mg^{2+}. The other type of cell adherence is physical (passive) adherence in which the cells should be left at 4 °C where, in this case, active adherence effects are eliminated. However, the major disadvantage of separating cells by adherence is the difficulty encountered in recovering the adherent cells from the surface into the suspension, which may be essential for further investigations. Several techniques have been suggested to recover adherent cells, such as scraping with a rubber policeman (bulb) at 4 °C, and washing with EDTA-containing medium. Detaching the adherent cells from the dish by scraping or by the use of chemicals may affect cell function in experimental systems. An alternative procedure for separating adherent cells which reduces the possibility of impairing cell function is by density gradient centrifugation, see Chapter 3.

Separation of blood cells by adherence columns includes the isolation of adherent monocytes from lymphocytes by passing over nylon wool columns, which also depletes B-cells and suppressor T-cell subpopulations (Levis and Robbins, 1972; Greaves and Brown, 1974); rayon wool columns (Kirchner et al, 1974; Oehler et al, 1977); glass bead columns (Shortman et al, 1971; Koller et al, 1973; Summers et al, 1974); G-10 bead columns (Ly and Mishell, 1974; Jerrells et al, 1980; Chien and Ashman, 1984). Jerrells et al (1980) reported a comparative study of the depletion of blood monocytes by using a Sephadex G-10 column method with other commonly applied procedures for the removal of monocytes. If a cell adherence technique is performed to collect monocytes, contamination with adherent B-lymphocytes and granulocytes (if present) will reduce the purity of the eluted monocytes. However, the presence of a higher concentration of serum (20–40%) can limit B-cell adherence to plastic and glass, but the removal of granulocytes can be achieved by incubating the adherent cells for 24 h at 37 °C before elution (Kenneth, 1981).

Nylon wool columns are especially useful for the preparation of non-adherent T-lymphocytes, since the procedure depletes adherent B-lymphocytes as well as monocytes (Danilovs et al, 1980). Further, Froelich et al (1983) reported the enrichment of natural killer cells (up to 90% purity) by incubating the non-adherent lymphocytes (obtained by adherence of cells to nylon wool) with Leu-1 monoclonal antibody and then mixing them with antibody-coated bovine erythrocytes. The pelleted cells were then centrifuged on a Ficoll cushion and the interface cell layer was found to be enriched for cells possessing natural killer activity. Blood eosinophils have also been purified from neutrophil-eosinophil enriched fractions by adherence to nylon wool (neutrophils usually adhere to nylon wool, while eosinophils do not) (Parrilo and Fauci, 1978; Koeffler et al, 1980).

In addition, adherence of leucocytes and platelets to cellulose has been used by Beutler et al (1976) and Ali et al (1983) to enrich blood reticulocytes and to prepare leucocyte-depleted erythrocyte fractions.

Since monocytes have a tendency to adhere to plastic surfaces (e.g. Petri dishes), this property can be used to isolate monocytes from non-adherent cells and to prepare pure lymphocyte fractions (Horwitz and Garrett, 1977; Gadeberg et al, 1979; Kumagai et al, 1979).

Some of the above adherence methods are discussed in Chapter 6.

4.5 PHAGOCYTOSIS

Cell populations such as monocytes and granulocytes have the ability to phagocytose solid particles, for example iron and latex particles. The phagocytic cells can also ingest antibody-coated or modified red cells obtained from homologous (human) or heterologous species, for example rabbit or sheep. This phenomenon of phagocytosis has been found useful for the depletion of phagocytic cells from other cells present in the suspension.

Phagocytosis can be achieved *in vitro* by incubating the cells at 37 °C for 45–60 min in the presence of serum as a source of Ca^{2+} and Mg^{2+}. Continuous and gentle mixing of the cell mixture is required for the efficient ingestion of the particles. In addition, if the particles are coated by IgG or complement, a higer percentage of cells will phagocytose the particles. Following phagocytosis, cells containing the particles can be sedimented by many techniques (e.g. centrifugation on a density gradient) due to their increased density.

Since some of the adherence techniques (Section 4.4.) also deplete adherent lymphocytes (Nathan et al, 1977), removal of phagocytic cells may be made selective by allowing them to ingest carbonyl iron particles. The iron-containing cells can then be removed by centrifugation on a Percoll or Ficoll cushion or by a magnetic field.

Carbonyl iron depletion of monocytes from whole blood has been reported by Rothbarth et al (1976), while Oehler et al (1977) described the removal of monocytes from blood mononuclear cells. Further, Sher and Glover (1976) reported the enrichment of blood eosinophils (up to 98%) by incubating the cell mixture (neutrophils and eosinophils) with carbonyl iron. The iron-containing neutrophils were then removed by magnet.

Phagocytosis of carbonyl iron and protein A-coated red cells by blood and bone marrow phagocytes is discussed in Chapters 3 and 6.

4.6   RED CELL ROSETTING

Separation of cells on the basis of presence of specific cell markers is one of the most reliable methods for positively selecting the desired cells. One of the applications in this area is the separation of lymphocyte populations via the technique known as 'rosetting' in which the cells form structures called rosettes. A rosette is a single lymphocyte which is attached to three or more red blood cells. Rosetting of the cells can be achieved by pelleting a certain ratio of lymphocytes and native or antibody-coated red cells under optimum conditions and in the presence of serum. After gentle resuspension of the mixture, if a subpopulation of lymphocytes bears receptors for a naturally occurring molecule or a previously attached ligand on the erythrocytes, these cells then bind the erythrocytes to form rosettes. This technique is frequently used for the negative or positive selection of cells by taking advantage of the differences in density and size between the rosetted and the non-rosetted cells. The rosetted cells may be recovered either by disruption of the rosettes or by hypo-osmotic lysis of the red cells attached to the lymphocytes (Platsoucas and Catsimpoolas, 1980c).

The most familiar rosette-forming cells are peripheral blood T-lymphocytes (Jondal et al, 1972) which form spontaneous rosettes with uncoated sheep red blood cells (E-rosettes). In addition, 50% of blood B-lymphocytes bind directly to mouse red blood cells to form rosettes (M-rosettes) (Stathopoulos and Elliot, 1974; Gupta and Grieco, 1975; Catovsky et al, 1976; Cherchi and Catovsky, 1980).

Further, it has been suggested that the morphologically termed 'large granular lymphocytes' in the lymphoid cells have an association with human blood natural killer cell activity (Timonen et al, 1981; Ortaldo et al, 1981; Abo and Balch, 1981; Luini et al, 1981). To study the natural killer phenomenon, large granular lymphocytes were separated from the lymphoid fraction (depleted from monocytes and B-lymphocytes) by centrifugation on a discontinuous Percoll gradient. The top cell fractions were then collected and depleted of E-rosette-forming cells. The remaining cells were found to contain up to 90% large granular lymphocytes. (Timonen and Saksela, 1980; Timonen et al, 1982).

Antibody-coated or modified red blood cells (i.e. carrying a ligand specific for a cell surface receptor) have also been used by many investigators to separate lymphocyte subpopulations by rosetting. A solution of chromic chloride is usually used for binding the ligand to the red cells and then those cells carrying the receptors are specifically rosetted (Ling et al, 1977; Parish and McKenzie, 1978). Purified human T-lymphocytes have been fractionated into T-helper (T_μ) and T-suppressor cells (T_γ) by rosette formation with ox erythrocytes coated respectively with rabbit IgM or IgG anti-ox red blood cell antibodies. The remaining cells which fail to form rosettes with both types of coated ox erythrocytes were classified as T_ϕ (Moretta et al, 1976 and 1977; Gupta and Good, 1978; Gupta et al, 1978). Further, complement-receptor-bearing lymphocytes have been rosetted by using sheep erythrocytes coated with the appropriate amount of heterologous IgM rabbit-anti-sheep red cell antibodies (Bianco et al, 1970; Parish and Hayward, 1974).

Some of the above rosetting techniques are detailed in Chapters 2 and 6.

4.7   LYSIS BY SPECIFIC ANTISERA AND COMPLEMENT

Elimination of distinct cell populations from a cell mixture by complement-mediated lysis (direct or indirect) can be used for the selective depletion of the unwanted cells. The unlysed cells remain intact and the method is, therefore, an example of negative selection.

This technique depends mainly on the availability of a specific antiserum against one or more markers present on the surface of the cells. Cell lysis can be achieved by incubating the cell mixture with the appropriate volume of antiserum and complement. Cells that possess the markers (e.g. antigens) will bind the antibodies. Following antigen-antibody binding the first component of the complement binds to the antigen-antibody complex, triggering a chain reaction of complement binding and activation involving the nine plasma proteins of the complement system; ultimately the final component binds and is inserted into the cell membrane, causing it to become leaky. Water is taken up into the cell and it lyses. The remaining nuclear material and cell debris can be removed by centrifugation on a density gradient, filtration and/or digestion (Cantor et al, 1972; Berridge and Okech, 1979; and Ali et al, 1983).

Direct complement-mediated lysis applies only to antibodies (e.g. monoclonal) which are of an immunoglobulin subclass that binds complement, for example mouse IgG_{2a} or IgM. The indirect method is useful with antibodies which are of an immunoglobulin subclass that does not bind complement, for example mouse IgG_1. In the latter technique, cells are incubated with the first antibody (e.g. mouse antiserum against the surface antigen) followed by a second incubation with the other antiserum (e.g. rabbit- or goat-anti-mouse antibody) which binds complement (Ledbetter et al, 1980).

Using complement-mediated lysis, it is essential to carefully select a suitable source for complement to avoid undesired effects on the unlysed cells. Serum sources have sometimes proved toxic to cells, therefore heterologous serum (e.g. rabbit or guinea-pig) should be pre-titrated for specific dependent cytotoxicity and for non-specific lysis against the desired cells. For studies which employ functional assays, additional screening is required. Ali et al (1983 and 1985) used autologous serum or plasma as a source of complement to lyse the donor's own bone marrow cells, to prepare erythroblasts and malignant plasma cells respectively. In culture, erythroblasts prepared in this way divided and differentiated. Further, the unlysed malignant plasma cells were able to synthesize and secrete paraprotein as detected by the plaque assay (Chapter 4). Compatible homologous serum or plasma may be the best alternative if autologous serum is unobtainable. However, in contrast to autologous serum, homologous serum as a source of complement may lower the viability of the remaining cells (F. Ali, unpublished data). In addition, the antibodies (monoclonal or polyclonal) should be tested at several dilutions to determine the amount required for optimum lysis under the individual laboratory's conditions.

Complement-mediated lysis has been applied to deplete blood T-lymphocytes by anti-θ antiserum (Takahashi et al, 1971). Falkoff et al (1982) described T-cell depletion from preparations of E-rosette negative blood mononuclear antibody by lysis with a monoclonal antibody (pan T) against T-cells. The resulting cell populations were found to be enriched for B-cells and monocytes. Removal of B-lymphocytes by using anti-immunoglobulin antiserum has also been described (Takahashi et al, 1971; Gmelig-Meyling et al, 1974).

Lysis of normal and sideroblastic bone marrow cells to prepare fractions enriched for erythroblasts, using both monoclonal and locally raised polyclonal antiserum against blood mononuclear cells, has been described by Ali et al (1983). Purification of malignant plasma cells from bone marrow of patients with myelomatosis by using the anti-mononuclear cell antiserum has also been reported by Ali et al (1985). Detailed technical information on bone marrow cell lysis has been included in Chapter 4.

A list of monoclonal antibodies against human cells, some of which can be used for complement-mediated lysis, may be obtained from Becton Dickinson.

4.8   AFFINITY SELECTION OF CELLS

Affinity chromatography and cellular immunoabsorbent methods are currently used for the separation or depletion of cells bearing distinct cell surface markers. Affinity methods depend mainly on the presence of specific cell surface antigens (e.g. immunoglobulin molecules, histocompatibility or blood group antigens), or receptors expressed on certain cell populations that can bind or adhere to an immobilized specific cell-surface ligand (e.g. antibodies to surface antigens, receptors or hormones). Immobilization of the ligand is usually achieved by applying a solid-phase supportive material (immuno-absorbent) to which the ligands are chemically bound by covalent linkage, or absorbed by adherence. Non-specific adherence of cells to the immobilized ligands can be reduced, in comparison to the selective binding of the desired cells, by proper treatment of the solid supports and adjustment of the conditions according to the nature of the ligand-cell surface receptor reaction. To recover the cells which were bound to the immobilized ligand, several techniques have been applied, such as the addition of a competitive binder, or changing the conditions so that the ligand-receptor bond becomes unstable (Platsoucas and Catsimpoolas, 1980d).

A number of substances have been used as solid-phase immuno-absorbents, such as glass beads and Degalan (Wigzell, 1976a and b), Sephadex G-200 (Schlossman and Hudson, 1973), Sepharose 6MB (Ghetie et al, 1978). These solid-phase immunoabsorbents are mostly used in the form of affinity chromatography columns in which purification is achieved through specific reaction or adherence between an affinity absorbent and the cell suspension to be purified. The non-adherent cells pass freely through the column. However, polystyrene plastic Petri dishes (Kedar et al, 1974) have also been used as flat surface immunoabsorbents from which the unbound cells are removed by gentle aspiration and washing. In principle, the solid-phase fractionation of cells on plastic Petri dishes, or 'panning', consists

of precoating polystyrene dishes with antigens, antibodies, immunoglobulin complexes, or antigen-antibody complexes (ligand-coated
dishes). The conditions should be standardized to allow specific
interactions between a component on the cell surface membrane and
the immobilized ligand attached to the surface of the dish. The
non-adherent cells can then be removed by gentle aspiration and
washing (Fong, 1983). In addition, affinity selection of cells can be
applied by using chemically modified fibres as solid-phase supports
(Edelman et al, 1971; Phillips et al, 1980). Modification of the fibres is
achieved by coating them with antigens, antibodies or lectin (Edelman
et al, 1971). Chemically modified fibres and surfaces can be used to
immobilize cells so that their relative position can be controlled,
recorded and rearranged under a variety of experimental conditions
(Edelman et al, 1971; Edelman and Rutishauser, 1974). This
application has many advantages, such as evaluating cell–cell interactions and cell mobility.

  Separation of cells on the basis of affinity is theoretically simple but
in practice is subjected to a number of difficulties. There may be
insufficient numbers of the cell surface molecules to enable stable
binding. The arrangement or properties of these receptors may be
inappropriate for the binding of cells to a solid support. Many solid
supports exhibit a natural adhesiveness for cells or have a physical
configuration that traps cells non-specifically. Furthermore, it may be
difficult to remove the bound cells from the solid support without
causing damage to the cells.

  Human B-lymphocytes (with surface immunoglobulin) and non-B-
lymphocytes have been separated by using Sephadex G-200 rabbit-
anti-human F(ab)$_2$ columns where T- and null lymphocytes pass
through the columns, while B-cells bind to the immunoabsorbent
materials (Chess et al, 1974; Chess and Schlossman, 1976 and 1977).
Columns packed with Sepharose pre-treated with the third component of the complement (C_3) have been used for the separation of
complement receptor-bearing lymphocytes (Casali and Perussia,
1977). The bound complement-receptor-positive lymphocytes were
recovered from the column by elution with a rabbit antiserum to
human C_3.

  Targan and Jondal (1978) reported the separation of Fc positive
lymphocytes. Their method employs the use of plastic dishes coated
with human IgG-rabbit-anti-human IgG antiserum for the fractionation of human blood effector lymphocytes (effector in natural killer
cytotoxic assays and in antibody-dependent cell-mediated cytotoxicity). The solid-phase selection of lymphocytes on monoclonal
antibody-coated dishes, or panning, has provided a valuable preparative method for purifying and enriching cell subsets. Applying this
technique, the separation of T-cell subsets (T-helper and T-suppressor

which bear receptors for IgG or IgM molecules respectively) has been reported by Fong et al (1981), Engleman et al (1981) and Tsoi et al (1982). They employed the use of Petri dishes coated with monoclonal antibodies specific for T-helper and for T-suppressor cells. Further, the purification of human immunoregulatory T-cells by the panning technique has been found useful for the assessment of T-cell function in human auto-immune disease states, for example rheumatoid arthritis (Tsoukas et at al, 1980).

Phillips and Babcock (1983) reported the preparation of monoclonal antibody (NKP-15) against natural killer (NK) cells and granulocytes. NKP-15 was then used for phenotypic characterization and for depletion of NK cells by panning.

The separation of blood basophils using Percoll gradients and panning techniques has been described by Landry and Findlay (1983).

Landreth et al (1982) reported the enrichment of surface Ig-negative human marrow cytoplasmic μ-chain-positive lymphocytes which were considered to be the immature precursors of B-lymphocytes. This was achieved by using monoclonal antibodies against murine B-lymphoma cells and affinity purified mouse-anti-rat Ig-coated dishes for cell depletion and recovery. This method should be found useful, for example, for the purification of pre-B-cells in order to study the requirement of B-lymphocyte maturation *in vitro* and for investigations of auto-immune and immunodeficiency disorders.

Separation of B-lymphocytes on the basis of their affinity to adhere to nylon fibres, giving an effluent population of highly enriched T-lymphocytes and 'null' cells, has been described by Danilovs et al, (1980).

Positive and negative selection of cells by affinity methods are included in Chapter 6.

4.9   CONTINUOUS FLOW CELL SORTING

Positive or negative selection of cells has been made possible by the development of a high-speed flow-system, a cell separation method for sorting and analysing individual cells. Separation of cells is on the basis of size and on the presence of specific cell surface markers, that is on physical and biochemical properties. Therefore, this system makes possible multiparameter measurement of each cell within a heterogeneous cell mixture. Sorting of a specific cell subpopulation provides cells for use in further experimental studies, such as *in vitro* culture and for analysing distinct cellular properties. There are numerous successful applications of flow-system technology to cell analysis and sorting, and the range of applications of this technique will continue to expand as both the preparation and staining methods of cells are advanced.

Using Fluorescence Activated Cell Sorter (FACS), the cells can be rapidly analysed (up to 10^7 cells/h) and separated individually for size (as measured by light-scattering or electronic volume) and fluorescence (intensity, colour or polarization). Evaluation of measured criteria against pre-selected properties form the basis for physical sorting of certain subpopulations of cells.

The general principle of sorting cells by using FACS is as follows. A fluid stream containing the single-cell suspension (stained with fluorescent dyes bound to specific cellular components) is introduced into a flow chamber. On entering the chamber, the fluid stream passes through a small ultrasonically vibrating nozzle which causes the stream to break, forming regularly spaced droplets of uniform size containing the cells. The beam from an argon-ion laser intersects the cell stream just below the nozzle. As the cells pass, one at a time, through the focused beam they scatter some of the light and, if labelled, they also fluoresce. Therefore, the presence of the cells is detected by a characteristic light-scatter signal and by one or more fluorescence signals. Light scattered by cells provides information on size and internal structure, whilst fluorescence yields quantitative information on constituents to which the stains are bound. Each cell is individually characterized by the intensity of the light it scatters and by the intensity, colour or polarization of fluorescence emitted while it is in the laser. These optical signals are amplified and converted into electrical signals by suitable photodetectors. The signals are then processed by a computer and the resulting data are displayed in a variety of ways, for example a profile histogram (number of events versus pulse height). For sorting the cells, characteristic signals from a single cell are analysed to determine whether or not the cell meets certain investigators' selected criteria. The droplets containing the desired cells are extracted from the main droplet stream by changing it electrically and can then be sorted into appropriate containers as they fall between positively and negatively charged plates. Uncharged droplets are collected in a separate container.

The applications of automated cell analysis and sorting are numerous, ranging from single-parameter to complex multiparameter analysis employing a computer-based system. Flow cytometry and sorting have been applied extensively to problems in cell biology and clinical research. The majority of studies to date have dealt with mammalian cells; however, subcellular organelles (e.g. nuclei, chromosomes and mitochondria) have also been sorted successfully. About 80% of all experiments with flow systems have dealt with the measurement of DNA (Arndt-Jovin and Jovin, 1978).

Sorting of fluorescently labelled cells has been used by Julius et al (1972) to demonstrate that antigen-binding cells are precursors to antibody-producing cells. Cell separation using FACS involving T-

and B-lymphocytes has also been described (Epstein et al, 1974; Kreth and Herzenberg, 1974; Cantor et al, 1975). Melamed et al (1972 and 1973) used acridin orange dye (to provide quantification of relative cellular RNA content) to characterize leucocytes from patients with leukaemias, lymphomas and other neoplasms. In addition, they have studied instrumental differential blood cell counts from patients undergoing chemotherapy. Kaplow and Eisenberg (1975) and Kaplow et al (1976) used light-scattering and absorption measurements to study and classify non-specific esterase- and peroxidase-positive leucocytes.

Studies on human bone marrow cells have also been reported by many workers. Beverley et al (1980) submitted monoclonal anti-myeloid (TG-1) antibody and complement-lysed bone marrow cells to cell sorting on the basis of light-scattering and were able to obtain erythroblasts of 94% purity in one fraction and to enrich haemopoietic progenitor cells in the other fraction. Robinson et al (1981) reported the preparation of human erythroblasts using monoclonal anti-glycophorin antibody with FACS. Cell suspensions containing over 90% erythroblasts were obtained in the glycophorin-positive fraction.

A review of automated cell sorting with flow system has been reported by Steinkamp (1977), Arndt-Jovin and Jovin (1978) and Price et al (1979).

4.10 PHASE PARTITION

Phase partition is a method for separating cells according to their surface chemistry (surface charge, bearing of specific receptors, lipid composition of cell membrane, hydrophobicity and surface tension). The phase systems are not detrimental to cells and these cells can then be recovered for further experimental studies, such as *in vitro* culture or metabolic studies.

If two immiscible water-soluble polymers are shaken together at a certain concentration, the mixture becomes turbid, but after standing for a while it will separate into two liquid phases in equilibrium and this is known as a two-phase system. The lower phase will contain a higher concentration of one polymer and the upper phase will be rich in the other polymer. Two-phase systems are usually used for the isolation of mammalian cells. In order to preserve the biological integrity of the cells during partition, the desired tonicity of the phase system can be achieved by adding salts, buffers, sugars and other substances. The cells (up to 10^7) are mixed with the phase and allowed to settle for a while. After settling, the cells will be selectively distributed between the polymers. However, several factors are involving in the determination of the distribution of cells between the upper phase, interface and the lower phase. These include polymer composition, molecular weight of polymers, ionic composition, cell surface properties and temperature.

There are several types of polymer combination that can be used for the separation of biological particles. For the purpose of cell separation, two-phase systems composed of dextran-polyethylene glycol or dextran–Ficoll are commonly used. A combination of these three polymers can also be used as three-phase systems.

Cell partition has been used for the separation of red cells from white cells and then granulocytes from lymphocytes (Walter et al, 1969a and b). The separation of human T- and B-lymphocytes has also been described by Walter and Nagaya (1975).

Many workers have reported separation methods involving several partition steps (counter-current distribution). This method was devised in order to obtain a higher percentage of the wanted cells which are only partially separated after using one partition step (Albertsson, 1971). Walter (1974) used counter-current distribution for the separation of red cells from white cells, neutrophils from lymphocytes and red cells of different stages of maturation from one another.

For more information on the separation of blood cells by partitioning see Walter (1982).

4.11   ELECTROPHORETIC METHODS OF CELL SEPARATION

Similar to cell partition, electrophoretic separation of cells is based on cell surface chemistry and mainly upon differences in cell surface charge density and hence electrophoretic mobility of the cells (Platsoucas et al, 1976). Differentiation phases or functional states of cells are usually expressed by different surface structure, for example by different surface charges. Therefore, one could expect that various cell populations behave in a different manner in an electric field. Since electrophoretic separation uses these differences in functional characteristics for the fractionation of cell populations from mixtures, it can therefore be a useful tool in membrane and cell research studies.

Electrophoretic separation has proved to be a mild, rapid and sensitive technique for large-scale cell preparations. It not only allows the isolation of protein without loss of activity, but also the separation of viable cells and cell organelles. With this system all requirements, including sterile conditions (which are essential for the separation of viable and metabolically intact cells) can be achieved.

Several electrophoretic methods have been applied for the separation of mammalian cells. However, the most commonly used techniques include continuous free-flow electrophoresis (Hannig, 1972) and density gradient electrophoresis (Boltz et al, 1973; Griffith et al, 1975).

Continuous free-flow electrophoresis employs a vertical separation chamber and a buffer solution that flows from top to bottom in the form of a thin film (about 0·6 mm thick). An electric field is set up perpendicular to the buffer stream. The cell suspension is injected into the streaming buffer through the top opening of the chamber. Within about 3–7 min, cells with different electrophoretic mobilities (i.e. different surface charge density) are deflected by different amounts and can be collected subsequently at the lower end of the chamber in a fraction collector, for example a 90-channel peristaltic pump.

On the other hand, density gradient electrophoresis utilizes an iso-osmotic density gradient medium, a commercially available apparatus usually used for polyacrylamide gels (Jovin et al, 1964), and a fraction collector. This technique offers the advantage of rapid separation of a relatively high number of cells (up to 10^8). Several factors affect density gradient separation of cells, and therefore careful consideration must be given to designing the apparatus and choosing the buffer and the gradient medium. The most suitable gradient material for cell electrophoresis is Ficoll with sucrose added to it to achieve the desired tonicity (Boltz et al, 1973). For more detailed information see Platsoucas (1983).

There are several applications of the electrophoretic methods of separation. Free-flow electrophoresis has been used by several workers for the separation and characterization of lymphoid and other haemopoietic cells. Isolation of T- and B-lymphocytes has been reported by Nordling et al (1972), and the separation of T- and B-cells and their subsets by Shortman et al (1975 and 1976).

Separation and characterization of cells by preparative density gradient electrophoresis have also been used for the fractionation of different mammalian cells. On the basis of cell surface charge, T-(Tμ, Tγ) and B-lymphocytes have been separated by Platsoucas et al (1980). In other experiments, Platsoucas et al (1979) described the separation of T-cell subsets (T-helper and T-suppressor) by density gradient electrophoresis. As determined by functional tests and cell surface marker analysis, T-cell subpopulations were found to be separated without modulation of their Fc receptors and changing of their properties. Fractionation of human bone marrow cells by density gradient electrophoresis has also been reported by Platsoucas et al (1981). They were able to separate the immature myeloid and erythroid cells from the mature cells (e.g. monocytes, small lymphocytes and granulocytes). Functional tests and cell culture of the separated cell fractions suggested that marrow T- and B-cell precursors can also be highly enriched for differentiation studies.

4.12   CLONING TECHNIQUES

With the increasing need to isolate and identify haemopoietic cells and peripheral blood precursors in order to study the mechanisms regulating proliferation and differentiation of cells, an *in vitro* culture technique has been introduced. Using semi-solid culture media, pure cultured cell populations arising as cohorts from single progenitors may be harvested from culture and can then be used for further functional and metabolic studies.

The development of the technique of culturing the precursor cells, known as colony forming units (CFU), in a semi-solid culture medium containing a colony stimulating activity (CSA; obtained from certain human tissues) to form colonies of granulocytes and macrophages (CFU-GM), has allowed study of the factors controlling proliferation of granulocytic series (Bradley and Metcalf, 1966). Factors controlling erythropoiesis have been extensively studied by growing the erythroid colonies in the presence of erythropoietin (Stephenson et al, 1971; Axelrad et al, 1974). Megakaryocytes (McLeod et al, 1976; Fauser and Messner, 1979) and lymphocytes (Rozenszajn, 1975; Claesson et al, 1977) have also been investigated by colony culture techniques.

The earliest haemopoietic cells are the pluripotent progenitor cells (Trentin, 1971; Lajtha, 1975; Weiss, 1981) which can be cultured in the presence of humoral substances, for example erythropoietin, CSA or BPA (burst promoting activity), to give colonies containing more than one lineage of haemopoietic differentiation—the CFU–GEMM (colony forming unit–granulocyte, erythrocyte, macrophage, and megakaryocyte) (Fauser and Messner, 1979). CFU–GEMM are formed earlier than the committed precursors which are capable only of developing a single cell line, for example CFU-GM and burst forming unit-erythroid (BFU-E). Individual committed precursor cells then generate maturing progeny under the influence of positive and negative regulatory factors.

Erythropoiesis includes the development of erythroid series from stem cells to the mature erythrocytes. Erythropoietin plays an important role in erythropoiesis and can be considered as the only specific regulator so far identified. BFU-E are the earliest erythroid committed cells and in culture they are able to give rise to large and usually diffuse colonies of erythroblast 'burst' after 14–17 days. The colony forming unit-erythroid (CFU-E) are more mature cells and can give rise to erythroid colonies consisting of between 8 and 50 cells after 7 days in culture. After a few divisions, CFU-E gives rise to the first recognizable erythroid precursor which is known as the proerythro-blast. Further maturation of these cells finally gives rise to the non-nucleated erythrocytes. (Iscove et al, 1974; Ogawa et al, 1976; Kaaba et al, 1984).

Granulopoiesis starts with the division of the earliest cell committed to granulocyte-macrophage colony forming unit, or CFU-GM. The maturation of CFU-GM is stimulated by humoral factors or CSA which are produced by other cells in tissue culture and mainly from macrophages (Golde and Cline, 1974; Moore, 1974). The precursor cell of a granulocytic series is the myeloblast and it has been suggested that neutrophils, eosinophils and basophils are derived from different distinct myeloblast precursors (Shoham et al, 1974; Fauser and Messner, 1979; Hall and Malia, 1984).

Monocytopoiesis leads to the formation of monocytes. The committed cells mature to monoblasts which, together with the proliferating promonocytes (produced by division of monoblasts) form the proliferating pool of the phagocytic cells *in vitro* (Goud and van Furth, 1975). Hall and Malia (1984) reported that bone marrow is the only source of monocytes and that the origins of monocytes and granulocytes are closely related. Therefore, the granulocyte-monocyte precursor will give rise to the circulating monocytes and then to the tissue macrophages. The regulation of monocyte production is closely associated with that of the neutrophil lineage.

Thrombopoiesis includes the production of thrombocytes or platelets by fragmentation of the cytoplasm of megakaryocytes. These cells originate in the bone marrow from pluripotent stem cells (CFU-GEMM). The stages of maturation of megakaryocyte includes megakaryoblast, promegakaryocyte and granular-megakaryocyte stages (Queisser et al, 1971). These stages are non-proliferative (i.e. DNA synthesis and cell division do not occur), but there is production of cytoplasmic contents from which platelets are produced. The level of circulating platelets is regulated by humoral thrombopoietin present in the plasma (McLeod et al, 1976; Hall and Malia, 1984).

Lymphopoiesis results in the formation of T- and B-lymphocytes and T-cell subsets. There is evidence to suggest that lymphocytes are derived from pluripotent stem cells capable of producing granulocyte, megakaryocyte and erythrocyte cell lineages. This evidence is derived for example, from the existence of both T- and B-cell deficiency which can be corrected by bone marrow transplantation and by studies of blast-cell transformation. The mechanisms responsible for regulating lymphopoiesis are not well understood (Micklem, 1979; Hall and Malia, 1984).

Erythroid cells obtained by cloning techniques have been used by several workers. Gregory and Eaves (1977) and Reid et al (1981) used harvesting of erythroblasts from bursts derived from peripheral blood or bone marrow BFU-E as a method for isolating erythroid cells. The erythroid colonies are recognized on the basis of appearance of haemoglobin-containing erthroblasts and by their time of appearance in culture. The configuration and the number of the BFU-E in culture have been studied by Ogawa et al (1977). They have reported that about 90 ± 6 bursts per 10^5 human bone marrow cells may be obtained. Reid et al (1981) suggested that after 10–11 days' culture the BFU-E contained two or more subcolony groups, in which subcolony size did not exceed about 50–100 cells. Erythroid cells harvested from BFU-E have been used by other investigators for various studies into the metabolism of differentiating erythroblasts (Baine and Benson, 1981). CFU-E and BFU-E numbers in human bone marrow have been studied by Ogawa et al (1976). They found that the mean number of marrow CFU-E is 75 colonies per 10^5 nucleated cells. Dainiak et al (1983) reported mean CFU-E and BFU-E in normal donors' marrows of 97 and 32 per 10^5 cells respectively. These results indicated that CFU-E and BFU-E numbers in human bone marrow can vary quite considerably.

The growth of CFU-GM *in vitro* has been described by several investigators and has been shown to be dependent on the presence of colony stimulating activity (CSA) (Golde and Cline, 1974; Moore, 1974). The CFU-GM progenitor does not usually give rise to a single type of colony but demonstrates the growth of both granulocytes and macrophages (Metcalf, 1981).

McLeod et al (1976) reported that impure preparations of erythropoietin also contain a factor able to stimulate the proliferation of megakaryocyte precursor. Based on this observation, Johnson and Metcalf (1977) and Fauser and Messner (1978) developed techniques which can be used for cloning mixed human colonies.

Satisfactory cloning techniques for culturing normal human T-lymphocytes have been reported by many workers (Rozenszajn et al, 1975; Claesson et al, 1977).

A method for separating normal mature bone marrow plasma cells by cloning has been described by Mendelow et al (1980). They separated plasma-cell-rich fragments from bone marrow suspension by buoyant density centrifugation. The fragments were then cultured using a simple suspension method. *In vitro* selective affinity of plasma cells and marrow stromal cells resulted in further concentration of plasma cells. After seven days the cultured fragments were disaggregated with trypsin, and stromal cells were then removed by their adherence properties. The non-adherent fraction was found to comprise approximately 85% plasma cells.

Metcalf (1981) described the techniques for culturing normal and leukaemic granulocyte-monocyte colonies in agar and the problems of harvesting and interpreting these cultures.

Methods for cloning and harvesting normal and abnormal bone marrow cells, especially erythroid cells, are discussed in Chapter 5.

Chapter 2

Collection and Identification of Cells

1. INTRODUCTION

1.1 HUMAN BLOOD CELLS

Blood cells are produced in the haemopoietic tissue located in specialized sites from which they are released into the circulation only when sufficiently mature. The major postnatal haemopoietic organs are the bone marrow, spleen, lymph nodes and thymus. For experimental purposes, venous blood is quite satisfactory for providing mature blood cells, since it is easily obtained in relatively large amounts.

Smears or cytocentrifuge preparations of peripheral blood cells stained with Jenner–Giemsa allow identification of the main types of blood cells. These include the white cells (leucocytes), red cells (erythrocytes) and platelets (thrombocytes). There are five types of white cells: lymphocytes, monocytes, neutrophilic granulocytes, eosinophilic granulocytes and basophilic granulocytes. The morphology and functions of peripheral blood cells are described in detail in many textbooks (Wintrobe et al, 1974; McDonald et al, 1978; Thompson, 1979). The relative percentages and the absolute numbers of the different types of leucocytes found in normal preparations of adult blood are shown in *Table* 2.1. Blood cells are normally easy to distinguish from one another by using conventional staining methods. However, accurate cytological characterization and detection of abnormalities in blood cells can be achieved using cytochemical and enzyme-specific staining methods, immunofluorescence staining or red cell rosetting.

The juvenile red cells, reticulocytes, may be distinguished from mature red cells by incubating the blood with a supravital stain of brilliant cresyl blue or methylene blue.

It is sometimes difficult to clearly differentiate monocytes from

Table 2.1. The differential count and absolute number of normal blood cells (from Dacie and Lewis, 1975a. *Practical Haematology*, Churchill Livingstone, Edinburgh.)

Cell type	% cells	Absolute number × 10⁹/l
Neutrophilic granulocytes	40–75	2·0–7·5
Large and small lymphocytes	20–45	1·5–4·0
Monocytes	2–10	0·2–0·8
Eosinophilic granulocytes	1–6	0·04–0·4
Basophilic granulocytes	<1	<0·01–0·1
Reticulocytes: adult and children	0·2–2·0	10–100
Infant (full term)		
and cord blood	2–6	mean 150

neutrophils and large lymphocytes. A more specific characterization of monocytes can be obtained by non-specific esterase staining with α-naphthyl acetate as the substrate (Grossi et al, 1978; Bevan et al, 1980) than with Jenner–Giemsa stain.

Peripheral blood lymphocytes have been classified as B-, T- and null lymphocytes (Miller and Mitchell, 1969; Katz and Benacerraf, 1972; Good, 1972; Foon et al, 1982). B-lymphocytes (thymus-independent and functional in humoral immunity) have surface immunoglobulin (SIg) as a cell specific marker which allows these cells to be detected by immunofluorescence staining. T-lymphocytes are thymus-derived and are responsible for the cell-mediated immunity and regulation of other lymphoid cell formation. They can be identified by surface receptors which have the ability to form rosettes with sheep red blood cells when mixed together under optimum conditions (Jondal et al, 1972). T-cells are further classified into three subpopulations on the basis of the presence or absence of Fc receptors. $T_M(T\mu)$-lymphocytes have receptors for the Fc portions of IgM molecules, $T_G(T_\gamma)$-cells have receptors for the Fc portion of IgG molecules whilst T_ϕ-cells lack these receptors (Webb and Cooper, 1973; Dickler et al, 1974; Chiao et al, 1974, 1975; Moretta et al, 1975, 1977; Ferrarini et al, 1975; Gmelig-Meyling et al, 1976; Chiao and Good, 1976). Non-specific esterase staining can also be used to distinguish T_M lymphocytes from T_G and T_ϕ cells (Grossi et al, 1978; Bevan et al, 1980). Furthermore, T-cell subsets have also been detected by surface antigens recognized by monoclonal antibodies (Stobo, 1982).

1.2 HUMAN BONE MARROW CELLS

In adult life the bone marrow is the dominant haemopoietic organ. On gross examination, bone marrow samples may be red, indicating active haemopoiesis, or yellow, indicating a haemopoietically inactive marrow. The red colour of marrow is due to the presence of haemoglobin from erythrocytes and their precursors. Red marrow is rich in haemopoietic cells together with fat cells and connective tissue, while the major cell type in yellow marrow is fat cells. After the age of about 50 years the proportion of active marrow declines and that of the fat increases. Bone marrow contains an apparently confused assortment of cells, with no clear pattern of organization. However, the cells are continually proliferating, differentiating and being discharged into the circulation at varying rates. The marrow not only discharges cells into the blood stream, but also receives them from the blood. The structure and function of bone marrow is discussed in many text books (e.g. Wintrobe et al, 1974; Erslev and Weiss, 1977; Hall and Malia, 1984).

Slide preparations of bone marrow cells stained with Jenner–Giemsa after the removal of fat and other non-haemopoietic tissue, show the various stages of differentiation of the peripheral blood cells from their precursors (McDonald et al, 1978). The earliest committed cells of each cell line, myeloblasts, erythroblasts, lymphoblasts, monoblasts and plasmoblasts, originate from a stem call (haemocytoblast) and cannot be reliably differentiated from one another by morphological appearance alone.

The myeloid series forms the majority of marrow cells. This cell line consists of myeloblasts, promyelocytes, myelocytes, metamyelocytes, band or stab cells and mature granulocytes (neutrophils, eosinophils, and basophils). The erythroid series includes proerythroblasts, early erythroblasts, intermediate erythroblasts, late erythroblasts, reticulocytes and erythrocytes. The lymphoid cell line similarly consists of a series of precursors and includes immature lymphoblasts which may differentiate into large and small lymphocytes. The monocytes and lymphocytes are thought to have a common precursor cell at some stage during their differentiation. The monocytic series consists of monoblasts, promonocytes and monocytes. Plasma cells (plasmocytes) are the progeny of lymphocytes, but some haematologists consider they constitute a separate series. Included in the plasma cell line are the plasmoblasts, proplasmocytes and plasmocytes. Platelets are derived from megakaryocytes. These arise from their precursor cells, the megakaryoblasts. Megakaryocytes are the largest cells in the bone marrow and occur infrequently. The differential cell count of normal marrow preparations is shown in *Table* 2.2.

Smears of bone marrow are routinely stained with Jenner–Giemsa and Perl's prussian blue for iron. The latter technique allows identification of sideroblasts and siderocytes, by staining cytoplasmic inclusions in the abnormal erythroblasts and erythrocytes respectively. Additional bone marrow stains such as sudan black or peroxidase stain can be used to identify myeloid cells. Periodic acid–Schiff (PAS) stain is used to detect lymphoblasts and abnormal

Table 2.2. Differential count ranges of bone marrow aspirates from 12 healthy subjects (from Wintrobe et al, 1974. *Clinical Haematology*, 7th ed. Philadelphia, Lea & Febiger).

	Mean (%)	Observed range (%)
NEUTROPHILIC SERIES (Total)	53·6	49·2–65·0
Myeloblasts	0·9	0·2– 1·5
Promyelocytes	3·3	2·1– 4·1
Myelocytes	12·7	8·2–15·7
Metamyelocytes	15·9	9·6–24·6
Band or stab cells	12·4	9·5–15·3
Neutrophilic granulocytes	7·4	6·0–12·0
EOSINOPHILIC SERIES (Total)	3·1	1·2– 5·3
Myelocytes	0·8	0·2– 1·3
Metamyelocytes	1·2	0·4– 2·2
Band or stab cells	0·9	0·2– 2·4
Eosinophilic granulocytes	0·5	0– 1·3
BASOPHILS AND MAST CELLS	<0·1	0– 0·2
ERYTHROCYTE SERIES (Total)	25·6	18·4–33·8
Proerythroblasts	0·6	0·2– 1·3
Early erythroblasts	1·4	0·5– 2·4
Intermediate erythroblasts	21·6	17·9–29·2
Late erythroblasts	2·0	0·4– 4·6
LYMPHOCYTES	16·2	11·1–23·2
PLASMA CELLS	1·3	0·4– 3·9
MONOCYTES	0·3	0– 0·8
MEGAKARYOCYTES	<0·1	0– 0·4
M:E RATIO	2·3	1·5– 3·3

erythroblasts. Esterase stains are used to differentiate monocytes from lymphocytes and granulocytic cells (Dacie and Lewis, 1984).

2. CELL SEPARATION MEDIA

Unless stated otherwise, all reagents are of Analar grade. If aseptic conditions are required, perform the work in a sterile hood using sterile equipment and solutions.

2.1 HEPES SALINE

Materials

    i. 1M Hepes buffer [4-(2-hydroxy ethyl)-1-piperazine-ethane sulphonic acid] pH 7·3 (Gibco): 1 ml.

    ii. NaCl; 0·9% (w/v) solution: 1 l.

Procedure

    a. Mix 1 ml Hepes buffer with 1 litre NaCl solution.

    b. Store at 4 °C.

2.2 BALANCED SALT SOLUTION (BSS) FREE OF Ca^{2+} AND Mg^{2+}

The following recipe yields a balanced (buffered) salts solution that is isotonic for human cells (osmolality 290–300 mmol/kg H_2O). This working solution is used at times when cell aggregation is to be avoided. Monocytes are particularly susceptible to aggregation.

Materials

    i. NaCl: 8·0 g.

    ii. KCl: 0·2 g.

    iii. Na_2HPO_4: 1·15 g.

    iv. KH_2PO_4: 0·2 g.

    v. Glucose: 0·2 g.

    vi. Sterile distilled water: 1 l.

    vii. 0·45 μm filter (Millipore).

Procedure

    a. Dissolve the above reagents in a small volume of sterile distilled water and make up to 1000 ml with distilled water.

    b. Sterilize the solution by passing through a 0·45 μm Millipore filter and store at 4 °C in a sterile container. Do not use if the solution is cloudy.

Comments

    a. For storage at 4 °C, make up a stock solution of 10 × concentration (conc) and dilute as required.

    b. To prepare Ca^{2+} and Mg^{2+} free 'Dulbeccos' phosphate buffered saline (PBS), dissolve the above reagents without glucose in 1 litre distilled water (or in 100 ml to obtain 10 × conc). To prepare

PBS with Ca^{2+} and Mg^{2+} add 0·132 g $CaCl_2 2H_2O$ and 0·1 g $MgCl_2 6H_2O$ per litre.

2.3 EAGLE'S MINIMAL ESSENTIAL MEDIUM (MEM)

This solution is buffered to pH 7·4 at 37 °C with 20 mmol/l Hepes buffer (1M) (P. de Souza and A. May, unpublished work).

Materials
  i. Sterile, pyrogen-free, distilled water: 81 ml.
  ii. 1M Hepes buffer, pH 7·3 (Gibco): 2 ml.
  iii. Eagle's MEM (Wellcome; 10 times working concentration): 10 ml.
  iv. 0·154M NaOH: 5·2 ml.
  v. Streptomycin: 100 µg/ml.
  vi. Penicillin: 200 units/ml.

Procedure
  a. Mix the above reagents. The osmolality should be 280–300 mmol/kg H_2O.
  b. Sterilize the solution by passing through a 0·45 µm Millipore filter and store at 4 °C in a sterile container.

Comments
It is necessary to test the osmolality with each new batch of Eagle's MEM. Adjust the volume of the distilled water to give a final osmolality of 280–300 mmol/kg H_2O.

2.4 BONE MARROW COLLECTING MEDIUM

Materials
  i. Eagle's MEM, pH 7·4 at 37 °C (Section 2.3): 50 ml.
  ii. Heat-inactivated foetal calf serum (HI-FCS): 25 ml.
  iii. Preservative-free heparin (Duncan Flockhart Co. Ltd.): 1000 units.

Procedure
  a. Mix the above reagents in a clean container, and measure the osmolality (280–300 mmol/kg H_2O).
  b. Sterilize by passing the medium through a 0·45 µm Millipore filter into a sterile bottle.

c. Aliquot 10–15 ml into sterile containers and store indefinitely at −20 °C.

Comments

Use 10 ml collecting medium for the collection of bone marrow aspirates from the sternum and iliac crest. The 15 ml sample is used for the collection of bone marrow obtained from the femur of patients undergoing hip-replacement surgery.

3. COLLECTION OF SPECIMENS

Blood and bone marrow samples from healthy subjects and patients should only be taken after obtaining their fully informed consent and in the UK the procedure must be approved by the Joint Ethics Committee.

3.1 BLOOD SAMPLES

Materials

Preservative-free heparin (Duncan Flockhart Co. Ltd.): 15 units/ml blood.

Procedure

a. Place blood into a tube containing heparin within 2 min of collecting the sample. Mix by gently inverting the tube.

b. Keep the tube on ice until required.

3.2 BONE MARROW SAMPLES

Normal bone marrow samples can be obtained from the femur of haematologically normal patients undergoing hip surgery or from the iliac crest of normal adults after the induction of anaesthesia for minor surgery. Diagnostic aspirates from the sternum or iliac crest of patients with blood disorders can also be used (P. de Souza and A. May, unpublished work).

Materials

    i. Bone marrow collecting medium (Section 2.4).

   ii. Heat-inactivated foetal calf serum (HI-FCS).

  iii. Sterile Kwill, 5 inch (Hinder-Leslies Ltd.).

Procedure

　　a. Mix the bone marrow sample with the collecting medium immediately after taking the sample.

　　b. Disrupt the marrow granules by repeated aspiration through a syringe and 19 or 25 gauge needle.

　　c. Transfer the cell suspension to a sterile plastic container and centrifuge at 1200 *g* for 7–10 min at room temperature.

　　d. Remove any fat which remains at the top of the suspending fluid with a sterile Kwill. Resuspend the sedimented cells in HI-FCS and mix gently using a 19 or 25 gauge needle and syringe.

　　e. Pass the cells through a sterile nylon gauze filter, if necessary, to remove cell aggregates, bone particles and connective tissue.

4.　PREPARATION OF BUFFY COAT

When blood from a normal subject is centrifuged, two layers may be observed. The upper fluid layer called plasma constitutes about 55% of the total blood volume, and the lower cell layer consists mainly of red cells and reticulocytes. The narrow, whitish band just above the red cell pellet is the buffy coat and this contains platelets and white cells. The preparation of buffy coat is useful to concentrate white cells after the removal of erythrocytes. It is also effective in removing the majority of platelets with the supernatant plasma. In addition, this method can be used to remove the mature erythrocytes from bone marrow cell suspensions in order to concentrate the nucleated cells.

Materials

　　i. Balanced salt solution (BSS) free of Ca^{2+} and Mg^{2+}, *or* Eagle's minimal essential medium (MEM).

　　ii. Wintrobe tube.

　　iii. Parafilm sealing tissue (Gallenkamp).

　　iv. Pasteur pipettes.

Procedure

　　a. Mix the anticoagulated blood or bone marrow sample with a syringe and needle, fill Wintrobe tubes carefully using Pasteur pipette to exclude bubbles from the column and seal with Parafilm.

　　b. Centrifuge at 400 *g* for 15 min at room temperature in a bench centrifuge.

　　c. Using a Pasteur pipette, discard the supernatant fluid and collect the following narrow, almost white coloured layer of cells (buffy coat) into a sterile tube containing BSS or Eagle's MEM.

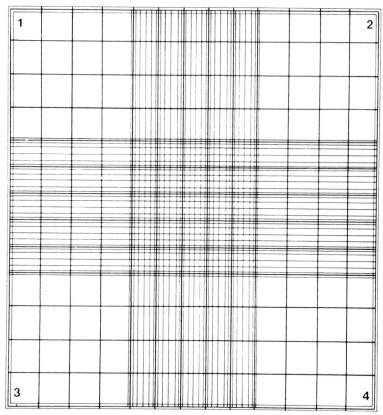

Fig. 2.1.Haemocytometer grid showing 'improved' Neubauer ruling with double line surrounding each group of 16 small squares used in all-glass chambers to produce the optical phenomenon of a single translucent boundary line.

d. Wash the cells twice with Eagle's MEM or BSS (800 g for 7 min). Resuspend in BSS or Eagle's MEM.

5.   CELL COUNTING USING HAEMOCYTOMETER

The haemocytometer chamber (*Fig.* 2.1) is used to count blood or bone marrow cells. In *Fig.* 2.1 the squares indicated by the numbers 1, 2, 3 and 4 are used for counting nucleated cells of blood or bone marrow cell suspensions.

In a haemocytometer that is 0·1 mm deep, the volume occupied by each of these squares under a coverslip is 10^{-4} ml.

Materials
   i. Haemocytometer and coverslip (Gallenkamp).
  ii. Pasteur pipettes.
 iii. Counting fluid: 3% (v/v) acetic acid.

Procedure
   a. Prepare the appropriate dilutions of the cell suspension just prior
to counting. The optimum concentration of cells for counting is $5-10^5$
cells/ml (50–100 cells per large square) after dilution in the counting
fluid.
   b. With a Pasteur pipette allow the cell suspension to flow under the
coverslip until the grid area is just full and not overflowing into the sides
of the chamber. If the chamber is overloaded, start again with a clean
haemocytometer, rather than removing excess liquid. Overfilling of the
chamber may cause loss of cells and can produce a dilution error.
   c. Allow cells to settle for at least 1 min.
   d. Count all of the cells in each of the four large squares (1–4 in *Fig.*
2.1). Some cells will be touching the outermost borders. Count only
those cells touching two of the outside borders (e.g. the upper and left).
Determine the average number of cells per large square. This is the
number of cells per 10^{-4} ml. Thus:

cells/ml = (average number per large square) $\times$ 10^4/ml $\times$ dilution factor.

Comments
   a. A number of errors can be introduced using this method. These
include dilution errors, loss of cells during pipetting, uneven suspension
of cells, overfilling or underfilling of the chamber, and counting of the
cells before they settle.
   b. Most of the data on cell counts in this book have been obtained
using a Coulter Counter (Model ZF) and Channelizer (Model C-1000).
This equipment has the advantage of giving accurate and rapid results.
Operate the Coulter Counter as directed by the manufacturers'
instructions for each model.
   c. For consistent cell counts it is important to use either the
haemocytometer or the Coulter Counter throughout the experiment.

6.   CYTOCENTRIFUGE PREPARATION

To obtain an accurate differential cell count, the cell preparation must
be well spread and adequately stained, and examination must be
systematic. If smears are used, differential cell counting should be done
in a manner that takes into account the distribution of cells according to

their size. The use of a cytocentrifuge which spreads cells onto a small area (6 mm diameter) on the slide overcomes this problem and also makes morphological examination of the cells much easier.

Materials
  i. Heat-inactivated foetal calf serum (HI-FCS) *or* bovine serum albumin (BSA): 2% (v/v) in buffered salt solution (BSS) *or* phosphate buffered saline (PBS).
  ii. Methanol (95%).

Equipment
  Cytospin (Shandon Southern).

Procedure
  a. Prepare a cell suspension containing $5–7 \times 10^4$ nucleated cells in 0·3 or 0·5 ml HI-FCS or BSA (to help the cells to stick to the slides). If the cell suspension contains a large number of mature erythrocytes, adjust the volume of cells accordingly in order to prevent the red cells from obscuring the morphology of the white cells.
  b. Centrifuge the cell suspension in the Cytospin (800 r.p.m.) for 10–15 min.
  c. Rapidly remove any residual moisture on the slide by blowing with a warm hair-dryer.
  d. Stain the slides within 24–48 h. To store the unstained preparations more than 48 h, fix the cells by dipping in methanol for 30 s.

Comments
If there are a lot of red cells, as in blood, adequate numbers of white cells for differential counting will not be present on the slide. Therefore, if necessary prepare a buffy coat cell suspension to concentrate the white cells.

7. CONVENTIONAL STAINING METHODS

7.1 JENNER–GIEMSA STAIN
The major categories of blood and bone marrow cells are quite easily identified using a conventional Romanowsky-type stain such as Jenner–Giemsa. This consists of a combination of methylene blue, which stains acidic components blue, and eosin which stains basic

components pink. The staining solution must be carefully buffered to ensure optimum ionization of side chains in the molecules which will take up the dye. In addition, the intensity of the stain will be uneven if the slide preparation is too thick. Jenner–Giemsa stain is useful primarily for evaluating abnormalities of white cells, red cells and platelets. For bone marrow samples it is useful for assessing anaemias, leukaemia, leukopenia, thrombocytopenia, hypoplasia, aplasia and other disorders.

Materials

   i. KH_2PO_4: 9·1 g/l.
  ii. Na_2HPO_4: 9·5 g/l.
 iii. Jenner's stain (BDH).
  iv. Giemsa's stain (BDH).
   v. Methanol.
  vi. DPX mountant (BDH).

Procedure

PREPARATION OF SOLUTIONS

   a. 0·066M Sörensen's phosphate buffer, pH 6·8: mix 50·8 ml KH_2PO_4 and 49·2 ml Na_2HPO_4 to give 100 ml of pH 6·8 solution.
   b. Buffered water: add 900 ml distilled water to 100 ml 0·066M Sörensen's buffer.
   c. Jenner's stain solution: mix 1 part Jenner's stain with 2 parts buffered water.
   d. Giemsa's stain solution: mix 1 part Giemsa's stain with 10 parts buffered water.

STAINING OF CELLS

   a. Fix the cells for 5 min in methanol.
   b. Stain for 3 min in Jenner's stain solution.
   c. Wash with distilled water.
   d. Stain with Giemsa's stain solution for 9 min.
   e. Rinse for 6 min with buffered water.
   f. Dry the slides by blowing with a warm hair-dryer. Apply DPX mountant and a coverslip to keep them free from dust.
   g. Examine under oil immersion.

Comments

Most of the Jenner–Giemsa stains of cell preparations described in this book were carried out using a Hema-Tek slide stainer (Ames).

7.2 DIFF-QUICK

Diff-Quick is a rapid staining method for blood and bone marrow cells, and allows a preliminary identification of the prepared cells. It is fairly satisfactory for the staining of thin films or cytocentrifuge preparations.

Materials
  i. Solution I: acid stain component (AHS).
  ii. Solution II: basic stain component (AHS).
  iii. Methanol *or* fixative (AHS).
  iv. Buffered water (*see* Section 7.1).

Procedure
  a. Fix the dry slides for 30 s in methanol.
  b. Stain for 30 s in solution I (red) and dry gently with tissue paper.
  c. Stain the slides in solution II (purple) for 30 s.
  d. Rinse for 10 s in buffered water and dry carefully.
  e. Add DPX mountant and cover with coverslip.

8. SPECIFIC STAINING METHODS

Cytochemical stains provide not only an accurate identification of cells but also demonstrate any abnormalities in individual blood or bone marrow cells.

8.1 BRILLIANT CRESYL BLUE

Reticulocytes are juvenile red cells which can be distinguished from mature erythrocytes by staining with brilliant cresyl blue or with new methylene blue (Dacie and Lewis, 1975b). The former stain reacts with the ribosomes which are present only in reticulocytes and forms a blue precipitate of granules or filaments (McDonald et al, 1978). In normal blood the percentage of reticulocytes is only about 0.2–2%.

Materials
  i. NaCl; 0.9% (w/v): 790 ml.
  ii. Brilliant cresyl blue: 0.8 g.
  iii. Thymol.

Procedure

PREPARATION OF STAINING SOLUTION

   a. Dissolve cresyl blue in the NaCl to prepare a 1% solution.
   b. Add a few crystals of thymol to prevent bacterial growth.
   c. Filter through a layer of filter paper and store in a clean, stoppered bottle.

STAINING OF CELLS

   a. Mix three drops of blood suspension with an equal volume of brilliant cresyl blue solution, and leave for 10–15 min at room temperature.
   b. Resuspend the cells gently and use a small drop to prepare a smear.
   c. Examine the cells without fixing and estimate the percentage of reticulocytes after counting 1000 red cells (choose an area where the red cells do not overlap with each other).

8.2   NON-SPECIFIC ESTERASE

The method of Yam et al (1971) with α-naphthyl acetate as substrate can be used to distinguish between monocytes and neutrophils or large lymphocytes. Monocytes and platelets give a strong, diffusely positive red-brown stain (*Fig.* 2.2). The granulocytic series stains negative. Non-specific esterase can also be used to detect T_M-lymphocytes (Grossi et al, 1978; Bevan et al, 1980). T_M-lymphocytes show a localized dot-staining pattern (*Fig.* 2.2), whereas T_G-, B- and null lymphocytes have a negative or diffusely granular, weakly positive stain.

Materials

   i. Fixative (keep at 4 °C):

Na_2HPO_4	200 mg
KH_2PO_4	1 g
Acetone	450 ml
Formalin	250 ml
Distilled water	300 ml

   ii. Pararosaniline solution (wear gloves and make fresh each time; dissolve by warming gently and then cool and filter):

Pararosaniline	200 mg
2M HCI	5 ml

   iii. Tube A. sodium nitrate (keep in a dark place): 80 mg.
   iv. Tube B. α-naphthyl acetate: 100 mg.

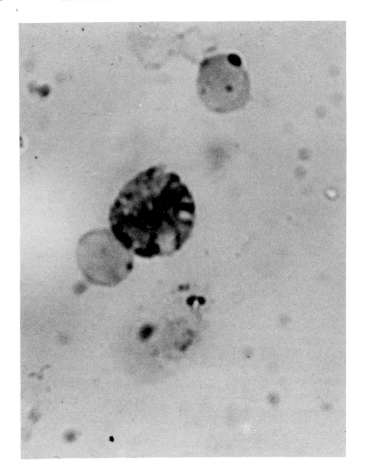

Fig. 2.2. Non-specific esterase staining of peripheral blood mononuclear cells. Note the strongly staining monocyte in the centre of the photograph and the characteristic dot-staining pattern in the T_M-lymphocytes.

v. Ethylene glycol monomethyl ether.

vi. 0·15M phosphate buffer, pH 7·4:

0·15M NaH$_2$PO$_4$.2H$_2$O	18 ml
0·15M Na$_2$HPO$_4$	82 ml

vii. Methyl green: 2% (w/v) solution; extract this solution at least three times with chloroform before use.

Procedure

    a. Prepare cytocentrifuge slides, dry in air and stain not more than 48 h later.

    b. Immediately before staining, fix the cells at 4 °C for 30 s.

    c. Wash the slides thoroughly three times with distilled water at room temperature and allow to air dry.

    d. To tube B add 5 ml ethylene glycol monomethyl ether. In a Coplin jar mix 1·5 ml of this solution with 27 ml 0·15M phosphate buffer.

    e. To tube A add 2 ml distilled water to dissolve the sodium nitrate, pipette 2 ml pararosaniline solution into the tubes, mix well, and after 1 min transfer and mix 1·8 ml of this solution with the phosphate buffer–α-naphthyl acetate–ethylene glycol monomethyl ether mixture (step *d*).

    f. Filter into another Coplin jar and adjust the pH to approximately 6·1.

    g. Stain the slides with the solution in the Coplin jar for 45 min at room temperature.

    h. Wash the slides three times with distilled water and dry gently using tissue paper.

    i. Counterstain with methyl green for 10 min in another Coplin jar.

    j. Wash well with distilled water and air dry.

    k. Cover the stained area with mountant and coverslip. Examine under the microscope using oil immersion.

8.3   PERL'S PRUSSIAN BLUE REACTION

Peripheral blood red cells with non-haem iron-containing granules in their cytoplasm are known as siderocytes. These stain nearly black with ordinary blood stains and are referred to as 'Pappenheimer bodies'; they become deep blue in Perl's stain (siderotic granules). In bone marrow, the sideroblast is the red cell precursor containing stainable iron granules. Normal erythroblasts contain up to five of these granules and those containing more than this are referred to as pathological sideroblasts (Bottomley, 1980). In this situation granules stain deep blue with Perl's stain (McDonald et al, 1978) and with light microscopy they may be seen either scattered through the cytoplasm or as a ring around the nucleus (Dacie and Lewis, 1975f).

Materials

    i. 0·2M HCl.

    ii. Potassium ferrocyanide: 2% (w/v) solution (prepare fresh each time, since it is unstable).

    iii. Neutral red: 0·05% (w/v) solution (filter before use).

Procedure

  a. Fix the cytocentrifuge preparation with methanol for 15 min and allow to dry.

  b. Add equal volumes of 0·2M HCl and 2% potassium ferrocyanide solution, mix and pour into a clean Coplin jar immediately before use. Stain the cells in this solution for 20 min at room temperature.

  c. Wash the stained slides for 10 min in distilled water.

  d. Counterstain the washed slides with 0·05% neutral red for 60 s, rinse thoroughly in distilled water and allow to dry in air.

  e. Cover with mountant and a coverslip, and examine with oil immersion. Any artifact iron is recognized by the iron not being in the plane of the smear.

Comment

Slides will fade after a few months.

8.4   SUDAN BLACK

This stain reacts with lipids including neutral fats, phospholipids and sterols. In leucocytes, sudan black positivity parallels the myeloperoxidase reaction. Cells of the lymphoid series are usually sudan black-negative, while granulocyte precursors and immature monocytes are strongly positive (Dacie and Lewis, 1975e and 1984). Granules in early and mature granulocytic series stain black (McDonald et al, 1978).

Materials

  i. Formaldehyde (40%): use as a fixative.

  ii. Solution A: dissolve 0·3 g sudan black in 100 ml of absolute ethanol. Mix well to dissolve the stain and filter to remove the large particles.

  iii. Solution B: dissolve 16 g of crystalline phenol in 30 ml of absolute ethanol and add the mixture to 100 ml water which contains 0·3 g disodium hydrogen phosphate ($Na_2HPO_4.12H_2O$). Shake vigorously until the phenol has dissolved and filter.

  iv. Staining solution: add 30 ml of solution A to 20 ml of solution B and filter. Keep at 4 °C for 2–3 months.

  v. 70% ethanol.

  vi. Jenner–Giemsa: as a counterstain.

Procedure

a. Prepare cytocentrifuge slides and fix them for 10 min in formalin vapour which can be obtained by placing a formalin-soaked filter paper in a 37 °C incubator. Wash gently 5–10 min in water.

b. Place the staining solution in a Coplin jar and submerge the slides in the solution for 30 min or for 1 h (to obtain stronger staining).

c. Wash slides in 70% ethanol for 2–3 min by waving them in the alcohol contained in a Coplin jar.

d. Wash with tap water for 2 min and dry.

e. Counterstain with Jenner–Giemsa and blot dry but do not mount.

Comments

As this stain is similar to the myeloperoxidase reaction it is generally used to distinguish acute lymphocytic leukaemia (negative) from acute myelogenous leukaemia (positive). It is appreciated that this stain gives better definition of granules in early granulocytic cells.

8.5 MYELOPEROXIDASE

The peroxidase reaction depends on the presence of peroxidase in the cytoplasm of cells. The reaction relies on the transfer of hydrogen (H) from various substrates to hydrogen peroxide, yielding a blue or brown derivative of the dye located at the site of enzyme activity in the cells.

Cells of the neutrophil, eosinophil and basophil series and mono-cytes are peroxidase-positive. Myeloperoxidase activity is shown as blue deposits (McDonald et al, 1978). Cells of the lymphoid and erythroid series are peroxidase-negative. This procedure is useful for distinguishing cells from the lymphoid and myeloid series (Dacie and Lewis, 1975c, 1984).

Materials

i. Fixative: a mixture of 1·25% glutaraldehyde and 1% formaldehyde in 0·1M phosphate buffer (pH 7·3). Mix 50 ml of a 25% solution of glutaraldehyde, 27·8 ml of a 36% solution of formaldehyde and add the buffer up to 1000 ml.

ii. Incubation mixture: add the following reagents in the order shown below and mix well after each addition (prepare just before use):

DAB (Sigma)	5	mg
Tris-HCl buffer, 0·05M, pH 7.6	10	ml
H_2O_2, 30% (w/v)	0.1 ml	

iii. Enhancer: dissolve $0.5\,g$ $CuSO_4$ or $Cu(NO_3)_2.3H_2O$ in 100 ml of Tris-HCl buffer, $0.05M$, pH 7·6.

iv. Counterstain: dissolve 10 g of Giemsa's stain in 100 ml of $0.066M$ phosphate buffer, pH 6·4.

Procedure

 a. Fix the freshly prepared slides for 1 min and then rinse in saline (9 g/l NaCl). Store at 4 °C for not more than 1 week.

 b. Immerse the slides in the incubation mixture for 1 min in a Coplin jar at room temperature.

 c. Wash briefly in Tris-HCl buffer (3 changes) and then submerge the slides in the reaction enhancer.

 d. Rinse in saline and keep in saline until counterstained.

 e. Counterstain for 10 min. Dry and mount in DPX.

8.6   PERIODIC ACID-SCHIFF (PAS)

The liberation of the carbohydrate moiety from glycoproteins and their subsequent oxidation to aldehydes form the basis of the PAS reaction. A positive reaction is given by polysaccharides, mucopolysaccharides, glycoproteins and mucoproteins. A positive reaction in blood cells generally illustrates the presence of glycogen. This is confirmed to be the case when the reaction is prevented by addition of saliva or diastase. PAS-positive material appears as red granules (McDonald et al, 1978). Developing granulocytic cells react positively at all stages of development. Matured polymorphonuclear neutrophils are strongly positive. Myeloblasts and myelocytes are weakly positive. The large specific granules of eosinophils are negative, although the background cytoplasm may be weakly positive (Dacie and Lewis, 1975d and 1984).

Materials

 i. Methanol: use as fixative.

 ii. Periodic acid ($HIO_4.2H_2O$), 10 g/l: make up fresh each time.

 iii. Schiff's reagent: dissolve 1 g basic fuchsin in 400 ml boiling distilled water and shake for 5 min. Cool solution to 50 °C and then filter. To the filtrate, add 1 ml of thionyl chloride ($SOCl_2$) and leave standing in the dark for 12 h. Then add 2 g of activated charcoal, mix by shaking for 1 min and filter. Store in the dark at 0–4 °C.

 iv. Rinsing solution: add 6 ml sodium metabisulphite (100 g/l), 5 ml 1M HCl and make up the volume to 100 ml with water.

  v. Counterstain: to 2 g Mayer's haemalum, add water to 100 ml.

Procedure

  a. Fix the film in methanol for 5–15 min.
  b. Wash in running tap-water for 15 min.
  c. Stain with periodic acid solution for 10 min.
  d. Wash in tap water and immerse in Schiff's reagent for 30 min at room temperature in the dark.
  e. Rinse the slides three times in the rinsing solution, then wash with distilled water for 5 min.
  f. Counterstain with Mayer's haemalum for 10 min.
  g. Blue in tap water for 5 min.
  h. Dry slides in air and mount with DPX mountant.

9. CELL SURFACE MARKERS

In general, cell surface markers are the most sensitive, specific and versatile probes for the detection of cell populations and subpopulations. The majority of the methods available for the detection of lymphocyte subpopulations are based on the presence of specific cell surface receptors (Platsoucas and Catsimpoolas, 1980c) and antigens (Fong, 1983), selectively expressed on certain lymphocyte populations. Such specific cell markers are often involved in immunological functions, such as antigen recognition, cell-mediated lysis and cell–cell interactions involved in the regulation of the immune response. Cell markers may also be products of differentiation pathways with unknown immunological functions or may be receptors for specific hormones, for example erythropoietin in the CFU-E, or for growth factors such as transferrin.

9.1 E-ROSETTING

Peripheral blood T-lymphocytes are identified by their surface receptors which have the ability to form structures known as rosettes with sheep red cells when both are mixed together under certain conditions. Each rosette (*Fig. 2.3*) is a single lymphocyte surrounded by a number of attached sheep red blood cells. The reaction is quite specific for the T-lymphocytes and all T-cells can form rosettes when conditions are made optimal (e.g. pH, the presence of Ca^{2+} and Mg^{2+}, time of incubation at 37 °C, time left at 4 °C, and size of the tube) (Platsoucas and Catsimpoolas, 1980a). In addition, the cell suspension should be of high viability and free of cell aggregates and debris. The procedure described below is based on that of Jondal et al

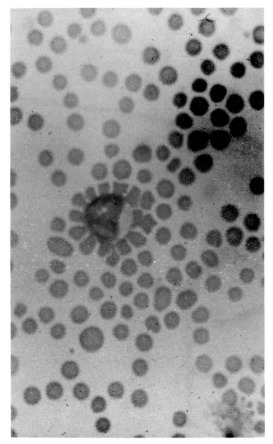

Fig. 2.3. Rosetting of sheep red blood cells by a peripheral blood T-lymphocyte. The cytocentrifuge slide was stained with Jenner–Giemsa.

(1972). By using this method the percentage of T-lymphocytes in mononuclear cell fractions of normal peripheral blood was determined as between 52–81%.

Materials

    i. Sheep red blood cells (SRBC) preserved in Alsevier's solution (not more than 10 days old).

    ii. Hepes-saline (pH 7·4).

    iii. Eagle's minimal essential medium (MEM).

    iv. Heat-inactivated foetal calf serum (HI-FCS).

    v. Toluidine blue: 0·1% in Eagle's MEM.

vi. Polyethylene tubes (Sarstedt) or any small tubes with conical bottom.
vii. Haemocytometer and coverslip (Gallenkamp): keep at 4 °C.

Procedure

PREPARATION OF 2% SRBC SUSPENSION

 a. Wash 1 ml of SRBC solution three times with Hepes-saline (800 g for 7 min at room temperature).
 b. Dilute a small volume of the sedimented SRBC to 2% (v/v) in Eagle's MEM.

FORMATION OF ROSETTES

 a. Into a small polyethylene tube add 0·1 ml of mononuclear cell suspension at a concentration of 3×10^6 cell/ml (prepared as described in Chapter 3, Section 4.1), 0·1 ml of the 2% SRBC suspension and 50 µl HI-FCS. Mix well.
 b. Incubate at 37 °C for 10 min in a water bath.
 c. Centrifuge the cells for 5 min at 200 g in a bench centrifuge.
 d. Leave at 4 °C overnight.

COUNTING OF ROSETTES

 a. Resuspend the rosettes gently using a cold Pasteur pipette and place a small drop on a cold haemocytometer.
 b. Add a small amount of toluidine blue, to show up the nucleated cells. Mix and cover gently with coverslip.
 c. Examine microscopically for rosettes. Discrimination between rosettes and red cell aggregates is facilitated by the blue staining of lymphocytes.
 d. Count at least 200 rosetted and non-rosetted cells. Any lymphocyte in contact with three or more SRBC is considered as a rosette.

Comments

 a. A lower percentage of rosettes will be obtained if the cell mixture is kept for a few hours at 4 °C.
 b. A number of modifications aiming to improve the rosette assay have been reported. The most commonly used technique is the treatment of SRBC with neuraminidase. This treatment enhances the binding of the sheep red blood cells to human T-lymphocytes and significantly reduces the fragility of the rosettes (Weiner et al, 1973). A

rapid method of rosetting (less than one hour) has also been described (Kaplan and Clark, 1974; Pellegrino et al, 1976; Kaplan et al, 1976) and employs SRBC treated with 2,S-amino-ethyl-isothiouronium bromide (AET).

9.2 ERYTHROCYTE–ANTIBODY–COMPLEMENT (EAC) ROSETTES

A number of blood cells possess receptors for various complement components. Such cell types include B-lymphocytes (Bianco et al, 1970; Bianco and Nussenzweig, 1971; Dierich et al, 1974), 'third population' cells in human (Perlmann et al, 1972), monocytes and granulocytes (Ross and Polley, 1975) and eosinophils (Gupta et al, 1976). In addition, up to 2% of peripheral blood T-lymphocytes bear receptors for complement (Chiao et al, 1974).

A significant subpopulation of B-lymphocytes bear receptors for the activated form of the third component of complement (C_3). These cells form rosettes (EAC) with the indicator cells (SRBC coated with non-haemolytic amount of IgM antibodies and treated with complement). The procedure described here is based on those of Bianco et al (1970) and Parish and Hayward (1974). The percentage of lymphocytes that have complement receptors in normal peripheral blood is between 10 and 25%.

Materials

i. Sheep red blood cells (SRBC) preserved in Alsevier's solution (not more than 10 days old).

ii. Rabbit-anti-SRBC (Wellcome): IgM anti-sheep red cell antiserum. The minimum titre of the serum added should be determined with each new batch.

iii. Hepes-saline.

iv. Eagle's minimal essential medium (MEM).

v. Heat-inactivated foetal calf serum (HI-FCS).

vi. Autologous plasma (1/45, v/v in Eagle's MEM): as a source of complement.

vii. Toluidine blue: for staining of lymphocytes to distinguish between rosettes and red cell aggregates.

viii. Haemocytometer and coverslip (Gallenkamp).

ix. Nylon-gauze filter (Millipore).

Procedure

PREPARATION OF 5% SRBC SUSPENSION (E)

a. Wash 1 ml of the SRBC suspension three times with Hepes-saline (800 g, for 7 min). Discard the supernant.

  b. Dilute a small volume (50 µl) of the sedimented SRBC to prepare 5% (v/v) suspension in Eagle's MEM.

PREPARATION OF INDICATOR CELLS (EAC)

  a. Dilute rabbit-anti-SRBC antiserum 1/1000 (v/v) in Eagle's MEM (determine the dilution experimently by initial titration as described below).
  b. In a clean container, mix equal volumes of 5% SRBC suspension and the diluted rabbit-anti-SRBC.
  c. Incubate the mixture at 37 °C for 1 h (the time is not critical).
  d. Centrifuge the tube at 500 *g* for 5 min in a bench centrifuge and resuspend SRBC to prepare 2% (v/v) suspension in Eagle's MEM.
  e. Add one drop of the diluted plasma (as a source of complement) to the 2% SRBC and incubate the mixture at 37 °C for 15 min only (time is very critical in this step).

FORMATION OF EAC-ROSETTES

  a. Prepare peripheral blood mononuclear cell suspension using either Percoll as described in Chapter 3, or by using Ficoll–Triosil (Chapter 6).
  b. Pass the mononuclear cell suspension through a fine-mesh nylon gauze filter to remove any cell aggregates.
  c. In a small clean tube, mix two parts each of EAC suspension and mononuclear cell suspension (3×10^6 cell/ml). To this mixture add one part HI-FCS and mix well.
  d. Incubate at 37 °C water bath for 10 min.
  e. Centrifuge at 200 *g* for 5 min and reincubate the tube for another 20 min.
  f. Let the tube stand for 10 min at room temperature.
  g. Resuspend the cells by strongly drawing them in and out of a Pasteur pipette to disperse any E-rosettes formed during the procedure.

COUNTING OF ROSETTES

For the estimation of the percentage of EAC-rosettes in the cell suspension follow the technique described in Section 9.1 above. However, it should be noted that monocytes and neutrophils (if present) can also form EAC-rosettes.

TITRATION OF ANTI-SRBC AND COMPLEMENT

  a. Dilute the rabbit-anti-SRBC antiserum, v/v with Eagle's MEM starting with the titre printed on the container supplied by the

manufacturer (e.g. 1/300, 1/600 and 1/1000 etc.) Perform the
EAC-rosette procedure as described above.
   b. Titrate the complement (patient's own plasma) using one drop
each of 1/20, 1/45 and 1/85 (v/v) dilutions in Eagle's MEM.
Check for EAC-rosetting in a manner similar to that described in the
above procedure.
   c. Use the concentration of antiserum and complement that is high
enough to give a maximum number of rosettes. Moreover, the
antiserum or complement concentration should not cause lysis of the
SRBC when incubated together.

Reproducibility
The percentage of EAC-rosettes was determined on two samples of
normal peripheral blood. The percentage was 9% and 19% respectively. These values were obtained using 1/1000 (v/v) dilution of the
anti-SRBC antiserum and 1/45 (v/v) dilution of the complement.
The morphology of the rosette structure is similar to that shown in *Fig.*
2.3 (F. Ali and A. May, unpublished work).

Comments
   a. It is possible to use erythrocytes from various sources. However,
human erythrocytes are to be avoided for EAC-rosetting since they
possess immune adherence receptors (Aiuti et al, 1974) and when
coated with complement may rosette amongst themselves.
   b. Titration of complement by adding one drop of 1/20 and 1/85
(v/v) diluted autologous plasma respectively gave 9% and 16%
EAC-rosettes, while a 1/45 dilution produced 19% EAC-rosettes.
Therefore a dilution of 1/45 was adopted for future experiments.
   c. Since rosetting is also characteristic of the monocytes it is
therefore necessary to identify the monocytes either by their capacity
to phagocytose iron particles (Chapter 3, Section 4.2) or by
morphological identification.
   d. The use of the IgM fraction of the anti-SRBC serum excludes
rosette formation due to Fc receptors (marker for the B-lymphocytes).

9.3   DIRECT FLUORESCENCE STAINING
This procedure can be used to detect cells that produce surface
immunoglobulin, such as peripheral blood B-lymphocytes. Cells are
incubated with a fluorescein isothiocyanate (FITC)-conjugated antibody and the antibody–antigen complex is made visible by irradiation
with light of a suitable wavelength under a fluorescence microscope.
Using this method, it is essential to avoid non-specific fluorescence

staining (false positive) of cells via the Fc receptors or due to labelled antibody aggregation. Non-specific binding of antibody to Fc receptors can be reduced by using F(ab)$_2$ fragments of immunoglobulin molecules. Any non-specific binding of F(ab)$_2$ aggregates to cells can be minimized by high-speed centrifugation. In addition non-specific staining will, in general, increase with increasing concentration of the conjugated antibody. Each new batch of antiserum, both test and control (non-immune serum) should therefore be titrated over a suitable dilution range to find the optimum concentration which gives minimal non-specific binding but effective specific staining. Cell suspensions for staining should be of high viability and essentially free of cell clumps and debris. By using this method the normal value of B-lymphocytes with surface immunoglobulin in peripheral blood is about 6%.

Materials
  i. Diagnostic FITC-conjugated F(ab)$_2$ (Behring).
 ii. Control FITC-conjugated F(ab)$_2$ (Behring).
iii. Phosphate buffered saline (PBS) Dulbecco 'A' (Oxoid tablets).
 iv. Sodium azide: 2% (w/v) solution
  v. Glycerol.

Equipment
  i. Leitz fluorescence microscope system.
 ii. Leitz Ploemopak filter system.
iii. Polyethylene tubes (Sarstedt).
 iv. Beckman 152 Microfuge or any other high-speed centrifuge.

Procedure
PREPARATION OF REAGENTS
  a. Phosphate buffered saline (PBS)-azide solution: completely dissolve one tablet PBS in 100 ml distilled water, add 1 ml sodium azide solution and store in a cool place.
  b. Staining solutions:
  i. Place a small volume of control and diagnostic FITC-conjugated F(ab)$_2$ reagents into two polyethylene tubes. Centrifuge for 1–3 min, in Beckman 125 Microfuge at room temperature and use the supernatants.
 ii. Prepare optimum dilution of antibody (determined by prior titration) in PBS–azide solution from each of the control and diagnostic FITC-conjugate reagents.

STAINING OF CELLS

 a. Into two separate tubes, transfer 50 µl of each of the diluted diagnostic and control reagents and then add 50 µl of the freshly prepared peripheral blood mononuclear cell suspension (3×10^6 cell/ml), prepared as described in Chapter 3 or 6.

 b. Leave the tubes at room temperature for 30 min, for the antibody–antigen reaction to occur.

 c. To remove excess labelled antibody, wash the cells three times with PBS–azide at 800 g for 5 min.

 d. Discard the supernatant, leaving the cells suspended in a small volume of PBS–azide solution.

 e. Add a small drop of glycerol to the cell suspension, mix gently with a Pasteur pipette, and place on a clean dry slide. Cover with a coverslip and examine using fluorescence microscope.

COUNTING OF CELLS

 a. Examine the cells under u.v. illumination within 24 h. The performances of different systems of u.v. light source, filter and objectives vary, so that each system must be checked for satisfactory results. For the Leitz fluorescence microscope, use an excitation wavelength of 495 nm by means of a Ploemopak filter. This produces a visible emission at 525 nm. Count the number of cells (at least 200 cells) with ordinary light, change to the u.v. light and estimate the number of positively stained cells. The stained cells appear as fluorescent apple green patches. Dead cells have bright homogeneous fluorescence.

 b. Check the control slide for negatively stained cells.

TITRATION OF REAGENTS

After ultracentrifugation titrate both diagnostic and control FITC-conjugated F(ab)$_2$ reagents over a dilution range. Dilute the reagents 1/20, 1/80 (v/v) with PBS–azide or use the dilution range which is suggested by the supplier. Follow the same procedure described above. For further experiments use the dilution of antibody that gives not more than 6% positively stained lymphocytes.

Reproducibility

The percentage of B-lymphocytes having surface immunoglobulin was estimated on two samples of normal peripheral blood. Using a reagent dilution of 1:80 (v/v), values of 4% and 5% were obtained.

Comments

   a. According to the instructions supplied by Behring, the diagnostic FITC-conjugated F(ab)$_2$ reagent is raised in rabbits against human Ig (IgG+IgA+IgM). The γ-globulin fraction is then isolated and conjugated with a standardized amount of fluorescein isothiocyanate (FITC). The IgG F(ab)$_2$ fragment is then obtained by enzymatic splitting with pepsin, purification and freeze drying. Control FITC-conjugated F(ab)$_2$ reagent is prepared from normal rabbit serum and used as a negative control.
   b. Sodium azide, a metabolic inhibitor, is added in order to prevent capping of the immunoglobulin at the apical end of the cell. Capping can be further reduced by staining the cell at 4 °C instead of room temperature.

10. DETERMINATION OF VIABILITY BY TRYPAN BLUE EXCLUSION

A rapid estimation of the percentage of viable cells in cell preparations can be achieved using trypan blue dye. Viable cells exclude the dye, while non-viable cells take up the dye and appear blue. The percentage of non-stained cells gives the percentage viability.

Materials

   i. Eagle's minimal essential medium (MEM).
   ii. Trypan Blue 0·4% (Gibco): dilute 1/4 (v/v) in Eagle's MEM.
   iii. Haemocytometer and coverslip.

Procedure

   a. Prepare cell suspension containing 3–6 × 10^6 cells/ml.
   b. Mix one part cell suspension with one part trypan blue and leave for 1 min.
   c. Place one drop on a clean, dry haemocytometer with a coverslip in place. Allow the cells to settle for at least 1 min.
   d. Count the percentage of viable and non-viable cells. Determine the percentage viability after counting at least 200 cells.

Chapter 3

Isolation of Blood Cells by
Centrifugation on Percoll Gradients

1. INTRODUCTION

In recent years centrifugation has proved to be one of the most useful techniques for the fractionation of biological particles. Different types of cells can be separated according to difference in buoyant density which is termed 'isopyknic' centrifugation, or according to variation in size as in the case of 'rate-zonal' centrifugation. Stokes' law describes the sedimentation rate (V) of a sphere with a diameter d in a gravitational field g:

$$V = \frac{d^2(\rho_p - \rho_l)\, g}{18\eta}$$

where ρ_p and ρ_l are the respective densities of the spherical particles (e.g. cells) and liquid (gradient material), and η is the viscosity of the liquid. Stokes' law adequately describes the behaviour of cells during isopyknic centrifugation, in which separation is effected on the basis of density. In addition, the above equation applies to velocity sedimentation in which separation is on the basis of size.

1.1 ISOPYKNIC CENTRIFUGATION (EQUILIBRIUM DENSITY CENTRIFUGATION)

The cells are sedimented on the basis of density through an increasingly dense medium (continuous density gradient) during the application of a gravitational force (g) by centrifugation. The density range of the gradient medium encompasses all densities of the cells present in the sample. The cells float in an equilibrium position after reaching a point where their density equals that of the medium. At this position (ρ_p and ρ_l) = 0, therefore sedimentation rate (V) = 0. Cells with a density greater than that of the gradient sediment to the bottom of the tube. The density gradient is formed from substances which will not perturb osmotic balance or ionic equilibria. These include very high molecular weight polymers of low osmolality. The cells are either applied to the top of the gradient or are mixed into the gradient medium with the dense solution, which helps to minimize streaming of the cells. Reproducibility requires careful temperature control and, in order to prevent perturbation, the centrifuge is operated with the brake in the 'off' position.

1.2   ISOPYKNIC CUSHIONING

A cell suspension is layered onto a high-density medium, the density of which varies according to the type of cells that are to be isolated. The basis of the cell separation is the same as the isopyknic centrifugation, but the cells collect at the interface between the media. A gravitational force is applied by centrifugation and at equilibrium those cells having a density lower than that of the cushion ($\rho_l > \rho_p$) are collected at the cushion/medium interface, whereas the more dense cells are found in the pellet ($\rho_l < \rho_p$) at the bottom of the tube. A discontinuous gradient may include a single density layer (single-step cushioning) or may be constructed from several cushions, one on top of the other, starting with the highest density at the bottom of the tube to the lowest density at the top. The cells are collected at the appropriate interface between medium of $\rho_l < \rho_p$ and medium of $\rho_l > \rho_p$.

1.3   DENSITY GRADIENT MEDIUM (PERCOLL)

Density gradient centrifugation has for many years been used for the separation of cells. The restrictions placed on using this technique have mostly been due to the physical properties of the gradient materials available for use. At the density required for optimum resolution, the conditions created by many media are far from the physiological norm, thus leading researchers to compromise between resolution (degree of purification) and retaining the biological integrity of the cells.

Isopyknic centrifugation has been facilitated by the introduction of Percoll (Pharmacia Fine Chemicals). Percoll is a colloidal suspension of silica particles coated with polyvinylpyrrolidone (PVP) which serves as a stabilizer and avoids silica toxicity to the cells. The suspension can be made isotonic and adjusted to physiological pH before preparation of density gradients.

Pure colloidal silica solutions (Ludox-HS; Pharmacia Fine Chemicals) was first reported as being useful for cell separation by Mateyko and Kopac (1963), and was then systematically evaluated by Pertoft and

Laurent (1968, 1977) and by Wolff (1975). It was found that unmodified silica solutions were unstable in the presence of salt at physiological pH and were toxic to cells. This instability and toxicity was decreased by the addition of polymers such as PVP, dextran and polyethylene glycol. However, a large excess of free polymer was required and this not only increased the osmolality and viscosity but was also difficult to remove from suspensions. Percoll (modified colloidal silica MCS, Pertoft and Laurent, 1977) was then developed to overcome these problems. Each silica particle has a 15–30 nm diameter and is irreversibly coated with PVP (Pertoft et al, 1978). Percoll suspensions are supplied at a density of about $1·13 \pm 0·005$ g/ml and can form gradients in the range $1·0$ to $1·3$ g/ml, which covers a density range sufficient for isopyknic separation of all human blood cells. Percoll has a very low osmotic pressure of 15–20 mmol/kg H_2O and can therefore give a density gradient virtually iso-osmotic throughout. It also has a low viscosity of 10 ± 5 centipoises (cP) at 20 °C which allows an equilibrium to be obtained rapidly. Percoll is easily removed from cells (Bergman et al, 1977), it can be sterilized by filtration and is completely non-toxic to cells (Pertoft et al, 1977; Kurnick et al, 1979). All of these characteristics make Percoll an excellent gradient medium for the separation of cells. Although Ficoll (Pharmacia Fine Chemicals), has been used for many years to separate blood cells and particularly peripheral blood mononuclear cells (Böyum, 1968), a major advantage of Percoll is its ability to generate a continuous density gradient when centrifuged at high g values.

Continuous density gradients of Percoll have previously been used by many workers for the separation of monocytes, lymphocytes and neutrophils (Kurnick et al, 1979; Gmelig-Meyling and Waldmann, 1980; Segal et al, 1980; Giddings et al, 1980). Modification of the starting density enables a good recovery of highly purified lymphocyte subpopulations (Ali et al, 1982). Isolated cells exhibit a high viability (Pertoft et al, 1977; Feucht et al, 1980).

Discontinuous Percoll gradients have been used to separate monocyte and lymphocyte subpopulations (Gutierrez et al, 1979; Ulmer and Flad, 1979). Kurnick et al (1979) also separated low density B-lymphocytes from T-lymphocytes. A complete up-to-date list of references of research carried out using Percoll may be requested from Pharmacia Fine Chemicals.

2. PREPARATION OF PERCOLL SOLUTIONS OF DIFFERENT DENSITIES

Percoll solutions are required at a range of starting densities since cells differ in their buoyant densities. Silica-containing solutions usually give a pellet at the bottom of the centrifuge tube, and deposits of silica on the walls of tubing used for separation. These deposits should be removed before drying by washing thoroughly with water immediately after use.

2.1 DIRECT DILUTION OF STOCK PERCOLL

The stock suspensions of Percoll may be diluted directly from the bottle to give the desired density (working solution) as described below.

Materials
  i. Stock Percoll (Pharmacia Fine Chemicals): mix before use.
 ii. $1 \cdot 2$M NaCl: 8% (w/v) solution.

Procedure
  a. Choose the final volume (V) of Percoll solution of the desired density. Place a volume of $1 \cdot 2$M NaCl equal to one-tenth of the final volume V, into a sterile container. The volume of purchased Percoll to be added to this solution is calculated by the following formula (work from Pharmacia Fine Chemicals reproduced by kind permission):

$$V_0 = V \frac{\rho - 0 \cdot 1\rho_{10} - 0 \cdot 9}{\rho_o - 1}$$

where: V_0 = volume of stock Percoll (from the bottle), ml
       V = volume of the final working solution, ml
       ρ = desired density of the final solution, g/ml
       ρ_o = density of stock Percoll (printed on the bottle), g/ml
       ρ_{10} = density of $1 \cdot 2$M NaCl = $1 \cdot 056$ g/ml
  b. Make up to the final volume with distilled water.
  c. Measure the density using the refractometer (Section 3).
  d. Measure the osmolality of the working solution. This should be in the range 280–300 mmol/kg H_2O.
  e. A graph identical to the one shown in *Fig.* 3.2 (p. 61) may be drawn to relate the volume of purchased Percoll to the final density.
Example:
To prepare 100 ml of working Percoll solution of density $1 \cdot 077$ g/ml in $1 \cdot 2$M NaCl, place 10 ml of $1 \cdot 2$M NaCl into a container. The calculated volume of stock Percoll (V_o) to add is:

$$V_0 = 100 \frac{1 \cdot 077 - (0 \cdot 1 \times 1 \cdot 056) - 0 \cdot 9}{1 \cdot 13 - 1}$$

= 54·9 ml (if stock Percoll density is 1·13 g/ml). Make up to 100 ml with distilled water.

Comment

The osmolality of the working solution prepared using 1·5M NaCl (9% w/v, as suggested by Pharmacia Fine Chemicals) was 325–330 mmol/kg H_2O. Since the optimum osmolality for most living human cells is 280–300 mmol/kg H_2O, higher osmolalities cause shrinkage of cells with alteration of their density. 1·2M NaCl is therefore the recommended concentration.

2.2 INDIRECT DILUTION OF PERCOLL

Iso-osmotic Percoll with the optimum osmolality of 290–300 mmol/kg H_2O can be obtained by mixing 9 parts of the purchased Percoll with 1 part 1·2M NaCl (8%, w/v) and diluting to the desired density with balanced salt solution or Eagle's minimal essential medium. For the separation methods described here Percoll solutions with the desired density were prepared by the indirect method.

Materials

   i. Percoll (Pharmacia Fine Chemicals): mix before use.
  ii. 1·2M NaCl (8%, w/v) solution. Pass through a 0·45 μm Millipore filter for sterilization.
 iii. Buffered salt solution (BSS).

Procedure

PREPARATION OF ISO-OSMOTIC PERCOLL

   a. Mix 9 parts Percoll with 1 part of sterile 1·2M NaCl.
   b. Measure the osmolality of the resulting iso-osmotic Percoll (280–300 mmol/kg H_2O).
   c. Store in a sterile bottle at 4 °C.

DILUTION OF ISO-OSMOTIC PERCOLL

In the methods described in this chapter Percoll solution is required at four different densities, namely 1·077, 1·083, 1·09 and 1·11 g/ml. These can be prepared by adding BSS to the iso-osmotic Percoll in the proportions shown in *Table* 3.1.

Table 3.1. Preparation of Percoll solutions of different densities using the indirect dilution method

Percoll Density g/ml	Equivalent volumes of solutions	
	Iso-osmotic Percoll	BSS or Eagle's MEM
1·077	5	3
1·083	15	8
1·09	15	5
1·11	17	3

Comments

a. Using the indirect dilution method, enough gradient solution of the required density can be prepared in advance, thereby reducing the risk of variation of the density from experiment to experiment. In addition, less time is required for preparation of the wanted cells.

b. Iso-osmotic Percoll can also be diluted with Eagle's minimal essential medium (MEM).

c. For sterilization, pass through a 0·45 μm Millipore filter.

3. DETERMINATION OF PERCOLL DENSITY BY CALIBRATION CURVE

The simplest way to determine the density of a given Percoll solution is by measuring the refractive index of the solution with a refractometer. The refractive index has a linear correlation with density (Pertoft and Laurent, 1977).

Materials

i. Percoll (Pharmacia Fine Chemicals): record the density of the purchased Percoll which is always printed on the label.

ii. Buffered salt solution (BSS).

Equipment

Refractometer (Atago).

Procedure

PREPARATION OF PERCOLL SOLUTIONS

a. Prepare iso-osmotic Percoll as described in Section 2.2.

b. Make up a series of dilutions of iso-osmotic Percoll (20%, 50% and 80%) in BSS or Eagle's MEM.

ESTIMATION OF REFRACTIVE INDEX (RI).

a. Set the refractometer to the lowest point on the middle scale (1·333) using distilled water. Clean and dry the plate with tissue paper after each measurement. Place a small volume of BSS and record the RI.

b. Measure the RI of the purchased Percoll (RI = 1·3518).

c. On a graph of RI against density join the two points as shown in *Fig. 3.1.*

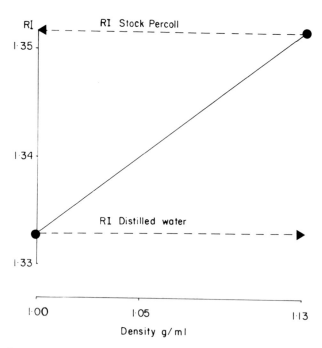

Fig. 3.1. The relationship between the density of purchased Percoll and its refractive index (RI).

d. Measure the RI of the iso-osmotic Percoll and then determine the RIs of the 20%, 50% and 80% soltions.

e. Plot another graph of RI against percentage iso-osmotic Percoll with best straight line drawn through the points as shown in *Fig. 3.2.*

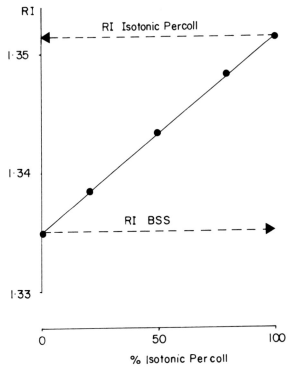

Fig. 3.2. The refractive indices (RI) of solutions containing different proportions of iso-osmotic Percoll and buffered salt solution (BSS).

APPLICATIONS

   a. To determine the density of any Percoll solution, measure the RI and extrapolate.

   b. The graph can also be used to prepare Percoll solution of any density. Use *Fig.* 3.1 to calculate the RI. From *Fig.* 3.2 determine the percentage dilution of iso-osmotic Percoll (with BSS or Eagle's MEM) to give the RI calculated from *Fig.* 3.1.

Comment
For good reproducibility a calibration curve should be plotted with each batch of the purchased Percoll.

4.   SINGLE-STEP DENSITY GRADIENT CENTRIFUGATION OF CELLS (ISOPYKNIC CUSHIONING)

The procedure described here can separate a population of cells into two layers. The first layer is formed at the interface between the suspending fluid and the Percoll solution, and the second layer is usually found as a sediment at the bottom of the tube (Ali et al, 1982).

4.1 HARVESTING OF MONONUCLEAR CELLS

Percoll of 1·077 g/ml density can be used for a rapid separation of blood mononuclear cell layer (MNL) (monocytes and lymphocytes) from the granulocytes and mature red cells.

Materials

   i. Preservative-free heparin (Duncan Flockhart Co. Ltd): 15 units/ml blood.
   ii. Percoll solution (density 1.077 g/ml): prepare as described in Section 2.2.
   iii. Buffered salt solution (BSS).
   iv. Heat-inactivated foetal calf serum (HI-FCS).
   v. 0·45 µm filter (Millipore).

Procedure

   a. Mix venous blood with heparin and prepare a buffy coat cell layer. Suspend the cells in the donor's own plasma (which has been centrifuged hard to sediment the platelets, *see* Comment 1) or in any physiological solution (BSS or Eagle's MEM).
   b. Count the total number of nucleated cells, and prepare cytocentrifuge slides for Jenner–Giemsa staining.
   c. Into a sterile container (or preferably a polycarbonate tube, supplied by MSE Scientific Instruments Ltd), carefully layer the buffy coat cell suspension onto an equal volume of Percoll solution using a syringe and 19 gauge needle.
   d. Centrifuge at 400 g for 15–20 min at room temperature in a bench centrifuge.
   e. Discard the supernatant (plasma or suspending medium). This also removes some of the remaining platelets.
   f. Harvest the mononuclear cells from the Percoll/plasma interface using a 19 gauge needle and syringe, and dispense 5 ml of cell suspension into each container. To recover all of the cells, also remove the medium lying immediately above the pellet of red cells and granulocytes.
   g. To sediment the separated MNL, add BSS to a final volume of about 15–20 ml for each 5 ml cell suspension, to decrease the density of the Percoll solution.
   h. Centrifuge at room temperature for 7–10 min at 1000 g.

i. Suspend the pelleted cells in the donor's own plasma, HI-FCS or any suitable medium.

j. Mix well using a syringe and needle or a vortex mixer. Count the total number of cells and prepare Jenner–Giemsa stained cytocentrifuge slides for morphological examination and for obtaining a differential cell count.

k. Determine cell viability using trypan blue exclusion.

l. Estimate the recovery of MNL using the total number and the differential count at the beginning and end of the procedure as follows:

$$\% \text{ Recovery} = \frac{\text{Total MNL cell number collected finally}}{\text{Total MNL cell number initially in the blood}} \times 100$$

Reproducibility

Separation of normal blood cells by Percoll cushioning allowed harvesting of monocytes and lymphocytes at the Percoll/suspending medium interface, while the granulocytes and mature red cells were sedimented to the bottom of the tube. From seven consecutive experiments, the mean percentage of each cell type was: 82% (SE 3·0) lymphocytes; 17% (SE 3·0) monocytes and 0·85% (SE 0·3) granulocytes. Cell viability was high (more than 90%). The recovery of isolated cells was more than 80% and the morphological appearance of the cells appeared to be unchanged.

Comments

a. To use the donor's own plasma, centrifuge at 2350 g for 7 min to sediment the platelets, and pass through a 0·45 μm Millipore filter.

b. For reasons of economy, it is necessary to use a buffy coat preparation rather than whole blood so that the volume of Percoll used can be kept to a minimum.

c. An alternative method for removing platelets from the MNL is by suspending the cells in a few drops of HI-FCS, and layer carefully onto 10 ml HI-FCS. Centrifuge at 400 g for 15 min. Discard the supernatant HI-FCS and repeat the procedure (using 5 ml HI-FCS) before suspending the cells in the suspending fluid.

d. A comparative study was performed using both Percoll and Ficoll–Triosil (Pharmacia Fine Chemicals, Chapter 6, Section 1) for the isolation of peripheral blood mononuclear cells from both whole blood and buffy coat.

The data indicated that Percoll is as effective as Ficoll–Triosil in preparing MNL. However Percoll is the preferred medium since its lower viscosity (10 ± 5 cP at 20 °C) allows rapid separation of cells (15–20 min) when compared with Ficoll–Triosil (30–40 min).

4.2 PREPARATION OF PURE LYMPHOCYTES

Depletion of phagocytic cells from the mononuclear cell suspension to obtain pure lymphocytes can be achieved by incubation with carbonyl iron particles (Rothbarth et al, 1976). The carbonyl iron loaded monocytes can then be sedimented by centrifugation on a Percoll cushion of 1·077 g/ml density, due to their increased density (Ali et al, 1982).

Materials

i. Preservative-free heparin (Duncan Flockhart Co Ltd): 15 units/ml blood.
ii. Carbonyl iron powder (Goodfellow Metals).
iii. Eagle's minimal essential medium (MEM).
iv. Buffered salt solution (BSS).
v. Heat-inactivated foetal calf serum; for cytocentrifuge slides.
vi. 0·45 μm filter (Millipore).

Equipment

Rotary mixer.

Procedure

STERILIZATION OF CARBONYL IRON POWDER

a. Place 1 g carbonyl iron powder into a clean, screw-capped bottle.
b. Sterilize by autoclaving at 15 lb/in^2 at 121 °C for 20 min.
c. Dry the bottle in an incubator at 37 °C. Store at room temperature.

INCUBATION WITH CARBONYL IRON

a. Mix whole blood with heparin and centrifuge (450 g for 15 min) to prepare the buffy coat. Place the buffy coat cell suspension and plasma in separate containers.
b. Centrifuge the plasma (2350 g for 7 min) to sediment the platelets and pass through a 0·45 μm Millipore filter. Suspend the cells in the filtered plasma (keep some of the plasma in a sterile container).
c. Prepare cytocentrifuge slides and stain with Jenner–Giemsa.
d. Prepare a mononuclear cell layer (MNL$_1$) using Percoll 1·077 g/ml as described in Section 4.1.
e. Count the total number of nucleated cells and prepare cytocentrifuge slides for both Jenner–Giemsa and non-specific esterase staining (Chapter 2).

 f. Add 10 ml of Eagle's MEM to the sterile carbonyl iron powder, mix well and add 50 μl of this suspension to each 1 ml of the mononuclear cell suspension (contains about 3–5 × 10^6 nucleated cells).
 g. Incubate the cell mixture for 45 min at 37 °C on a rotary mixer. Shake the tube occasionally using a vortex mixer (or by hand) to avoid sedimentation of the carbonyl iron particles and to prevent aggregation of the monocytes.

DEPLETION OF PHAGOCYTIC CELLS
 a. With a syringe and 19 gauge needle resuspend the cell mixture and carefully layer onto an equal volume of 1·077 g/ml Percoll solution.
 b. Prepare a second batch of mononuclear cell layer (MNL$_2$) and harvest them at the interface. Wash twice and suspend with BSS, Eagle's MEM or the patient's own plasma. The pellet will contain the carbonyl iron-loaded monocytes.
 c. Count the total cell number and prepare stained cytocentrifuge slides for morphological examination and differential counting.
 d. Calculate the recovery of lymphocytes at the interface from the total cell number at the first and second MNL as follows:

$$\% \text{ Recovery} = \frac{\text{Total lymphocyte number in MNL}_2}{\text{Total lymphocyte number in MNL}_1} \times 100$$

Reproducibility
Incubation of mononuclear cells with carbonyl iron depleted the cells of monocytes and pure lymphocyte preparations were obtained. The mean percentages of the remaining cells from four experiments were: lymphocytes 96% (SE 2·6); monocytes 1·8%; granulocytes 1·6%. The mean recovery of lymphocytes from three preparations was 95% (SE 1·5). The recovery of B-lymphocytes after carbonyl iron depletion of monocytes was measured on one occasion using direct fluorescence staining and was found to be complete. The morphology of the prepared lymphocytes appeared to be normal (*Fig. 3.3*).

Comment
EDTA anti-coagulant should be avoided because it chelates Ca^{2+} and Mg^{2+} which are necessary for the carbonyl iron phagocytosis by monocytes.

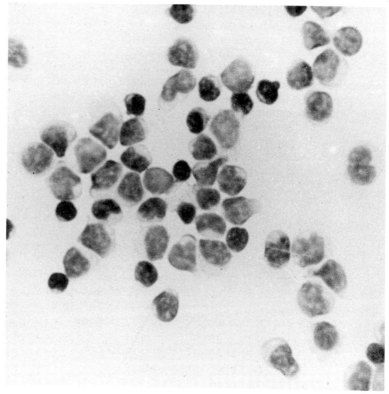

Fig. 3.3. Jenner–Giemsa staining of normal peripheral blood lymphocytes purified from mononuclear cells using carbonyl iron depletion of monocytes.

5. BANDING OF LEUCOCYTES BY DISCONTINUOUS PERCOLL GRADIENT

Banding of the mononuclear cell layer (MNL) on a discontinuous gradient of Percoll gives highly enriched monocyte and lymphocyte fractions. The methods described here can separate a population of cells into two bands, which form at the interface between Percoll layers of different densities during centrifugation. Cell separation by discontinuous Percoll gradients is useful when a high-speed centrifuge (which is required to generate the continuous density gradient of Percoll) is not available.

5.1 BANDING OF MONOCYTES AND LYMPHOCYTES

The method described here was established by Al-Sumidaie et al (1984).

Materials

   i. Preservative-free heparin (Duncan Flockhart Co Ltd):
15 units/ml blood.

   ii. Eagle's MEM × 10 (Gibco): prepare iso-osmotic MEM by
adding distilled water (1:9, v/v) and adjust to pH 7·4 with NaOH.

   iii. Iso-osmotic Percoll solution: prepare as described in Section
2.2 using Eagle's MEM 10 ×.

   iv. Percoll solution of 1·077 g/ml density (Section 2.2).

   v. Buffered salt solution (BSS).

   vi. Heat-inactivated foetal calf serum (HI-FCS).

   vii. Polycarbonate tube (MSE Scientific Inst) *or* siliconized glass
container (Appendix D).

Procedure

PERCOLL SOLUTIONS

Percoll solution is required at three different densities: 1·057, 1·066
and 1·074 (± 0·005) g/ml. These can be obtained by preparing
42%, 50% and 56·6% Percoll in iso-osmotic Eagle's MEM.

BANDING OF CELLS

   a. Layer the heparinized blood or buffy coat cell suspension onto
the same volume of Percoll solution (1·077 g/ml) (placed in a
polycarbonate tube or a siliconized glass container) using a syringe and
19 gauge needle. Prepare MNL as described in Section 4.1. Wash the
recovered cells twice and resuspend in cold BSS.

   b. Count the total number of cells and prepare cytocentrifuge slides
for staining with both Jenner–Giemsa and non-specific esterase
(Chapter 2).

   c. Centrifuge the MNL at 400 g for 7 min in a bench centrifuge.

   d. Discard the supernatant and resuspend the pelleted cells with
2 ml of Percoll solution (1·074 g/ml).

   e. Transfer the cells into a new tube and onto the surface of the cell
suspension carefully layer using a syringe and needle 2 ml of Percoll
solution (1·066 g/ml) by allowing the Percoll solution to run on the
side wall of the tube.

   f. Using the same technique, place the third layer of Percoll (1·057
g/ml) on the top of the two previous solutions (three layers should be
visible).

   g. Centrifuge the tube at 2200 g for 90 min at room temperature
in a bench centrifuge.

   h. Discard the supernatant Percoll solution (1·057 g/ml) above
the mononuclear phagocyte (monocyte) band (*Fig.* 3.4) and collect the
cell layer. Repeat the same technique to collect the next band of cells

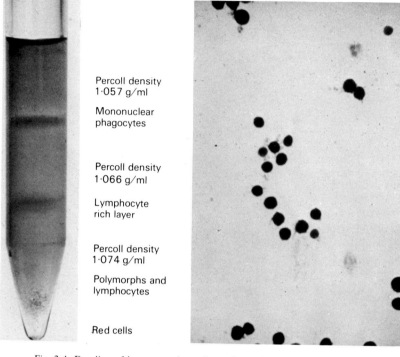

Percoll density
1·057 g/ml

Mononuclear
phagocytes

Percoll density
1·066 g/ml

Lymphocyte
rich layer

Percoll density
1·074 g/ml

Polymorphs and
lymphocytes

Red cells

Fig. 3.4. Banding of leucocytes by a discontinuous density gradient of Percoll (left); non-specific esterase staining of monocytes (mononuclear phagocytes) obtained from the discontinuous density gradient (right).

(lymphocytes). The remaining cell band at the bottom of the tube contains polymorphs (neutrophils), some red cells and lymphocytes.

i. Count the total number of cells and prepare at least two cytocentrifuge slides for each band of cells. Stain with both Jenner–Giemsa and non-specific esterase (Chapter 2) to estimate the percentage of lymphocytes and monocytes in each cell band.

j. Check the viability of the recovered cells (if required) by dye exclusion of trypan blue.

k. Calculate the recovery of the nucleated cells (monocytes or lymphocytes) from the discontinuous gradient of Percoll as follows:

$$\% \text{ Recovery} = \frac{\text{Number of cells (monocytes or lymphocytes)}}{\text{Number of cells (monocytes or lymphocytes)}} \times 100$$

$$\text{in the MNL cells}$$

Reproducibility

Banding of mononuclear cells by a discontinuous density gradient of

Percoll produced highly enriched bands of monocytes and lymphocytes which formed at the interface between the Percoll layers (*Fig.* 3.4). From 100 experiments using normal subjects, the mean percentage of monocytes collected at the 42%–50% interface was 83% (SD ± 10) and the mean percentage of lymphocytes collected at the 50–56·6% interface was 92% (SD ± 6). Other bands (one at the top and the other at the bottom of the gradient) were discarded. The mean recovery of monocytes was 78% (SD ± 10) and of lymphocytes was 80% (SD ± 6). The morphology of the recovered cells was unchanged. The mean viability of monocytes was 97% and of lymphocytes was 98%.

Comments
  a. It is preferable to use polycarbonate tubes to prevent adherence of monocytes with subsequent reduction in recovery.
  b. Sufficient amounts of sterile Percoll of each density may be prepared in advance and stored at 4 °C. Solutions are stable at physiological pH and osmolality.

5.2 A RAPID METHOD FOR THE FRACTIONATION OF MONONUCLEAR CELLS

Mononuclear cells can also be fractionated into monocytes and lymphocytes by discontinuous density gradients of Percoll using a method reported by Weetman et al. (1983).

Materials
  i. Preservative-free heparin (Duncan Flockhart Co Ltd): 15 units/ml blood.
  ii. Buffered salt solution (BSS).
  iii. Iso-osmotic Percoll solution (Section 2).
  iv. Heat-inactivated foetal calf serum (HI-FCS): for cytocentrifuge slide preparation.
  v. Conical tube: 15 ml capacity.

Procedure
PERCOLL SOLUTIONS
Prepare 40%, 48% and 53% iso-osmotic Percoll in BSS.

FRACTIONATION OF CELLS
  a. Collect venous blood in heprain and prepare a mononuclear cell layer (MNL) as described in Section 4.1. Wash the cells twice with BSS.

b. Suspend the pelleted mononuclear cells in 3 ml 53% Percoll solution in a conical tube and onto the top of this solution layer 3 ml 48% and 1 ml 40% Percoll solution using a syringe and needle (*see also* Section 5.1).

c. Centrifuge at 400 g for 20 min at room temperature.

d. Collect the two bands of cells and proceed as described in Section 5.1 (Step *h* onwards).

Reproducibility

Fractionation of MNL on a discontinuous density gradient of Percoll produced a significant enrichment of monocytes and lymphocytes in the fractions. In 14 experiments, more than 90% pure monocytes were collected at the 40–48% interface and more than 95% pure lymphocytes recovered from the bottom of the tube. Other bands were discarded. Purity was determined by non-specific esterase staining (Chapter 2). The morphology of the cells was unchanged. Recovery of the cells was variable (60–80%).

Comments

a. The monocyte fractions were irradiated with 3000 rads following isolation to eliminate contaminating lymphocytes but leaving monocyte function intact.

b. The separated cells were used to demonstrate production of thyroglobulin antibodies with autologous thyroglobulin-primed monocytes.

6. PREPARATION OF A CONTINUOUS DENSITY GRADIENT OF PERCOLL

A preformed continuous density gradient is stable and can be prepared up to a week in advance.

6.1 GENERATION OF THE GRADIENT

When a solution of Percoll in 0·12M NaCl is centrifuged at < 10 000 g in an angle-head rotor, the coated silica particles will sediment in an uneven distribution thus forming a density gradient. Since Percoll is a polydispersed or heterogeneous colloid, its component particles sediment at different rates, producing a very smooth gradient. The gradient forms isometrically around the starting density and becomes progressively steeper with time. A gradient of Percoll formed by centrifugation will change continuously during high speed centrifugation. Prolonged centrifugation of Percoll at high *g* force results in all of the colloid sedimenting in a hard pellet at the base of the tube. Gradients of many shapes and ranges can be formed by varying the starting density and the centrifugation conditions. The 'S' shaped gradient curve is characterized by a fairly flat region occupying most of the centrifuge tube. This enables cells of very similar buoyant densities to be separated with high resolution.

The method described here can be used for the generation of 10, 20 and 50 ml Percoll gradients.

Materials
Percoll solution, of known starting density (Section 2.2).

Equipment
i. MSE 25 angle-head rotor (MSE Scientific Inst.).
ii. Polycarbonate tubes, with aluminium screw-top caps (MSE Scientific Inst.).

Procedure
a. Place the diluted Percoll solution into a polycarbonate tube and cap tightly. Prepare two gradients if density marker beads are used to monitor the gradients (*see* Section 6.2).
b. Centrifuge in an MSE 25 angle-head rotor, with the brake off, for 45 min at 20 000 *g* and 4 °C. Use a balanced polycarbonate tube containing either identical gradient materials or distilled water.
c. Allow the gradient to warm up to room temperature before use.
d. To store the gradient, keep the tube in a stable, upright position at 4 °C. Use preferably within 3 days.

Comments
a. A minimum of centrifugal force of about 10 000 *g* should be used for Percoll in 0·12M NaCl in order to self-generate gradients in angle-head rotors. Rotor geometry and tube size have a marked effect on the shape of the curve. As the angle of the rotor comes closer to the vertical, the path length for the formation of the gradient becomes shorter and the gradient forms more rapidly.
b. It is not possible to use swing-out rotors for self-generating gradients, due to the long path length and unequal *g* force along the tube.

6.2 DETERMINATION OF FRACTION DENSITY BY DENSITY MARKER BEADS

Density marker beads provide a simple and rapid method for measuring the fraction density of a continuous density gradient of Percoll. The position of the cells within the gradients can also be located. Therefore, density marker beads can be used as an external marker (for monitoring gradient shape and range) in a centrifuge tube containing identical gradient material to the one used for the experiment.

Materials

i. Percoll solution (10 ml) of a known density (Section 2.2): generate the density gradient as described in Section 6.1.
ii. Density marker beads (Pharmacia Fine Chemicals).
iii. Heat-inactivated foetal calf serum (HI-FCS).
iv. Polycarbonate tube (MSE Scientific Inst.): 15 ml capacity.

Procedure

PREPARATION OF BEAD SUSPENSION

Add 1 ml distilled water to each of the ten vials and leave the beads to swell for at least 18 h at 4 °C. Store at 4 °C and use when required.

CENTRIFUGATION ON PERCOLL GRADIENT

a. Transfer 20 µl (220 µl for 50 ml gradient) of bead suspension from the first nine vials (as suggested by the manufacturers) to a tube containing 1 ml (5 ml for 50 ml gradient) HI-FCS (use a new disposable tip for each vial). Mix well using a syringe and needle.
b. Gently, layer the bead suspension onto the preformed Percoll gradient and centrifuge at 1400 g for 15 min. This tube can be used as a counter-balance in the rotor during centrifugation of the tube containing the cell suspension.
c. Record the distribution of the coloured beads (*see Fig. 3.5*) throughout the gradient.
d. Measure the distance (in mm) of each band from the bottom of the tube using millimetre graph paper.
e. Plot a graph of density versus distance (mm) from the bottom of the tube (*Fig. 3.6*).

Comments

a. A simple but laborious method of measuring the density of the

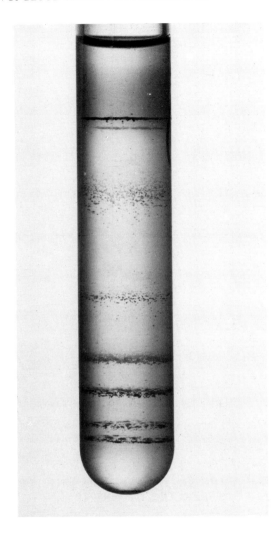

Fig. 3.5. Banding of density marker beads through a preformed Percoll gradient with starting density of 1·083 g/ml.

fractions without the use of a refractometer or density marker beads is to weigh a known volume of Percoll solution from each fraction.

   b. In order to store the density marker beads, add merthiolate (0·01%, w/v) and do not freeze.

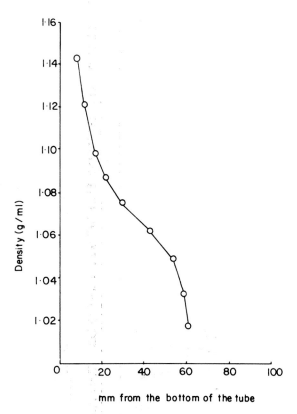

Fig. 3.6. The use of coloured density marker beads in the calibration of a preformed Percoll gradient of starting density of 1·083 g/ml.

7. FRACTIONATION OF LEUCOCYTES ON A PREFORMED PERCOLL GRADIENT

This method is useful for obtaining cell populations for which there is only a small difference in density between each cell type. Successful cell separation can be obtained with initial samples not exceeding 80×10^6 cells/ml for each of 10 ml of gradient materials.

7.1 FRACTIONATION OF MONONUCLEAR CELLS

Isopyknic centrifugation of mononuclear cells on a continuous density gradient formed from Percoll of starting density 1·083 g/ml can be used to separate monocytes from lymphocytes. The monocytes are greatly enriched in the low density fractions whereas fractions of higher density contain only lymphocytes. If neutrophils and eosinophils are present in the pre-Percoll layer of cells they can be located in the lower fractions of the gradient just above the red cell layer.

Materials

    i. Preservative-free heparin (Duncan Flockhart Co Ltd): 15 units/ml blood.

    ii. Percoll solution (1·077 g/ml): prepare as described in Section 2.2.

    iii. Preformed density gradient of Percoll with starting density of 1·083 g/ml (Section 2.2): generate the gradient as described in Section 6.1.

    iv. Buffered salt solution (BSS).

    v. Heat-inactivated foetal calf serum (HI-FCS).

Procedure

CENTRIFUGATION OF CELLS

    a. Layer the heparinized blood or buffy coat cell suspension onto an equal volume of Percoll (density 1·077 g/ml) and prepare a mononuclear cell layer (MNL) as described in Section 4.1. Suspend the recovered cells in 1 ml BSS or HI-FCS.

    b. Count the total number of nucleated cells and prepare cytocentrifuge slides for Jenner–Giemsa staining.

    c. Gently layer the cell suspension onto the top of the preformed gradient of Percoll, using a syringe and 19 gauge needle.

    d. Centrifuge at 1400 g for 15 min in a bench centrifuge at room temperature.

FRACTIONATION OF GRADIENT MATERIAL

    a. Discard 2 ml from the top of the gradient, and collect 0·5 ml fractions into a set of tubes using a 1 ml syringe and needle. Wash the syringe thoroughly with BSS after collection of each fraction.

    b. To sediment the isolated cells, add 5 ml BSS to each tube, and centrifuge at 800 g for 7 min.

    c. Wash the pelleted cells once in 2 ml BSS. Discard the supernatant and resuspend in 0·3–0·5 ml HI-FCS or BSS.

    d. Count the total number of cells in each fraction, prepare cytocentrifuge slides and stain with Jenner–Giemsa for morphological evaluation and differential counting.

    e. Check the viability by trypan blue exclusion.

Table 3.2 Fractionation of peripheral blood mononuclear cells using equilibrium density gradient centrifugation on Percoll of starting density 1·083 g/ml

Fraction No.	Monocytes (%) Expt.		Lymphocytes (%) Expt.		Neutrophils (%) Expt.	
	1	2	1	2	1	2
Pre-Percoll	16	15	76	84	7	0·5
3	—	84	—	16	—	0
4	90	77	9	23	1	0
5	45	56	54	44	1	0
6	19	31	80	69	0·6	0
7	0·4	5	97	92	2	3
8	0	11	97	85	3	4
9	0·2	2	90	96	9	2
10	0	2	49	87	51	11
11	0	1	18	89	82	10

f. Calculate the recovery of cells from the gradient as follows:

$$\% \text{ Recovery} = \frac{\text{Total cell number (monocytes or lymphocytes) collected from the fractions}}{\text{Total cell number (monocytes or lymphocytes) layered onto the gradient}} \times 100$$

Reproducibility

Continuous equilibrium density gradient centrifugation of mononuclear cells (prepared from normal blood samples) separated the monocytes from the bulk of the lymphocytes. In two experiments (*Table* 3.2) the monocytes were greatly enriched (90% and 84%) in the fractions of low density compared with the original mononuclear cells (16% and 15% in experiments 1 and 2). Certain fractions of higher density contained up to 97% lymphocytes. Neutrophils (if present) were found in the lowermost dense fractions of the gradient. For example, in the first preparation the fraction containing 82% neutrophils was enriched from 7% neutrophils originally in the mononuclear cell layer. Platelets contaminate the least dense fractions and bind to the monocytes. This was avoided to a significant extent by prior preparation of a buffy coat (*see* Chapter 2, Section 4). The morphology of the separated cells was found to be unchanged.

Comments

a. Cell clumps should be removed from the suspension before layering onto the Percoll gradient. This can be achieved by passing the cells through a sterile nylon gauze filter.

b. Sufficient amounts of the sterile gradient material can be prepared in advance and stored at 4 °C. This solution is stable at physiological pH and osmolality.

c. The above gradient (1·083 g/ml density) can be used for the separation of granulocytes from red cells. Centrifuge the heparinized blood on a Percoll cushion (1·077 g/ml density) as described in Section 2.2. Collect the layer of granulocytes just above the red cells at the bottom of the tube. Wash and layer the cells onto the preformed gradient. Collect cell fractions to just above the pink band of cells. Wash twice with BSS and prepare cytocentrifuge slides for Jenner- –Giemsa staining to estimate the percentage of neutrophils.

7.2   SEPARATION OF B- AND T-LYMPHOCYTES

Equilibrium centrifugation of either blood mononuclear cells or of pure lymphocytes obtained by carbonyl iron (or glass bead adherence) removal of monocytes on a continuous density gradient of Percoll can be successfully used to isolate lymphocyte subpopulations. B-lymphocytes with surface immunoglobulin can be detected in the regions of low density and T-lymphocytes in the regions of higher density (as shown by sheep red cell rosetting). T_M-lymphocytes with their characteristic positive 'dot' pattern after non-specific esterase staining can be found mainly in the region of higher density. By equilibrium density gradient centrifugation, there is always a preferential enrichment of T-lymphocytes, either in the presence or absence of monocytes (Ali et al, 1982).

Materials
   i. Preservative-free heparin (Duncan Flockhart Co Ltd): 15 units/ml blood.
   ii. Percoll solution 1·077 g/ml density (Section 2.2).
   iii. Percoll solution of 1·083 g/ml density (Section 2.2): prepare the continuous density gradient as described in Section 6.1.
   iv. Buffered salt solution (BSS).
   v. Heat-inactivated foetal calf serum (HI-FCS): for cytocentrifuge slides.
   vi. Carbonyl iron powder (Goodfellow Metals).
   vii. 0·45 µm filter (Millipore).

Equipment
Rotary mixer.

Procedure

PREPARATION OF CELLS

   a. Collect venous blood from a normal donor and place into a collecting vessel containing heparin. Prepare mononuclear cells using Percoll (Section 4.1).
   b. To obtain autologous plasma, transfer about 10 ml of the blood into another tube, centrifuge at 1400 *g* for 7 min in a bench centrifuge. Collect and recentrifuge the plasma for 10 min at 2350 *g* to sediment the platelets. Sterilize by passing through a 0·45 μm Millipore filter.
   c. Count the total number of nucleated cells in the remaining blood sample. Prepare cytocentrifuge slides for both Jenner–Giemsa and non-specific esterase staining (Chapter 2).
   d. Retain a small volume of the cell suspension (about 0·3 ml containing 3×10^6 cells/ml) to estimate the percentage of T-lymphocytes.
   e. Remove the monocytes either by incubation with carbonyl iron as described in Section 4.2, or by adherence, *see* Chapter 6.

FRACTIONATION OF CELLS

After preparation of pure lymphocytes, mix the cells using a needle and syringe and layer gently onto the preformed density gradient of Percoll. Centrifuge and collect the fractions as described in Section 7.1.

IDENTIFICATION OF ISOLATED CELLS

Use some of the recovered cells for surface immunoglobulin fluorescence staining (to detect B-lymphocytes) and for E-rosette formation (to detect T-lymphocytes). Determine the percentage of monocytes and T_M-lymphocytes in the fractions, for example by staining for non-specific esterase (*see* Chapter 2).

Reproducibility

T- AND B-LYMPHOCYTES

Equilibrium centrifugation of either blood mononuclear cells or pure lymphocytes on a continuous density gradient gave lymphocyte fractions containing between 92% and 99% T-lymphocytes as shown by sheep red blood cell rosetting. Simultaneous sedimentation of carbonyl iron-loaded monocytes gave a clear picture of the distribution of B-lymphocytes (with surface immunoglobulin) throughout the density gradient. *Table* 3.3 shows the results from the two experiments done in this way. Fractions containing up to 40% B-lymphocytes could

Table 3.3. Fractionation of monocyte-depleted mononuclear cells to study the distribution of B- and T-lymphocytes using equilibrium density gradient centrifugation on Percoll of starting density 1·083 g/ml

Fraction No.	*Density marker beads collected Expt. No.		$10^6 \times$ cells/ml Expt. No.		Lymphocytes (%) Expt. No.		Monocytes (%) Expt. No.		SIg^+ (%) Expt. No.		E-rosettes (%) Expt. No.	
	1	2	1	2	1	2	1	2	1	2	1	2
Pre-Percoll	—	—	-	-	85	92	15	5	—	5	79	71
1	—	Blue	2·7	0·6	—	—	—	—	30	—	—	—
2	—	Blue and orange	1·7	1·3	—	96	—	4	39	—	—	26
3	—	Green	0·7	1·2	87	77	13	22	39	35	50	40
4	—	Green and few red	1·1	1·6	99	68	1	32	22	22	75	19
5	—	Red	4·5	1·6	100	66	0	33	5	19	80	45
6	—	Red	8·4	1·4	100	93	0	7	2	10	90	74
7	—	Few red	6·4	4·8	99	97	0·5	3	7	3	82	83
8	—	Nil	2·5	11·5	100	99	0	1	2	3	92	91
9	—	Blue	2·0	16·5	97	99	0	0·5	5	3	81	92
10	—	Blue	2·0	7·9	98	98	0	—	6	4	81	93

*The buoyant densities (g/ml) of density marker beads are: blue, 1·018; orange, 1·033; green, 1·049; red, 1·062; blue, 1·075; orange, 1·087.

be obtained. These fractions were contaminated with T-lymphocytes, null lymphocytes, residual monocytes and dead cells. Fractions enriched in T-lymphocytes (90% and 93%) were found in the pure lymphocyte fractions in the lower part of the gradient. Significant numbers of B-lymphocytes are still present in the more dense fractions containing a greater number of cells but in these fractions they are greatly out-numbered by the T-lymphocytes. A tube with the density marker beads was run in parallel with the test tube in experiment 2 and the densities of the B- and T-lymphocytes recovered were estimated. B-lymphocytes with surface immunoglobulin were found to be concentrated in the region of low density (1·03–1·065) g/ml and T-lymphocytes in the region of higher density (1·06–1·08) g/ml. From eight experiments, two using mononuclear cells, two using glass bead adherence removal of monocytes and four using carbonyl iron, the mean percentages of T-lymphocytes were found to be increased from 82% (range 73–88%, SE 3·0) in the pre-Percoll layer, to 95% (range 92–99%, SE 0·93) in the most T-lymphocyte-enriched fraction from the gradient, which was often the fraction containing most cells (*Table* 3.4). The mean percentage of the non-lymphoid cells (monocytes and granulocytes) in these gradient fractions was 2·5% (range 0·5–13%, SE 0·46). There was always more than one fraction that was highly enriched in T-lymphocytes. The recovery of

Table 3.4. Non-specific esterase staining of lymphocyte fractions obtained by continuous density gradient centrifugation on Percoll of 1·083 g/ml density (By courtesy of Elsevier Biomedical Press B.V.)

Fraction No.	Lymphocytes (%)	T-lymphocytes (%)	T_M-lymphocytes (%)	Diffuse-staining lymphocytes (%)
Expt. I.				
4	55	—	—	—
5	93	81	36	53
6	99	82	48	52
7*	100	93	68	33
8	100	91	66	35
9	97	74	76	21
10	83	—	51	32
Expt. II				
5	89	—	29	59
6	99	—	54	45
7	96	—	73	23
8*	100	—	81	19
9	100	—	83	17
10	90	—	80	10

*Fraction with the highest cell number.

T-lymphocytes from the gradient was measured in two experiments and was found to be 69% and 70%. On one occasion the recovery of B-lymphocytes from the gradient was measured and found to be 63%. The mean viability of the mononuclear cells remained the same (99% and 98%) before and after carbonyl iron depletion of the monocytes, but the value dropped from 98% to 94% after E-rosette formation. The mean viability of eight T-lymphocyte fractions obtained from the gradient, as measured by trypan blue exclusion before E-rosetting, was 96·9% (SE 0·63).

T_M-LYMPHOCYTES

In two experiments, the fractions were studied for non-specific esterase staining (*Table* 3.4). T_M-lymphocytes were found preferentially in the lower part of the gradient, and those with negative or diffuse staining in the upper part. Diffuse-staining lymphocytes included T_G-, B- and null lymphocytes but not all of those in the upper part of the gradient can be accounted for by the B- and null lymphocytes, which suggests that even though there was considerable overlap, T_G- and T_M-lymphocytes were separated to some extent on the basis of density, so that the major T-lymphocyte-containing fraction is also enriched in T_M-cells.

Comments

a. There was some variation in the distribution of T-lymphocytes on the gradient from the different experiments. This may be due to technical inconsistencies. These include variation in the volume of the cell suspension layered or collected from the gradient and, possibly, the application of g force by inadvertently using different places in the centrifuge rotor (i.e. different radii). Standardization of the running conditions should decrease the differences. In addition, differences in the degree of enrichment of T-lymphocytes in the fractions may be more apparent than real because of differences in the viability of lymphocytes affecting rosetting efficiency (Platsoucas and Catsimpoolas, 1980a). They may, however, simply reflect the use of different donors. In some cases the carbonyl iron-loaded monocytes that did not sediment to the bottom of the tube still contaminated the T-lymphocyte fraction. The number of carbonyl iron particles ingested by these monocytes was perhaps not sufficient for the increase in density required for their sedimentation to the bottom of the gradient. Therefore, it may be better to sediment the carbonyl iron-loaded monocytes first, using Percoll cushion (1·077 g/ml density) as described in Section 4.2, and then layer the remaining cells onto the preformed gradient.

b. T-lymphocytes are commonly prepared by E-rosetting with separation of the rosetted cells from non-rosetted by pelleting the former through 1·077 g/ml Ficoll or Percoll (Jondal et al, 1972; Feucht et al, 1980). The removal of sheep red blood cells and the rosetting procedure itself may involve some loss of viability (Kay et al, 1977). The binding of sheep red blood cells to T-lymphocytes may bring about metabolic changes which might not be wanted (Larsson et al, 1978; Bevan et al, 1980). Equilibrium density gradient centrifugation of human peripheral blood mononuclear cells is rapid and non-disruptive and other workers have shown that T-lymphocytes are unaffected by their contact with Percoll. It is concluded that this would be an extremely useful method for obtaining viable and highly enriched T-lymphocyte fractions from normal human peripheral blood, although their selective enrichment in T_M-cells should be remembered.

c. In two experiments, a small volume of the cell suspension in the fractions was used to estimate the percentage of cells that form EAC-rosettes (Chapter 2, Section 9.2). The results showed that between 10 and 20% EAC-rosettes can be obtained in the lower fractions (fraction 10 onwards). In one experiment, the rosetted cells were successfully sedimented by using Ficoll–Triosil and the attached SRBC were then removed by lysing with NH_4Cl (Chapter 6, Sections 1.1 and 7.4 respectively).

8. ENRICHMENT OF PERIPHERAL BLOOD RETICULOCYTES

Preformed density gradient of Percoll with starting density of 1·11 g/ml can be used for the fractionation of normal blood erythrocytes giving, in the most enriched fractions, a seven-fold enrichment of reticulocytes. The reticulocyte-rich fractions can be obtained relatively free of white cells (Peters, 1982).

Materials

    i. Preservative-free heparin (Duncan Flockhart Co Ltd): 15 units/ml blood.
    ii. Percoll solution of 1·11 g/ml density (Section 2.2): generate the density gradient as described in Section 6.1.
    iii. Buffered salt solution (BSS).
    iv. Heat-inactivated foetal calf serum (HI-FCS).

Procedure

    a. Place blood from a normal subject into a tube containing heparin and prepare a buffy coat.

  b. Collect the buffy coat together with the top layer of red cells and plasma in separate containers.

  c. Suspend the cells in 1 ml autologous plasma (which was centrifuged at a high speed to sediment the platelets) and mix well.

  d. Carefully, layer the cell suspension onto the preformed gradient of Percoll.

  e. Centrifuge at 1200 g for 15 min at room temperature.

  f. Discard 2 ml supernatant from the top of the gradient together with the upper layer of cells until the first pink band of cells.

  g. Collect at least 5 fractions (0·5 ml each) into separate tubes.

  h. Wash the recovered cells twice with BSS.

  i. Resuspend with 0·5 ml autologous plasma. Use a small volume of the cell suspension in each tube for reticulocyte staining (Chapter 2, Section 8.1) and estimate the percentage of reticulocytes in the suspension.

Reproducibility

Fractionation of human erythrocytes on a continuous density gradient of Percoll produced a significant enrichment in the percentage of reticulocytes. In two separate experiments, the top cell fractions (pink colorations) were still contaminated with white cells and were therefore discarded. However, in the first fraction collected with insignificant white cell contamination there was an enrichment of reticulocytes from 1·2% and 0·8% in the original buffy coat–red cell layer to 6·4% and 5·3% respectively. Lower percentages of reticulocytes were obtained further down the gradient.

Comments

  a. The seven-fold enrichment of reticulocytes from normal blood was sufficient for the study of globin chain synthesis in normal blood (Peters et al, 1983a). These studies showed that reticulocyte fractionation on Percoll made no difference to the results obtained and therefore leaves these cells metabolically intact.

  b. The percentage of reticulocytes in the reticulocyte-rich layer was only about 7%, but this could be improved by taking a smaller (0·2 ml) fraction of cells.

Further applications

The above method has also been used for the following studies:

  a. Equilibrium density centrifugation of a blood sample obtained from a patient with non-microspherocytic haemolytic anaemia increased the percentage of reticulocytes from 24% in the original red cell layer (pre-Percoll layer) to 98% and 95% (duplicate separation) in the top fractions. The lower fractions collected from both gradients contained less than 0·5% reticulocytes. Red cells of different stages of maturation were then used for the measurement of hexokinase activity (*see* Chapter 1, Section 1.2) (M. Wagstaff, Department of Haematology, Welsh National College of Medicine, Cardiff).

b. Since the density of red cells is dependent upon their intracellular haemoglobin concentration, and Percoll seems to have no detrimental effect on the metabolism of these cells, then equilibrium density centrifugation on Percoll provides a rapid means for separating two populations of red cells if they differ in terms of intracellular haemoglobin concentration, as for example occurs in some cases of sideroblastic anaemia (A. May and S. Peters, unpublished).

9. ISOLATION OF CORD BLOOD AND EARLY POST-NATAL BLOOD RETICULOCYTES

Preformed gradients of Percoll with increasing density (1·09 g/ml) can be used to prepare highly enriched reticulocyte fractions. Fractionation of cord blood and early post-natal blood on this gradient can yield fractions containing up to 95% and 30% reticulocytes respectively when starting with reticulocyte percentages of 2–20% and about 2% respectively in the original samples (Sweet, 1985).

Materials
    i. Preservative-free heparin (Duncan Flockhart Co Ltd): 15 units/ml blood.
    ii. Buffered salt solution (BSS).
    iii. Percoll solution of density 1·09 g/ml (Section 2.2): generate the gradient as described in Section 6.1.
    iv. Heat-inactivated foetal calf serum (HI-FCS).

Procedure
    a. Layer the heparinized blood on top of the preformed Percoll gradient.
    b. Centrifuge for 15 min at 1200 g at room temperature.
    c. Remove the upper white cell bands to just above the pink cell layer, using a syringe and needle.
    d. Collect the pink band of cells, which contains most of the reticulocytes, to just above the dark red cell layer.
    e. Wash the collected cells twice with BSS.

f. Suspend the pelleted cells with HI-FCS and centrifuge at 400 g for 10 min to remove the BSS.

g. Resuspend in HI-FCS. Use a small volume of the cell suspension for brilliant cresyl blue staining to estimate the percentage of reticulocytes (Chapter 2, Section 8.1.).

Chapter 4

Purification of Bone Marrow Cells Using Specific Antisera and Complement

1. INTRODUCTION

The main impetus for devising cell separation procedures has been the increasing interest in human cell differentiation, in particular the development of blood elements from haemopoietic stem cells, and in the behaviour of lymphoid cells during the immune response.

Preparation of specific bone marrow cell populations using physical methods such as equilibrium centrifugation is not highly effective because of the extreme heterogeneity of cell type, size and density within each differentiating cell type.

Contamination of bone marrow with peripheral blood when obtained by conventional aspiration also adds to the heterogeneity of the aspirate. More specific methods are therefore required for obtaining a pure bone marrow cell population.

Separation procedures based on differentially expressed cell surface markers constitute the most promising technique for the preparation of subpopulations with defined characteristics. The use of complement-mediated lysis of unwanted cells, a method of negative selection, is a well-established immunological technique. Cells coated with antibody are lysed when complement is added. This method has been used successfully for more than 20 years (Oda and Puck, 1961; Möller and Möller, 1962; Cann and Herzenberg, 1963). More recently, lysis of target cells can also be achieved with highly specific monoclonal antibodies (Beverley et al, 1980). The complement system is the name given to one of the triggered enzyme systems of blood plasma and consists of a series of nine proteins which are responsible for complement-mediated cell lysis. Following antigen–antibody binding the first component of complement binds to the antigen–antibody complex, triggering a chain reaction of further complement binding and activation; ultimately the final component binds and is inserted into the cell membrane, causing it to become leaky. Osmotic incompetence would then lead to swelling and, finally, to rupture of the cell. The remaining cell debris and nuclear materials can be removed by filtration or digestion. The advantages of the technique are its relative simplicity and the fact that a large number of nucleated cells can be processed. In addition, the length of time taken to prepare the cells is independent of the number of cells required. It is possible to process more than one bone marrow sample at a time. The disadvantage of this method is that the eliminated population of cells cannot be recovered. Also in some situations, the relevant marker-bearing cells are not adequately lysed. Complement-mediated lysis requires the use of a monodisperse cell suspension with a high percentage of viable cells (not less than 85%). Non-viable cells will absorb antibodies and complement, reducing the amount available for reacting with the viable cells. In addition, to avoid cytotoxicity the donor's own plasma or serum must be used as a source of complement (F. Ali, unpublished observation).

2. CENTRIFUGATION OF BONE MARROW CELLS ON PERCOLL GRADIENTS

Equilibrium centrifugation of bone marrow cells on a Percoll gradient can be used to separate the bulk of nucleated marrow cells from the red cells and mature granulocytes. Simultaneous removal of the dead cells, stromal and fibrin aggregates can also be achieved by discarding the uppermost fractions of the Percoll gradient. Moreover, density gradient centrifugation on Percoll is useful for enriching cells at different stages of differentiation. During the maturation of the myeloid and erythroid cells there is an increase in density (Olofsson et al, 1980) so that a reasonable separation of their stages of differentiation can be achieved using equilibrium density gradient centrifugation of marrow cells on Percoll.

Materials
   i. Percoll solution of starting density 1·083 g/ml; prepare and generate the continuous density gradient as described in Chapter 3, Sections 2.2 and 6.1.
   ii. Eagle's minimal essential medium (MEM).
   iii. Heat-inactivated foetal calf serum (HI-FCS): for cytocentrifuge slides.
   iv. Fine-mesh nylon gauze filter (Millipore).

Procedure

PREPARATION OF CELLS

    a. Prepare bone marrow buffy coat cells suspended in 1 ml Eagle's MEM or HI-FCS.

    b. Remove all cell aggregates by passing through a fine mesh nylon gauze filter.

    c. Estimate the cell number, and prepare cytocentrifuge slides for Jenner–Giemsa staining.

FRACTIONATION OF CELLS

    a. Carefully layer the bone marrow cell suspension (not more than 80×10^6 cells/ml) onto the preformed Percoll gradient.

    b. Centrifuge and collect the fractions as described in Chapter 3, Section 7.

    c. Pool the fractions containing the wanted cells.

    d. Check the viability using trypan blue exclusion, and use the cells for any further experimental studies.

Reproducibility

Equilibrium density gradient centrifugation of two normal bone marrow samples and one sample from a patient with primary acquired sideroblastic anaemia was carried out. Analysis of the fractions showed that the erythrocytes usually form a band of cells near to the bottom of the gradient (except in the case of sideroblastic anaemia where the hypochromic erythrocytes have a lower density) and some may appear in fractions of lower density. Dead cells and stromal aggregates are found at the upper fractions (1–4) of the gradient, mainly above the principal cell layers.

    Centrifugation of bone marrow cells on a continuous density gradient of Percoll was not effective in separating one cell type from another but did, however, fractionate the granulocytic precursors according to the stage of differentiation as shown in *Table* 4.1. The most immature cells (e.g. myeloblasts) were found in the least dense fractions of the gradient and the more mature cells were concentrated in the more dense fractions.

Comments

    a. If only the removal of the red cells is required, collect all the bone marrow cell layers above the red cell fraction after centrifugation on the Percoll gradient.

    b. Prior centrifugation of bone marrow cells on Percoll is also useful for cell sorter analysis, since removal of red cells will reduce the time

Table 4.1. Fractionation of normal bone marrow cells and distribution of different stages of myeloid maturation on a continuous density gradient of Percoll of starting density 1·083 g/ml

Fraction No.	Myeloid (%)		Erythroid (%)		Lymphocytes and monocytes (%)		M1 (%)		M2 (%)		M3 (%)	
	Expt. 1	Expt. 2	Expt. 1	Expt. 2	Expt. 1	Expt. 2	Expt. 1	Expt. 2	Expt. 1	Expt. 2	Expt. 1	Expt. 2
*Whole marrow	63	-	18	-	18	-	-	-	-	-	-	-
3	36	21	39	42	24	37	7	0	27	5	66	95
4	-	10	-	47	-	43	-	few	-	few	-	few
5	-	10	-	54	-	36	-	few	-	few	-	few
6	68	10	18	34	15	56	6	10	29	10	65	80
7	-	10	-	46	-	44	-	5	-	20	-	75
8	59	17	22	17	19	66	6	0	40	29	55	70
9	62	32	12	18	27	50	11	3	33	22	57	75
10	87	21	1	16	12	63	10	8	40	21	52	71
11	89	60	2	24	10	16	3	1	23	16	75	83
12	92	74	0·5	16	8	11	1	1	19	5	81	94
13	69	-	23	{red	8	-	0	-	15	-	86	-
14	62	-	30	{cells	8	-	0	-	14	-	87	-

*Differential count was estimated as a mean of seven haematologically normal bone marrows. M1 = myeloblasts and promyelocytes; M2 = myelocytes and metamyelocytes; M3 = stab forms and neutrophils.

required for sorting and removal of debris and irreversible aggregates will prevent blocking of the fine tubes and orifices.

c. It is preferable to remove the free nuclei of the dead cells, which if remaining would obscure morphological identification of cells. Their high molecular weight DNA, which tends to stick to the outer cell membranes, would cause clumping of the cells present in the upper fractions. This can be eliminated by using deoxyribonuclease (DNAase) to digest the DNA as described in Section 3.3 below.

d. Fractionation of bone marrow cells on a continuous density gradient of Percoll has been used in the study of the uptake and distribution of ^{59}Fe by erythroblasts during differentiation, in order to compare iron uptake into haem by erythroblasts from sideroblastic marrows with that by age-matched erythroblasts from normal marrows (May et al, 1982).

3. DEPLETION OF MYELOID CELLS WITH MONOCLONAL ANTI-MYELOID ANTIBODY

In a single step all mature myeloid cells and their recognizable precursors, except for few early myeoblasts can be removed using the monoclonal anti-myeloid antibody TG-1 (Beverley et al, 1980) and complement. After lysis 2–4-fold enrichment of erythroid cells can be obtained. A significant increase in the percentages of monocytic and lymphocytic cells can also be achieved (Ali et al, 1983).

3.1 SOURCE OF COMPLEMENT

In the lysis procedure the donor's own (autologous) plasma or serum must be used as a source of complement to avoid toxicity from non-ABO blood group antibodies present in compatible (homologous) plasma or serum, or from species-specific antibodies present, for instance, in rabbit (heterologous) serum.

Autologous blood should be collected not more than two days before the aspiration of bone marrow samples and is placed into a tube containing preservative-free heparin. EDTA (ethylene-diaminetetraacetic acid) should be avoided because it chelates the Ca^{2+} and Mg^{2+} in plasma usually necessary for the haemolytic pathway.

Materials

i. Plastic tube containing lithium heparin (Sarstedt): or any container containing preservative-free heparin (15 units/ml blood).

ii. Filters: 0·45 μm (Millipore).

Procedure

   a. For collection of plasma, centrifuge the blood at 1400 g for 10 min. To obtain the serum, incubate anti-coagulant-free blood at 37 °C for 15 min to allow the clot to form, before centrifugation.

   b. Collect the supernatant plasma or serum into a clean tube and recentrifuge at 2350 g for at least 7 min to sediment the platelets.

   c. Collect the supernatant and sterilize by passing through a 0·45 µm Millipore filter. Store at 4 °C, or −20 °C for not more than 3 days.

Comments

   a. Haemolysis of red cells was sometimes evident when serum was being prepared as a source of complement (i.e. the supernatant became red due to release of haemoglobin).

   b. Alternatively, plasma or serum from ABO- and Rh-compatible normal donor should be used as a source of complement. Plasma or serum from patients with complement deficiency should be avoided.

3.2 LYSIS OF CELLS

Lysis can be achieved by incubating the bone marrow cells with monoclonal antibody TG-1 and complement by either a one-step or two-step procedure. In the one-step method, TG-1 and complement are added together. The procedure is useful when only the removal of the myeloid cells is desirable. The two-step procedure includes pre-incubation of the bone marrow cells with the antibody followed by the removal of the excess antibody and then addition of complement. Incubation for 30 min at 4 °C is sufficient for binding adequate amounts of TG-1 for lysis. Such a procedure is useful if more than one antibody is to be used to lyse the unwanted cells. Each new batch of TG-1 solution should be titrated against a small number of bone marrow cells to determine the smallest volume which removes all the recognizable myeloid cells and which gives a high viability and recovery of the remaining cells.

Materials

   i. Autologous plasma: as a source of complement (not more than 2 days old).

   ii. TG-1 antibody solution: prepare as described by Beverley et al, (1980).

   iii. Eagle's minimal essential medium (MEM).

   iv. Heat-inactivated foetal calf serum (HI-FCS): for cytocentrifuge slides.

v. Plastic screw-top tubes (Sterilin).
vi. Filter: 0·45 μm (Millipore).
vii. Nylon gauze filter (Millipore).

Procedure

ONE-STEP LYSIS METHOD

   a. Prepare a bone marrow buffy coat suspended in Eagle's MEM.
   b. Count the total number of cells and prepare cytocentrifuge slides for Jenner–Giemsa staining.
   c. Add the optimum volume of TG-1 antibody (determined by prior titration of each new batch). Mix well using a syringe and 19 gauge needle.
   d. Keep on ice for 30 min with occasional mixing to disrupt aggregated cells (using a vortex mixer).
   e. Add to the cell mixture the appropriate volume of autologous plasma as a source of complement (200 μl for each 2×10^6 bone marrow cells) and mix well using a vortex mixer.
   f. Incubate in a water bath at 37 °C for 30 min with occasional mixing of the tube to resuspend the aggregated cells.
   g. Add Eagle's MEM (two parts to one part cell suspension), mix well using the syringe and 19 gauge needle and pass the cell suspension through a nylon gauze filter to remove the stroma of the lysed cells.
   h. Centrifuge the cells at 400 g for 10 min at room temperature.
   i. Resuspend the sedimented cells with Eagle's MEM and refilter if residual stroma can still be detected.
   j. Digest the free nuclei with DNAase as described below.
   k. Count the total cell number, and prepare cytocentrifuge slides for Jenner–Giemsa staining.

TWO-STEP LYSIS METHOD

In this procedure keep the cells on ice for 30 min with the optimum amount of TG-1 as described above (steps *a–d*) and then wash three times with cold Eagle's MEM. Add complement and treat the cells as described above (steps *e–k*).

TITRATION OF TG-1 ANTIBODY

   a. Place the same volume of bone marrow buffy coat cell suspension (2×10^6 cells per 0·1 ml Eagle's MEM) in each of 5 tubes.
   b. Add TG-1 solution in volumes of 0 (as control), 25, 50, 200 and 400 μl and mix well.
   c. Proceed as described above (step *d* onwards).

d. Use the volume of TG-1 that lysed all the recognizable myeloid cells.

Reproducibility

Treatment of normal or abnormal bone marrow cells with TG-1 and autologous plasma (as a source of complement) lysed all the recognizable myeloid cells present in the cell suspension. Subsequently, removal of the myeloid cells produced a significant enrichment of the erythroid, monocytic, and lymphocytic cells in the final preparations. *Fig.* 4.1. shows the results of using TG-1 on marrow from 2 normal subjects; 1 patient with multiple myeloma (myelomatosis) and another with primary acquired sideroblastic anaemia. At the appropriate titre virtually all the myeloid cells were lysed leaving only a few

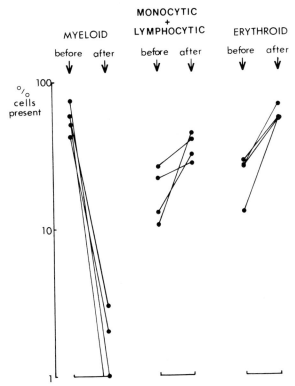

Fig. 4.1. Complement-mediated lysis of normal and abnormal human bone marrow cells using the anti-myeloid antibody TG-1. (By courtesy of Blackwell Scientific Publications).

myeloblasts. The other cells appeared unaffected. The viabilities of the remaining cells from two preparations using normal bone marrow samples were 92% and 98% and the recoveries were 35% and 41% respectively. Cell recovery of one experiment using bone marrow cells from a patient with primary acquired sideroblastic anaemia was 65%. Titration of two batches of TG-1 antibody solution shows that 200 μl of TG-1 was enough to remove all the myeloid series from 2×10^6 bone marrow cells in the presence of 200 μl plasma as a source of complement.

Comments

   a. Cloning of hybrids of the monoclonal antibody TG-1 was achieved by limiting dilution. The hybrids were obtained from a fusion for which BALB/c mice were immunized with the glycoprotein fraction of thymocyte membranes (Beverley et al, 1980). Culture medium from the clone was used for the lysis of cells. This was passed through a Millipore filter, made into 2 and 5 ml aliquots and stored at $-20\,°C$ or $-70\,°C$. The monoclonal antibody TG-1 may be available from Department of Haematology, University College Hospital, London.
   b. Differences in the recoveries of myeloid-depleted cells after complement-mediated lysis may be partly due to trapping of cells by stromal aggregates. In addition, the washing procedure may decrease the yields. Great care should therefore be taken when handling the cells throughout the whole method.
   c. Complement-mediated lysis of normal bone marrow cells using TG-1 and homologous plasma or serum as a source of complement removed all the myeloid cells. However, morphological analysis revealed an abnormal morphology of the remaining cells.

3.3   DIGESTION OF FREE NUCLEI

The free nuclei of the lysed cells must be removed since they tend to obscure morphological identification of the remaining cells. In addition, their high-molecular-weight DNA tends to stick to the outer cell membranes causing aggregation of the unlysed cells (Rutishauser and Edleman, 1977). Removal of the free nuclei can be achieved by DNAase digestion.

Materials

   i. Eagle's minimal essential medium (MEM).
   ii. DNAase (Sigma, DN-25); prepare 2 mg/ml solution of freeze-dried DNAase in Eagle's MEM. Filter, sterilize through a 0·45 μm Millipore filter and store in aliquots at $-20\,°C$.

iii. Nylon gauze filter (Millipore).

Procedure
   a. After antibody lysis of the marrow cells (not more than 5×10^6 nucleated cells/tube), suspend the cells in 0·5 ml Eagle's MEM.
   b. Add 200 μl DNAase solution and incubate the cells at room temperature for 20 min with occasional mixing on a vortex mixer.
   c. Filter through a nylon filter. Add Eagle's MEM and disrupt the cells with a needle and syringe.
   d. Centrifuge at 500 g for 7 min. Discard supernatant, wash once with Eagle's MEM and use the cells for any further studies after preparing cytocentrifuge slides for Jenner–Giemsa staining.

Reproducibility
Treatment of the unlysed bone marrow cells with DNAase was found to be essential. Handling of the cells was made easier and good cytocentrifuge slides were obtained for the examination of the morphology of the remaining cells. Cell viability was measured in three preparations before and after DNAase digestion and found to be unaffected. During the course of experiments a higher concentration (20 mg/ml) of DNAase was added and found to be more consistently effective without decreasing the viability of the remaining cells. The procedure of DNAase digestion was adopted for all future experiments using at least 200 μl of 2 mg/ml DNAase solution. In addition, in some preparations more than one digestion step was carried out to achieve better removal of the free nuclei.

3.4   FRACTIONATION OF MYELOID-DEPLETED MARROW CELLS ON PERCOLL GRADIENTS

Further concentration of nucleated bone marrow cells after the removal of myeloid series can be achieved by centrifugation on a continuous density gradient of Percoll.

Materials
   i. Percoll solution of starting density 1·083 g/ml: prepare and generate the density gradient as described in Chapter 3, Sections 2.2 and 6.1.
   ii. TG-1 monoclonal antibody (Section 3).
   iii. Eagle's minimal essential medium (MEM).
   iv. Heat-inactivated foetal calf serum (HI-FCS): for cytocentrifuge slide preparation.

v. Nylon gauze filter (Millipore).

Procedure

   a. Prepare bone marrow buffy coat cells suspended in Eagle's MEM, count the total number of cells and prepare cytocentrifuge slides for Jenner–Geimsa staining.
   b. Lyse the myeloid cells using TG-1 and complement as described in Section 3.
   c. Digest the free nuclei with DNAase as described in Secton 3.3. Suspend the remaining cells in 1 ml Eagle's MEM. Pass the cell suspension through a nylon gauze filter to remove cell clumps.
   d. Count the total number of cells, and prepare cytocentrifuge slides.
   e. Mix and carefully layer the cell suspension onto the preformed density gradient of Percoll using a syringe and 19 gauge needle.
   f. Centrifuge and collect the fractions as described in Chapter 3, Section 7.
   g. Suspend the cell fractions in HI-FCS or any suitable medium and determine the total number of cells in each.
   h. Prepare cytocentrifuge slides for all the fractions. Stain with Diff-Quick or Jenner–Giemsa and estimate the percentage of each cell type.
   i. Calculate cell recovery using the total cell number in the pre-Percoll layer and total cell number of all fractions:

$$\% \text{ Recovery} = \frac{\text{Total cell number from all fractions}}{\text{Total cell number from pre-Percoll layer}} \times 100$$

Reproducibility

Fractionation of the unlysed bone marrow cells on a continuous density gradient of Percoll after incubation with TG-1 and complement improved the enrichment of the erythroid, monocytic and lymphocytic cells. *Table* 4.2 shows the results of the two experiments carried out in this way. In Experiment 1, fraction 5 contained 70% erythroblasts and fractions 10, 11 and 12 of experiment 2 gave 71%, 79% and 89% respectively. No pure erythroblast fractions were obtained. In experiment 1, the percentage of monocytes was 81% in fraction 9 and in fraction 11, 82% of the cells were lymphocytes. In both experiments the only nucleated cells in the red cell layer (fractions 12, 13 and 14 of experiment 1 and 13 and 14 of experiment 2) were late erythroblasts and a few lymphocytes. However in the fractions containing most cells there was rather less enrichment.

Table 4.2. Fractionation of TG-1 treated bone marrow cells on a continuous Percoll gradient of starting density 1·083 g/ml. The bone marrow was obtained from a patient with myelomatosis (Expt. 1) and from a patient with primary acquired sideroblastic anaemia (Expt. 2)

Cell fraction	Myeloid (%)	Erythroid (%)	Monocytes and lymphocytes (%)	Plasma cells (%)
Expt. 1				
Whole marrow	63	28	15	0·5
+ TG-1	3	55	32	11
Fraction 2	2	22	74	2
Fraction 3	1	21	68	10
Fraction 4	0	63	32	5
Fraction 5	-	70	16	14
Fraction 6	1	45	36	9
Fraction 7	3	40	57	0
Fraction 8	-	-	-	-
Fraction 9	7	9	84	0
Fraction 10	-	-	-	-
Fraction 11	1	17	82	0
Fractions 12, 13 and 14	-	-	-	-
Expt. 2.				
Whole marrow	44	30	28	1
+ TG-1	2	56	40	2
Fraction 2	3	83	8	8
Fraction 3	0	61	35	4
Fraction 4	0·6	57	12	1
Fraction 5	1	60	39	0
Fraction 6	0·2	64	34	0
Fraction 7	1	65	33	0·3
Fraction 8	0	50	49	0·6
Fraction 9	0	40	59	0·6
Fraction 10	0	71	29	0
Fraction 11	0	79	22	0
Fraction 12	0	89	10	0
Fractions 13 and 14	-	-	-	-

Comment

On one occasion, using bone marrow cells obtained from a patient with primary acquired sideroblastic anaemia which was depleted of myeloid cells, fractionation of erythroblasts according to their stages of maturation was studied. The results showed that there was a significant enrichment of erythroblasts at different stages of differentiation, where the least mature cells are the least dense and are therefore concentrated in the top fractions of the gradient. With increasing density the fractions were increasingly enriched in the more mature erythroid cells.

4. PREPARATION OF POLYCLONAL ANTIBODIES AGAINST PERIPHERAL BLOOD MONONUCLEAR CELLS

Lysis of bone marrow monocytes and lymphocytes can be achieved by complement-mediated lysis using an antiserum raised in rabbit against human peripheral blood mononuclear cells (anti-MNL), which has been absorbed extensively with red blood cells obtained from the donor for immunizing the rabbit. The absorption step is necessary to remove the cross-reactivity of this antiserum with other bone marrow cells having common antigenic determinates, such as the blood group antigens (Ali et al, 1983).

4.1 PRODUCTION OF ANTISERUM

A normal New Zealand white rabbit weighing 2–4 kg is suitable for the production of anti-human peripheral blood mononuclear cell antibodies. Materials for injection must be kept sterile to reduce the risk of bacteria and endotoxin contamination.

Materials

 i. Percoll solution 1·077 g/ml density; prepare as described in Chapter 3, Section 2.1.
 ii. Preservative-free heparin (Duncan Flockhart Co. Ltd): 15 units/ml blood.
 iii. Isotonic saline (NaCl): (0·9% w/v).
 iv. Filters: 0·45 μm (Millipore).

Procedure

FIRST INJECTION

 a. Collect about 20 ml blood into a sterile tube containing heparin. Prepare mononuclear cells (MNL) suspended in 0·5 ml isotonic saline using Percoll.
 b. Count the total cell number and prepare cytocentrifuge slides for Jenner–Giemsa staining.
 c. Inject about 4×10^6 cells in a volume of 0·5 ml isotonic saline into the ear vein of the rabbit.

SECOND INJECTION (BOOSTER DOSE): NINETEEN DAYS LATER

 a. Collect venous blood (40 ml) in heparin from the original volunteer and prepare mononuclear cells suspended in 0·5 ml of isotonic saline.
 b. Prepare cytocentrifuge slides for Jenner–Giemsa staining.

c. Inject the rabbit intravenously with 10–13 × 10⁶ MNL in 0·5 ml saline.

COLLECTION OF ANTISERUM

a. 20 days later bleed the rabbit, collect about 30 ml of blood and allow to clot.
b. Collect the serum after centrifugation at 1400 g for 10 min.
c. Pass the serum through a 0·45 µm filter into sterile tubes, heat at 56 °C for 30 min to inactivate the complement.
d. Store at −20 °C as aliquots (5 ml). This is known as non-absorbed anti-human peripheral blood–mononuclear cell antiserum (non-abs.anti-MNL).

PRODUCTION OF NEW BATCHES OF ANTISERUM

a. Reinject the same rabbit with a booster dose (about 10–13 × 10⁶ cells per 0·5 ml isotonic saline) of freshly prepared mononuclear cells from the original donor.
b. Ten days later, bleed the rabbit and collect the antiserum.

TESTING THE ANTISERUM

Before absorption of unwanted antibodies each batch of antiserum should be tested for lysis of bone marrow cells in the presence of complement. The procedure used is the one-step lysis as described in Section 3.2, using 0·1–0·4 ml non-abs.anti-MNL and 0·5 ml autologous or homologous plasma or serum as a source of complement for each 3 × 10⁶ bone marrow cells in 0·1 ml Eagle's MEM.

Reproducibility

The same rabbit was injected four times with booster doses of freshly prepared MNL obtained from the original volunteer. All the antiserum collected showed a strong lytic activity against bone marrow cells, except for a few plasma cells. Therefore, these antisera were used for the purification of malignant plasma cells (Section 7).

4.2 ABSORPTION WITH RED CELLS

Unabsorbed rabbit antiserum contains a high titre of red cell agglutinating and cytotoxic antibodies. These can only be removed by extensive absorption against leucocyte-depleted red cells prepared from the blood of the donor of the mononuclear cell layer (MNL) used for immunization (Section 4.1).

A. Preparation of pure peripheral blood erythrocytes

Leucocytes and platelets can be removed from whole blood using a method based on that described by Beutler et al, (1976). This procedure entails the passing of blood cells through a column of microcrystalline cellulose and α-cellulose at room temperature. The red cells and reticulocytes pass through the column but the leucocytes and platelets adhere irreversibly.

Materials

i. Preservative-free heparin (Duncan Flockhart Co. Ltd): 15 units/ml blood.

ii. α-cellulose (Sigma): weight 2 g.

iii. Microcrystalline cellulose (Sigma): weight 2 g.

iv. Hepes–saline buffer (Chapter 2).

v. Percoll 1·077 g/ml: prepare as described in Chapter 3, Section 2.2.

vi. Acetic acid: 3% (v/v) in distilled water.

vii. Non-absorbent cotton wool.

Procedure

PREPARATION OF CELLULOSE COLUMN

a. Mix the α-cellulose and microcrystalline cellulose in a clean container and add 15 ml Hepes–saline. Leave to settle for 5–7 min.

b. Discard the supernatant and wash three times with Hepes–saline.

c. Plug the bottom of a 5 ml plastic syringe with a small piece of prewetted non-absorbent cotton wool. Clamp the column in a vertical position and pack with 3 ml of α-cellulose.

d. Wash the column for 1 min with Hepes–saline.

DEPLETION OF WHITE CELLS

a. Collect blood into heparin, and prepare MNL using Percoll (as described in Chapter 3, Section 4.1).

b. Collect the interface layer of cells into a separate tube. Wash the pelleted granulocytes and red cells twice with Hepes–saline (800 g for 7 min) to remove the Percoll.

c. Resuspend the cells in 1:3 (v/v) parts of Hepes–saline (maximum volume 8 ml) and pour into the cellulose column.

d. Collect the eluted red cells into containers on ice.

e. Wash the red cells twice in Hepes–saline. Discard as much as possible of the supernatant Hepes–saline.

f. Check for the presence of white cells using a haemocytometer. Dilute a small volume of red cells in Hepes–saline and then make a 1:1 (v/v) solution in acetic acid (white cell counting fluid). Cover with cover slips and examine under the microscope. If a lot of white cells are detected pass the red cell suspension through a second column containing a new batch of α-cellulose.

g. Use red cells immediately or store at 4 °C for not more than 3 days (wash once with Hepes–saline before use).

Comments

Discard as much as possible of the red cell diluent fluid before mixing with the antiserum in order to avoid diluting the antiserum.

B. Absorption of antiserum

Extensive absorption of the antiserum with packed red cells must be carried out repeatedly until no agglutination is observed, even under the microscope. A pair of red cells adhering together is still considered as indicative of agglutination.

Materials
    i. Red cells: purified as in Section A.
    ii. Hepes–saline buffer.
    iii. Screw-topped tube (Sterilin).
    iv. Filter: 0·45 μm (Millipore).

Procedure

INCUBATION WITH PURE RED CELLS

a. Mix one or two parts antiserum and one part of packed red cells.
b. Incubate at 37 °C in a water bath for at least 1 h with occasional mixing.
c. Centrifuge at 2350 *g* for 7–10 min at room temperature to sediment the agglutinated red cells.
d. Collect the supernatant antiserum into a clean container.
e. Repeat the incubation procedure with packed red cells until no agglutination is observed when examined under the microscope.

MICROSCOPICAL EXAMINATION OF RED CELLS

a. Dilute the sedimented red cells 1:4 (v/v) with Hepes–saline and mix well.

b. Place about 20 µl of the red cell suspension on a clean microscopic slide and cover with another slide (the drop should occupy only the central area).

c. Examine the red cells using the X40 objective of the microscope after pressing down on the top slide to make the liquid spread and the cells disperse. Under these conditions red cells in rouleaux formation are completely disrupted; whilst agglutinated red cells remain together.

TITRATION OF THE ABSORBED ANTISERUM

a. Filter the absorbed anti-MNL antiserum through a 0·45 µm Millipore filter.

b. Store 0·1 ml aliquots at −20 °C or −70 °C in sterile screw-top tubes.

c. Titrate the absorbed antiserum against a small number of bone marrow cells as described in Section 5.1 below. Record the range of volumes which eliminate the majority of the monocytic and lymphocytic cells and which give a high viability and recovery of the remaining cells.

Comments

Complete absorption of all agglutinated antibodies from 5 ml antiserum may need about 3–5 incubations with packed red cells prepared from 40 ml blood.

5.   COMPLEMENT-MEDIATED LYSIS OF BONE MARROW MONOCYTES AND LYMPHOCYTES

By adding the appropriate volume of the absorbed anti-mononuclear cell antiserum (abs.anti-MNL; Section 4) and complement, a selective lysis of the majority of bone marrow cells of the monocyte and lymphocyte lineages can be achieved. In addition, this antiserum can be used with bone marrow cells obtained from patients with primary acquired sideroblastic anaemia to prepare a cell suspension highly enriched with erythroblasts (Ali et al, 1983).

The optimum volume of the absorbed antiserum to be added can be determined by prior titration against small numbers of bone marrow cells. Any effect on viability, recovery or enrichment of the remaining cells can also be tested in advance. During the preparation of a large number of cells, a compromise must therefore be reached between enrichment and loss of viability. The initial titration step is necessary since there will be some lytic activity against erythroid and myeloid cells when high concentrations of antiserum are added. This may be due to the presence of common antigens on peripheral blood mononuclear cells, which have been lost during the differentiation of erythroblasts to red cells. Subsequent elimination of these antibodies will not be achieved even after thorough red cell absorption.

Each new batch of abs.anti-MNL should also be tested for lytic activity using a small number of normal bone marrow cells and different volumes of the absorbed antiserum. This will give a rough estimate of the amount of antiserum needed to achieve lysis. In subsequent experiments a much finer antiserum titration can be carried out for each marrow sample.

5.1 LYSIS OF CELLS

Complement-mediated lysis of bone marrow monocytes and lymphocytes can be achieved by incubating the marrow cells with the polyclonal antiserum (abs.anti-MNL) using either a one-step or two-step procedure as described in Section 3.2.

Each new batch of antiserum should be titrated against a small number of bone marrow cells to estimate the appropriate volume of antibodies, which removes all the recognizable monocytic and lymphocytic cell lineages but keeps the viability and recovery of the remaining cells high.

Materials

   i. Abs.anti-MNL antiserum (Section 4).
   ii. Autologous plasma: as a source of complement (not more than two days old).
   iii. Eagle's minimal essential medium (MEM).
   iv. DNAase (Sigma, DN-25): 2 mg/ml in Eagle's MEM.
   v. Heat-inactivated foetal calf serum (HI-FCS): for cytocentrifuge slide preparation.
   vi. Trypan blue (Gibco): 1/4 (v/v) in Eagle's MEM.
   vii. Screw-topped tubes (Sterilin).

Procedure

TITRATION OF ANTISERUM

   a. Prepare bone marrow buffy coat cells suspended in Eagle's MEM. Count the total number of cells. Prepare cytocentrifuge slides for Jenner–Giemsa staining to estimate the percentage of each cell type.
   b. Place into 4–5 screw-topped tubes an equal number of bone

marrow cells (1.5×10^6 or 3×10^6 cells per 50 μl and 100 μl Eagle's MEM).

   c. To each tube add a different amount of abs.anti-MNL (an approximate range of volumes must be determined by initial titration with each new batch).

   d. Add an equal volume (0.4–0.5 ml to each 3×10^6 bone marrow cells) of autologous plasma as a source of complement.

   e. Incubate the tubes at 37 °C for 1 h with occasional mixing using a vortex mixer.

   f. Centrifuge at 450 g for 7 min.

   g. Discard the supernatant and add DNAase (200 μl of 2 mg/ml Eagle's MEM for each 3×10^6 cells). Leave the tubes for 20 min at room temperature.

   h. Add 1 ml Eagle's MEM, mix and centrifuge at 450 g for 7 min.

   i. Resuspend the cells with Eagle's MEM and measure the viability of the remaining cells using trypan blue exclusion.

   j. Prepare cytocentrifuge slides and stain with Diff-Quick or Jenner–Giemsa stain.

   k. Examine with a microscope under oil immersion to estimate the percentage of each cell type after counting at least 200 cells.

LARGE SCALE CELL PREPARATION

Choose the volume of absorbed antiserum that is sufficient to lyse unwanted cells but which gives a high recovery and viability of the remaining cells. Carry out the above procedure using a large number of tubes each containing not more than 5×10^6 cells. This avoids aggregation of bone marrow cells, in particular the monocytes, and a subsequent reduction in antibody targeting.

Reproducibility

Treatment of bone marrow cells with abs.anti-MNL antiserum and complement (autologous plasma) selectively lysed the monocytic and lymphocytic cells, when the optimum volume of antiserum was added. *Fig.* 4.2 shows the results obtained using the abs.anti-MNL on five normal bone marrows. In three preparations, high titres of antiserum were used and even though the monocytic and lymphocytic cells were lysed, so also were some of the myeloid and erythroid cells. The mean viability of the resistant cells from four of these preparations was 91.7%. Differences in cell lysis were observed in different bone marrow samples. In general, monocytes are responsible for the observed differences. The addition of insufficient amounts of complement lowered the efficiency of lysis of monocytes and lymphocytes. In the work described here the optimum volume of complement used was

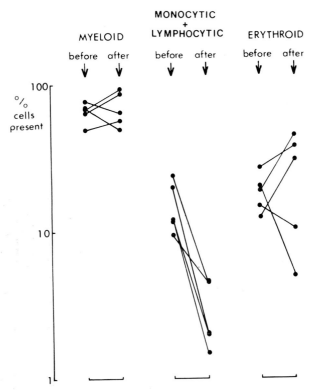

Fig. 4.2. The effect of absorbed anti-MNL alone on normal human bone marrow cells. (By courtesy of Blackwell Scientific Publications).

400–500 μl for each 3×10^6 nucleated cells suspended in 50–100 μl Eagle's MEM.

Lysis of bone marrow cells obtained from three patients with primary acquired sideroblastic anaemia (ringed sideroblasts 80%, 60% and 61%) and one patient with secondary sideroblastic anaemia (15% ringed sideroblasts) associated with carcinoma of the prostate is shown in *Fig.* 4.3. The results showed that monocytic and lymphocytic cells were selectively lysed but the results with the primary sideroblastic marrows differed from normal marrows in that the myeloid cells were relatively more sensitive to lysis than the erythroid cells so that they could also be removed, resulting in a significant enrichment in the percentage of erythroblasts in the suspension. Marrow cells from a secondary sideroblastic patient in the one experiment performed using complement-mediated lysis behaved more like those of normal bone marrow. Using primary sideroblastic marrows, cell suspensions containing 94%, 84% and 92% erythroblasts were obtained from

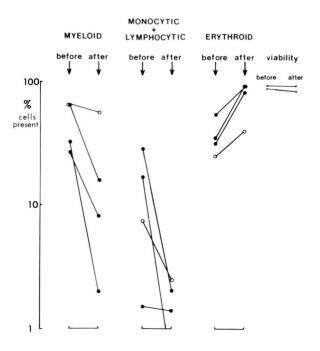

Fig. 4.3. The effect of absorbed anti-MNL antiserum on sideroblastic bone marrow cells: ●, primary; ○, secondary. (By courtesy of Blackwell Scientific Publications).

36%, 32% and 55% erythroblasts in the original samples. Cell viability of one of these preparations was 88% (94% originally). Recovery of the erythroid cells at the optimum volume of antiserum was estimated in one experiment and found to be 45%. The addition of a high concentration of antiserum decreased the recovery to 34%. The morphology of the remaining cells appeared to be unchanged. Large scale cell preparations performed using 9×10^6 and 30×10^6 cells per tube initially increased the percentage of erythroblasts from 55% and 32% in the original bone marrow cell suspensions to 87% and 74% in the final preparations. However, in the preliminary titration step using a small number of bone marrow cells (3×10^6 cells) the percentage of erythroblasts obtained was 92% and 82% respectively. The cells from two preparations were also examined for long-term viability as described below (Section 5.2). Reproducibility of the method was carried out using a new batch of antiserum and there was essentially no difference in the results.

Comments

a. In one experiment, the addition of 100 µl and 200 µl complement instead of 500 µl for each 3×10^6 cells reduced the efficiency of lysis of the monocytic and lymphocytic cells.

b. In general, monocytes are responsible for the observed differences in cell lysis between bone marrow samples. It is possible that there may be monocytes in some bone marrow samples which express different surface antigens from those present on the monocytes used for immunizing the rabbit.

c. Similar results were obtained when abs.anti-MNL and complement were added simultaneously (one-step lysis) and on incubating the cells with the antiserum at 4 °C for 30 min before adding complement (two-step lysis).

d. In the titration, using normal bone marrow cells, the myeloid and erythroid cells were also lysed when high concentrations of the abs.anti-MNL antiserum were added.

e. There are at least three possible explanations for the high enrichment of erythroblasts from patients with primary acquired sideroblastic anaemia using abs.anti-MNL alone. One is that the sideroblastic erythroblasts at all stages of maturity are more resistant to lysis. Another is that early erythroblasts are more resistant than late erythroblasts and the sideroblastic marrow samples contain relatively immature erythroblasts. The third is that the myeloid cells in this condition are more sensitive to lysis.

f. After lysis of sideroblastic marrow, the remaining myeloid cells can be removed by complement-mediated lysis using TG-1 antibody (*see* Section 3).

g. A rough estimation of the recovery of erythroblasts from bone marrow from the titration step can be evaluated by attributing the signs + + where the ratio of nucleated red cells to erythrocytes is the same or greater than the original bone marrow buffy coat, and + where the cell ratio is lower than that of the original. However, the exact percentage recovery of the cells in the final preparation should be estimated reliably using the total cell number and cytocentrifuge cell differentials.

h. For time economy prepare two slides after titration, one for Diff-Quick staining and the other for Jenner–Giemsa staining if required at a more convenient stage.

5.2 CELL CULTURE

Cell culture can be used as evidence for continuous viability of the isolated cells to show that they can grow and differentiate in culture. The effect of the absorbed anti-mononuclear cell antiserum (abs.anti-MNL) on the purified bone marrow erythroblasts from patients with primary acquired sideroblastic anaemia can be examined by *in vitro* cell culture. Cell viability is considered unaffected if the erythroid cells are able to divide and differentiate in culture.

Materials

    i. Heat-inactivated foetal calf serum (HI-FCS).
    ii. Eagle's minimal essential medium (MEM).
    iii. Alpha (α)-medium (Flow Labs.) containing 3% (v/v) HI-FCS *or* pooled AB serum (Chapter 5, Section 2.4); *or* Iscove's modification of Dulbecco's modified Eagle's medium with 10% HI-FCS and antibiotics.
    iv. Trypan blue 0·4% (Gibco): 1/4 (v/v) in Eagle's MEM.

Equipment

    i. Humidified incubator (Burkard, Lab-line).
    ii. CO_2 cylinders.

Procedure

Aseptic techniques should be used throughout.
    a. Mix the sterile cells with 0·5 α-medium *or* Iscove's modified Dulbecco's medium.
    b. Incubate the cells at 37°C in 5% CO_2 in air in a humidified incubator.
    c. Measure the viability of the cells using trypan blue exclusion after one and two days' culture.
    d. Prepare cytocentrifuge slides for both Jenner–Giemsa and Perl's staining (Chapter 2) to evaluate the morphology of the cultured cells and to count the percentage of each cell type present.

Reproducibility

In culture, the erythroblasts prepared using complement-mediated lysis (Section 5.1) were found to be dividing and differentiating, so that even if some antibody was bound to these cells it seems to have done them little harm.

One and two days' culture of two preparations of erythroblasts showed that the morphology of the growing cells appeared to be unchanged (*Fig.* 4.4) and the cells were seen to be dividing. Non-erythroid cells (myeloid series) increased by division of their blasts in one of these experiments so that the percentage of erythroblasts dropped from 94% to 64% after one day's culture. The viability of the cultured cells was 98%. In the other preparation, the

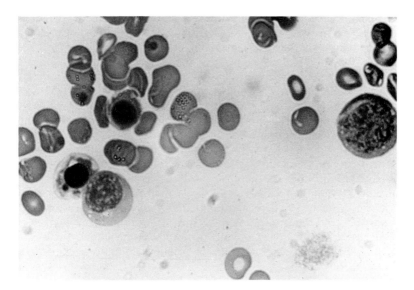

Fig. 4.4. Erythroid cells separated from bone marrow from a patient with primary acquired sideroblastic anaemia, after two days in culture.

percentage of erythroblasts after 48 h incubation increased to 95% (before culture 87%). Perl's staining of the cultured cells showed the presence of ringed sideroblasts and the percentage of these had, in fact, increased from 61% before culture to 90% after 48 h incubation of the cells.

Comments

The increase in ringed sideroblast percentage after two days in culture could be a natural result of culturing this particular bone marrow. Unfortunately, no control was carried out to see whether this was a specific consequence of antibody damage to the cells, or a result of eliminating monocytes and macrophages normally responsible for removing some of these cells. An alternative possibility is that the 'normal' early erythroblasts were selectively lysed, leaving the sideroblastic ones intact.

6.   PURIFICATION OF ERYTHROBLASTS BY COMPLEMENT-MEDIATED LYSIS WITH TWO ANTIBODIES

Lysis of non-erythroid cells present in the bone marrow cell suspension using specific antisera and complement can be used for the purification of erythroblasts from normal and abnormal bone marrows (Ali et al, 1983). This involves complement-mediated lysis of myeloid, monocytic and lymphocytic cells using a monoclonal antibody TG-1 (Beverley et al, 1980) directed against myeloid cells (Section 3), and a rabbit-anti-human peripheral blood mononuclear cell antiserum that has been extensively absorbed against mature erythrocytes (abs.anti-MNL, Section 4). Using these antibodies, in sequential or simultaneous fashion, cell suspensions can be prepared which are highly enriched in erythroblasts (80% or more). With the simultaneous lysis method a good recovery (90% or more) and high viability (90% or more) can be obtained if the optimal volume of abs.anti-MNL is added. Using this method of purifying erythroblasts, the main problem is that the residual unlysed cells may sometimes contain up to 15% monocytes. These contaminating cells may be removed, however, by density gradient centrifugation and carbonyl iron ingestion as described in Chapter 3. In addition, the monocytes may be depleted by inducing adherence to plastic or glass beads (*see also* Chapter 6).

6.1   SEQUENTIAL LYSIS OF NON-ERYTHROID CELLS

In this method lysis of bone marrow cells is carried out first with TG-1 antibody and complement. Free nuclei are removed with DNAase, and a second complement-mediated lysis step is then carried out with the absorbed anti-mononuclear cell antiserum (abs.anti-MNL).

Materials

    i. Monoclonal and polyclonal antibodies (Sections 3 and 4).
    ii. Autologous plasma: as a source of complement (not more than two days old).
    iii. Eagle's minimal essential medium (MEM).
    iv. DNAase (Sigma, DN-25): 2 mg/ml in Eagle's MEM.
    v. Heat-inactivated foetal calf serum (HI-FCS): for cytocentrifuge slides.
    vi. Trypan blue 0·4% (Gibco): 1/4 (v/v) in Eagle's MEM.
    vii. Screw-topped tubes (Sterilin).

Procedure

LYSIS WITH TG-1

    a. Prepare bone marrow buffy coat cells suspended in Eagle's MEM. Count the total number of cells and prepare cytocentrifuge slides for Jenner–Giemsa staining.

b. Incubate the bone marrow cells with the optimum volume of TG-1 and complement (determined by prior titration, *see* Section 3) to achieve lysis of myeloid cells.

c. Remove the free nuclei by digestion with DNAase (Section 3.3).

d. Count the total number of cells and determine the viability using trypan blue exclusion.

e. Prepare cytocentrifuge slides to evaluate the percentage of each cell type remaining in the suspension.

TITRATION OF ABS. ANTI-MNL

a. Use a small number (1.5×10^6 cells per tube) of the remaining cells for carrying out a titration of abs.anti-MNL over a range estimated previously with each new batch of the absorbed antiserum (Section 4.2B).

b. Remove the free nuclei by incubating with DNAase solution; determine viabilities, estimate recoveries and prepare cytocentrifuge slides for Diff-Quick or Jenner–Giemsa staining.

LARGE SCALE CELL PREPARATION

From the previous titration, choose the appropriate volume of abs.anti-MNL to prepare a large number of erythroid cells. Use a number of tubes each containing not more than 5×10^6 myeloid-depleted bone marrow cells.

Reproducibility

Complement-mediated lysis of non-erythroid cells using the two antibodies sequentially on three bone marrow samples from haematologically normal patients, and one from a patient with iron deficiency anaemia, produced highly enriched erythroid cell preparations. In all experiments except one, the TG-1 removed the myeloid cells completely. The residual myeloid cells in this preparation must, however, have been affected by the TG-1 since they were removed during the second incubation. In all preparations except one, the monocytic and lymphocytic cells were successfully removed using the abs.anti-MNL. The percentages of erythroblasts were increased from 13–35% (mean 22.5%, SE 4.86) in the original marrow to 82–94% (mean 89.2%, SE 2.6) in the enriched cell preparations (*Fig.* 4.5). The viability of the remaining cells after using both antibodies was high (86%, 96% and 91%). Recoveries of the erythroblasts after TG-1 lysis were 58% and 28% and after the abs.anti-MNL this fell to 24% and 18% respectively (59% and 36%

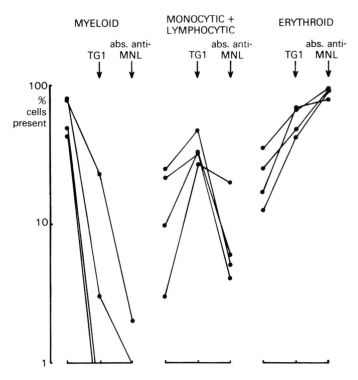

Fig. 4.5. The effect of the sequential complement-mediated lysis of bone marrow cells by TG-1 and absorbed anti-MNL antiserum. (By courtesy of Blackwell Scientific Publications.)

erythroblasts were therefore lost in the abs.anti-MNL stage). Cell morphology appeared unchanged.

In one experiment large scale cell preparation using 14×10^6 cells in one tube was not as successful at enriching erythroblasts (72%) as the initial titration step (90%). About half of the monocytes and lymphocytes remained, whereas most of these cells had been removed in the titration step. When a large number of tubes were used each containing only 3×10^6 cells, erythroblast enrichment was similar to that in the titration step (94% and 91% respectively).

Comments

a. Although the above method is straightforward, a procedure is described below which not only improves the yield of erythroid cells but which can also be carried out in only 2½ h.

b. When more than 14×10^6 cells are reacted in a single tube, the efficiency of cell lysis is reduced (*see* Section 5.1, *Procedure*). In addition, monocytes were found to be the main contaminant when iron-deficient marrow was used. With this marrow, monocytes were resistant to lysis, both in titration and large scale cell preparation.

c. Sequential complement-mediated lysis of human bone marrow, using TG-1 and then abs.anti-MNL, produced almost pure preparations of erythroblasts from normal, sideroblastic and megaloblastic bone marrows (Ali et al, 1983). Equilibrium density gradient centrifugation on Percoll enabled the collection of fractions selectively enriched in cells of different stages of maturation, thus allowing for investigation of changes associated with differentiation, as for example, ferritin content.

d. Polyclonal or monoclonal antibodies against the two well known erythroblast surface markers, Rhesus antigens (Rearden and Masouredis, 1977) and glycophorin (Gahmberg et al, 1978), are already available. Positive selection of erythroblasts (up to 90%) using anti-glycophorin monoclonal antibody and cell sorter analysis has been reported by Robinson et al (1981).

6.2   SIMULTANEOUS LYSIS OF NON-ERYTHROID CELLS

In this method, bone marrow cells are incubated with TG-1 monoclonal antibody, followed by absorbed anti-mononuclear cell antiserum (abs.anti-MNL) before addition of complement to lyse the target cells (myeloid, monocytic and lymphocytic cells). The two antisera can be used together without any problems of mutual inhibition. The time taken for purifying erythroblasts is about 2½ h.

Materials

    i.   Monoclonal and polyclonal antibodies (Sections 3 and 4).

    ii. Autologous plasma: as a source of complement (not more than 2 days old).

    iii. Eagle's minimal essential medium (MEM).

    iv. Heat-inactivated foetal calf serum (HI-FCS): for cytocentrifuge slides.

    v.   DNAase (Sigma, DN-25): 2 mg/ml in Eagle's MEM.

    vi. Trypan blue (0·4%; Gibco): 1/4 (v/v) in Eagle's MEM.

    vii. Screw-topped tubes (Sterilin).

Procedure

TITRATION OF TG-1 AND ABS.ANTI-MNL

    a. Prepare bone marrow buffy coat suspended in Eagle's MEM, count the total number of cells and prepare cytocentrifuge slides for Jenner–Giemsa staining.

b. Aliquot 1·5 or 3×10^6 cells (in volumes of 50 μl and 100 μl respectively) into 4 or 5 screw-topped tubes.

c. Add the appropriate volume of TG-1 (determined by prior titration of each new batch, Section 3). Keep the tubes on ice for 30 min for the antibody-antigen reaction to occur.

d. Centrifuge the cells at 450 *g* for 3 min, and discard the supernatant.

e. Add the abs.anti-MNL in several volumes, the range of which was determined by previous titration (*see* Section 4).

f. Add 0·7–0·8 ml autologous plasma for each 3×10^6 bone marrow cells.

g. To obtain cell lysis incubate the tubes at 37 °C (water bath) for 40 min with occasional mixing to prevent monocyte aggregation.

h. Centrifuge the cells at 450 *g* for 5 min, and discard the supernatant.

i. Add the DNAase solution (about 200–400 μl for each 3×10^6 cells) and leave at room temperature for 20 min.

j. Wash the cells twice with Eagle's MEM (800 *g* for 5 min at room temperature).

k. Determine the viabilities and estimate recoveries.

l. Prepare cytocentrifuge slides (two slides for each tube) for staining with Diff-Quick or Jenner–Giemsa to evaluate the enrichment and morphology of erythroblasts.

LARGE SCALE CELL PREPARATION

Choose the volume of absorbed antiserum (abs.anti-MNL) which removed non-erythroid cells but did not reduce cell viability or recovery of the remaining cells. Use a large number of tubes, each containing not more than $4–6 \times 10^6$ bone marrow cells.

Reproducibility

Complement-mediated lysis of bone marrow cells using both antibodies simultaneously allowed a significant enrichment of erythroblasts. In five consecutive experiments using normal bone marrow cells the initial concentrations of erythroblasts ranged between 6–39% (mean 20·6%, SE 5·4). After lysis this was increased to 78–97% (mean 85%, SE 3·1) as shown in *Fig.* 4.6. The viabilities of the enriched cells were 83% and 95% when autologous plasma was used as the source of complement. Furthermore, the morphology of the purified erythroblasts was normal (*Fig.* 4.7a and b). Recoveries, measured on two occasions, were 94% and 90% respectively.

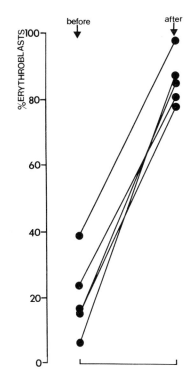

Fig. 4.6. The effect of the simultaneous complement-mediated lysis of normal bone marrow cells by TG-1 and absorbed anti-MNL antiserum.

Comments

a. When homologous compatible serum from several patients or from one normal donor was used as a source of complement, lower viabilities were obtained (67% and 74% respectively).

b. A comparative study of the sequential and simultaneous lysis of bone marrow cells was carried out using haematologically normal bone marrow samples. The results indicated that there was effectively no difference between the enrichment of erythroblasts obtained using sequential or simultaneous lysis. In addition, there was essentially no difference in the viability of the cells prepared by the separate procedure.

c. Using the sequential lysis of cells with homologous serum as a source of complement, a close examination of the morphology of the remaining cells revealed abnormal changes, even after TG-1.

d. In one experiment a third method was tried in which the abs.anti-MNL was added first. The cells were incubated with the

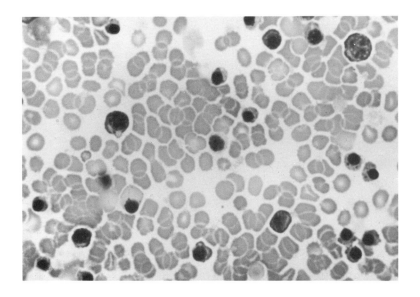

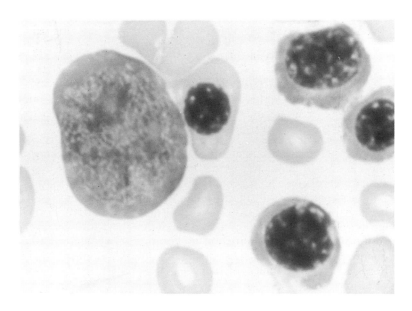

Fig. 4.7. The morphology of erythroid cells purified from normal bone marrow using simultaneous complement-mediated lysis of non-erythroid cells. Magnification *a.* × **360** (top) and *b.* × **600** (bottom).

abs.anti-MNL at 37 °C for 30 min. They were then centrifuged, the abs.anti-MNL was discarded and TG-1 was added. The cells were left at 4 °C for 30 min, complement was added and lysis achieved by incubation at 37 °C for 40 min followed by DNAase digestion using 200 µl of (1·3 mg/ml) DNAase.

The results showed that there were no differences between using TG-1 first, or the abs.anti-MNL. Examination of the slides showed that the digestion of free nuclei was improved by adding higher concentration of DNAase.

e. It was found by Mahmoud et al (1974) that antisera raised in two rabbits against neutrophils and myeloblasts, and then absorbed with human erythrocytes from a pool of donors, would lyse neutrophils and myeloblasts. This has possibly stimulated several groups of workers to raise heterologous antisera against matured neutrophils, and against leukaemic myeloblasts. Controlled experiments comparing the action of these two antisera, together with that of TG-1, have not yet been carried out. However, preliminary results suggest that TG-1 may be replaced by anti-neutrophil and anti-myeloblast antisera. A monoclonal antibody that lyses all non-erythroid bone marrow cells would be the ideal method for preparing erythroblasts, but such an antibody has not yet been reported.

f. Beverley et al (1980) submitted TG-1 and complement-lysed bone marrow cells to cell sorting on the basis of light-scattering and were able to obtain erythroblasts of 94% purity in one fraction. A slightly reduced purity of erythroblasts was obtained using a method of cell-sorting based on lower angle (i.e. cell size) and 90 ° light-scattering. It has been shown that it is possible to obtain 78–80% erythroblasts from human bone marrow (J. Hodgetts, 1984). By this technique it took 2 h to obtain 1×10^6 cells and the recovery was 57%. Using sequential complement-mediated lysis of non-erythroid cells described in this chapter, a cell suspension containing 90% erythroblasts was obtained. This was then sorted using light-scattering and 99% purity was achieved (88% of these cells were late erythroblasts). Anti-glycophorin monoclonal antibody and FACS have also been used by Robinson et al (1981) to prepare erythroblasts.

g. Two main problems were found to be associated with the use of complement-mediated lysis of non-erythroid cells. One was that high titres of the antiserum reacted with the erythroblasts. Even though trypan blue exclusion was effective at the optimum titre used for preparation of erythroblasts (as described), careful metabolic experiments are required to test for any antibody-induced abnormalities. For instance, the ability of the prepared cells to take up iron for haem and ferritin synthesis should be compared with both the original marrow and a control sample of unlysed cells which have been subjected to the same procedure. In addition, fluorescence staining analysis of bone marrow cells, reacted with the abs.anti-MNL and labelled with fluorescent sheep $F(ab)_2$ anti-rabbit Ig, should be carried out to estimate the extent of cross-reaction with the erythroblasts. The other problem arose from the presence of residual unlysed cells, usually monocytes. Contamination of erythroid cells using normal marrow, although an infrequent occurrence, shows about 15% monocytes. A reliable method for removing contaminating cells, if contamination does occur, should therefore be available. The most reliable methods for removing monocytes may be density gradient centrifugation, carbonyl iron ingestion and density gradient centrifugation (Chapter 3), adherence (Chapter 6) or ingestion of fluorescent latex particles and separation on the FACS.

h. Other workers have used harvesting of erythroblasts from bursts derived from peripheral blood and bone marrow burst forming units-erythroid (BFU-E) as a method of purifying erythroid cells. The colonies are described and distinguished as erythropoietic on the basis of appearance of haemoglobin-containing erythroblasts and their time of appearance in culture (Gregory and Eaves, 1977; Reid et al, 1981). Ogawa et al (1977) showed that about 90 ± 6 bursts per 10^5 human marrow buffy coat cells may be obtained, and Reid et al (1981) suggested that after 10 or 11 days' culture the bone marrow bursts contained two or more subcolony groups, in which subcolony size did not exceed about 50–100 cells. Therefore, to obtain 1×10^6 developing erythroblasts, about 10×10^6 bone marrow buffy coat cells will need to be plated. It is possible that this technique may be improved by further enriching the buffy coat cell suspension in BFU-E. Erythroid cells harvested from BFU-E have been used for various investigations into the metabolism of differentiating erythroblasts (Baine and Benson, 1981). Development in these circumstances is not always normal and deductions regarding normal *in vivo* erythroid differentiation cannot be made (Reid et al, 1981).

i. Lourenco et al (1978) have separated human bone marrow cells by three centrifugations through bovine serum albumin preparations of different pH and density. Using this method a fraction containing greater than 90% late-forming erythroblasts with a very low percentage of immature red cell precursors was obtained.

Further Studies

In this study the purified normal and abnormal erythroblasts have been used for the study of ferritin content (Ali et al, 1983; Hodgetts et al, 1986a) and to investigate iron uptake and ferritin synthesis in human erythroblasts (Hodgetts et al, 1986b). It is possible that further characterization of ferritin could be carried out including purification, isoelectric focusing, sub-unit analysis, measurement of iron content and iron binding and release studies. It is conceivable that some of these studies would involve the preparation of large numbers of erythroid cells. It is unlikely that large numbers of erythroid cells would be obtained from a single bone marrow sample, therefore erythroblast preparations from several normal bone marrows would be pooled, if such study is desirable. Interestingly there is some evidence that ferritin synthesis is related to the stages of maturation of the erythroid cells (Konijn et al, 1979). It is suggested that human erythroid cells prepared by complement-mediated lysis could be studied at different maturation stages to assess their ability to accumulate iron, synthesize ferritin and subsequently to synthesize haemoglobin.

In addition the prepared erythroblasts can be used for the preparation of sub-cellular particles such as mitochondria, in order to study their properties.

It is believed that these studies would give a clearer insight into erythroblast metabolism.

7. PURIFICATION OF MALIGNANT PLASMA CELLS

This section describes the preparation of enriched plasma cell suspensions from bone marrow obtained from patients with myelomatosis, using an antiserum raised in a rabbit against peripheral blood mononuclear cells (MNL) as described in Section 4.1. In the presence of complement, anti-MNL antiserum (heat-inactivated rabbit antiserum) added at an appropriate volume lysed all bone marrow cells and erythrocytes except for the plasma cells. Higher doses of the antiserum would result in plasma cell lysis (this may indicate the presence of antibodies against these cells). Their resistance to lysis at the optimum volume may be due to the presence of fewer common antigens between the plasma cells and normal peripheral blood mononuclear cells than there are between the other nucleated bone marrow cells and blood monocytes and lymphocytes. When using anti-MNL a high trypan blue exclusion viability of the purified plasma cells can be obtained. Moreover, their functional activity with respect to paraprotein secretion is preserved as shown by protein A plaque assay. The prepared cells are still able to secrete the class of paraprotein that was originally detected in the serum of the patient. The number of plaques can be reduced significantly by incubating the isolated plasma cells with cycloheximide, indicating *de novo* protein synthesis. The cells can also be stored for as long as desired in liquid nitrogen and after thawing are still viable and can synthesize paraprotein (Ali et al, 1985).

These characteristics demonstrate that this method is efficient in allowing the recovery of viable plasma cells and should prove useful in obtaining sufficient cells for further study of the metabolism of malignant plasma cells. In addition, the prepared plasma cells can be used to obtain nucleic acids (e.g. RNA) and normal and abnormal cell proteins.

7.1   ENRICHMENT BY PERCOLL CUSHIONING

Fractionation of bone marrow cells obtained from patients with myelomatosis on a Percoll cushion of 1·077 g/ml density (or Ficoll–Triosil, Chapter 6) can be used to separate the plasma cells at the suspending medium/Percoll interface. In addition, some myeloid, nucleated erythroblasts and mature red cells will sediment at the bottom of the tube, therefore increasing the percentage of plasma cells at the interface cell layer.

Materials
  i. Percoll solution of 1·077 g/ml density: prepare as described in Chapter 3, Section 2.2.
  ii. Eagle's minimal essential medium (MEM).
  iii. Heat-inactivated foetal calf serum (HI-FCS): for cytocentrifuge slides.

Procedure
  a. Prepare bone marrow buffy coat cells, count the total number of cells and prepare cytocentrifuge slides for Jenner–Giemsa staining.
  b. Carefully, layer the cell suspension onto the same volume of Percoll solution placed in a sterile container.
  c. Centrifuge (400 g for 20 min) and collect the cell layer at the Eagle's MEM/Percoll interface (not more than 5 ml per 20 ml container) using a syringe and 19 gauge needle.
  d. Dilute the recovered cells 1:3 (v/v) in Eagle's MEM and centrifuge to sediment the cells. Wash once with Eagle's MEM to remove the Percoll.
  e. Count the total number of cells, and prepare cytocentrifuge slides for Jenner–Giemsa staining.
  f. Calculate the recovery of plasma cells using the following formula:

$$\% \text{ Recovery} = \frac{\text{Number of plasma cells in pre-Percoll layer}}{\text{Number of plasma cells collected at the interface}} \times 100$$

Reproducibility
Isolation of bone marrow samples obtained from patients with myelomatosis on Percoll cushions produced a concentration of plasma

cells at the interface layer of cells, together with an efficient sedimentation of the mature erythrocytes to the bottom of the tube. Fractionation of five bone marrow samples by Percoll cushioning produced an increase in the percentage of plasma cells from 17–60% (mean 37%, SE 2) in the original marrow samples to 25–70% (mean 49%, SE 1·9) in the final preparations. The recovery of these cells after Percoll separation was measured in one of these experiments and found to be 95%.

7.2 NEGATIVE SELECTION OF PLASMA CELLS

In this method bone marrow cells obtained from patients with myelomatosis are fractionated first by Percoll cushioning (as described in Section 7.1). The collected cells are then incubated with the optimum volume of non-absorbed rabbit-anti-human blood mononuclear cell layer antiserum (anti-MNL) and complement to lyse the unwanted cells and keep the plasma cells intact.

Materials
    i. Anti-MNL antiserum (Section 4.1).
    ii. Autologous plasma: not more than two days old (as a source of complement).
    iii. Percoll solution of 1·077 g/ml density: prepare as described in Chapter 3, Section 2.2.
    iv. Eagle's minimal essential medium (MEM).
    v. DNAase (Sigma, DN-25): 2 mg/ml in Eagle's MEM.
    vi. Heat-inactivated foetal calf serum (HI-FCS): for cytocentrifuge slides.
    vii. Trypan blue, 0·4% (Gibco): 1/4 (v/v) in Eagle's MEM.
    viii. Screw-topped tubes (Sterilin).

Procedure

SEPARATION BY PERCOLL CUSHIONING
    a. Prepare bone marrow buffy coat cells suspended in Eagle's MEM, count the total number of cells and prepare cytocentrifuge slides for Jenner–Giemsa staining.
    b. Carefully, layer the cell suspension onto the same volume of Percoll solution and proceed as described in Section 7.1.

TITRATION OF ANTI-MNL ANTISERUM
    a. Into a set of 4 or 5 screw-topped tubes, aliquot 100 µl of bone marrow cell suspension ($1·5 \times 10^6$ cells).

   b. Add anti-MNL antiserum in a range of volumes determined by initial titration (as described in Section 4.2 for the absorbed antiserum).
   c. Add 0·4–0·5 ml autologous plasma for each 1·5–3 × 10⁶ marrow cells. Mix the cells in each tube with a vortex mixer.
   d. Incubate at 37 °C in a water bath for 1 h to allow lysis of target cells.
   e. Centrifuge at 450 g for 5 min and discard the supernatant.
   f. Add 200 µl DNAase solution and incubate the cells for 20 min at room temperature to digest the free nuclei from the lysed cells.
   g. Wash the cells twice with Eagle's MEM.
   h. Determine cell viability using trypan blue exclusion and estimate recoveries.
   i. Prepare cytocentrifuge slides (two slides for each tube) for staining with Diff-Quick or Jenner–Giemsa to evaluate the purity and morphology of the plasma cells.

LARGE SCALE CELL PREPARATION

Choose the volume of anti-MNL that is enough to lyse unwanted cells but which gives a high recovery and viability of the remaining cells. Perform the above procedure using large number of tubes each containing not more than 4 × 10⁶ bone marrow cells. This avoids aggregation of marrow cells and subsequent reduction in antibody targeting.

Reproducibility

In the presence of complement, lysis of bone marrow cells obtained from six patients with myelomatosis produced a high enrichment of plasma cells. The percentage of plasma cells increased from 17–60% (mean 42%, SE 2·7) in the initial bone marrow cell suspension to 72–99% (mean 73%, SE 3·0) in the final cell preparation as shown in *Fig.* 4.8. In four preparations plasma cells represented more than 90% of the remaining cells. In two experiments some myeloid cells resisted lysis, giving a lower percentage of plasma cells. On other occasions cells which were more lymphoid-like than plasma-cell-like remained.

   Fractionation of bone marrow cells on Percoll cushions resulted in an increase in the percentage of plasma cells of about 18–34% (*see* Section 7.1 for details).

   The mean viability of the enriched cells was 87% when autologous plasma was used as the source of complement. Furthermore, the morphology of the isolated cells was unchanged (*Fig.* 4.9).

   Large scale cell preparation in 2 of these experiments (using 12 and 35 × 10⁶ cells per tube) gave a low recovery of the enriched plasma cells due to cell loss caused by clumping which mainly occurred during

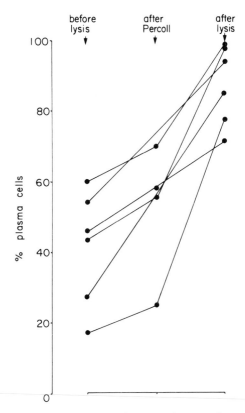

Fig. 4.8. The effect of non-absorbed anti-MNL antiserum on bone marrow cells from patients with myelomatosis.

DNAase treatment. However, on one occasion the bone marrow cells (30×10^6 cells) were divided into a series of tubes which increased the recovery of the plasma cells to 63%.

Comments

a. In the results of the experiments mentioned above, titration was only performed on three occasions (all of which yielded over 90% plasma cells) due to the insufficient number of marrow cells.

b. The main sources of contamination were cells of the granulocytic lineage or lymphocytes. When granulocytes remained they were usually heavily vacuolated and had started to degenerate. If required, their complete removal could be achieved either by freezing the cells in liquid nitrogen (Section 7.3B), since this was found to destroy them, or by lysis with TG-1 and complement (*see* Section 3). In one separate

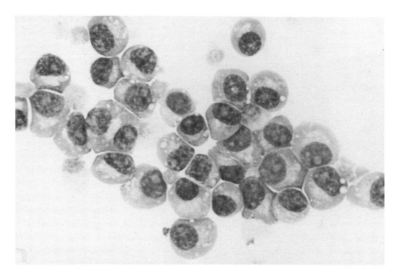

Fig. 4.9. Plasma cells prepared by complement-mediated lysis of bone marrow cells obtained from a patient with myelomatosis. (By courtesy of Blackwell Scientific Publications.)

experiment, the anti-MNL antiserum was added to the cells first after Percoll separation. The enrichment of plasma cells was determined and was found to be increased from 54% after Percoll separation to 76% after lysis with anti-MNL. The unlysed cells were then incubated with TG-1 (Section 3) to remove contaminating myeloid cells. The results show that the percentage of plasma cells was further increased to 93%.

c. Since this antiserum is normally very effective at removing lymphocytes, considerable contamination was seen in one of the experiments performed. This probably indicates that they are abnormal myeloma lymphocytes or possibly a population of non-B-lymphocytes normally present in low number, which has become expanded in this disease.

d. Since trypan blue exclusion of the separated cells was effective, it can be assumed that the intracellular contents were essentially intact. In addition, iron-loaded plasma cells have been reported to occur in certain conditions of iron overload (Karcioglu and Hardison, 1978).

Ferritin assay (Jones and Worwood, 1978) was performed with 14×10^6 and 3×10^6 cells of which 99% and 93% respectively were plasma cells. The results show that these cells contain a considerable amount (about 4–7 times the amount) of ferritin in peripheral blood lymphocytes and about the same amount as in blood monocytes. Obviously no conclusion can be drawn from these findings, but they demonstrate that this method of separating plasma cells can provide cells of adequate purity and numbers for investigating their metabolism and biochemical properties.

7.3 PARAPROTEIN SECRETION BY ISOLATED PLASMA CELLS

The functional activity of the fresh and stored plasma cells prepared as described in Section 7.2 can be tested by their ability to synthesize and secrete immunoglobulin, and this can be shown by a plaque assay (Ali et al, 1985). Sheep red blood cells (SRBC) with protein A (*see* Comment *a*) covalently bonded to their surfaces are mixed with rabbit-anti-human immunoglobulin, complement, the separated cells and agar. Immunoglobulin secreted by a cell will be bonded by the rabbit antiserum, which in turn is bonded by the protein A on the SRBC. The presence of the antibody–antigen complex on the SRBC causes activation of the complement system and results in lysis. Plaques of lysed SRBC therefore appear around each cell secreting antibody, allowing the number of cells secreting antibody to be determined. The plaque numbers can be reduced significantly by incubating the prepared cells with the protein-synthesis inhibitor cycloheximide (Helinek et al, 1982) to indicate that the plaques are not produced by passively-absorbed immunoglobulin released by damaged cells.

The method of plaque assay described here is based on that described by Gronowicz et al (1976) and Bird and Britton (1979).

A. Paraprotein secretion by fresh cells

Materials

  i. Rabbit-anti-human antisera (DAKO): use IgG, IgM and IgA antisera.

  ii. Complement (Flow Labs.): dilute the lyophilized guinea pig serum 1/4 (v/v) in BSS.

  iii. Sheep red blood cell (SRBC) (Tissue Culture Services) preserved in Alsevier's solution: use when 1 week old and for up to 3 weeks thereafter.

  iv. Hank's buffered salt solution (BSS).

  v. Chromic chloride ($CrCl_36H_2O$): dissolve $0.132\,g$ in $10\,ml$ distilled water.

  vi. Protein A (5 mg vials) (Pharmacia Fine Chemicals): dissolve in $10\,ml$ ($0.5\,mg/ml$) normal saline and aliquot 20 lots of $0.5\,ml$. Store at $-40\,°C$.

  vii. Agar (Difco-Bacto).

viii. DEAE-dextran (Pharmacia Fine Chemicals): prepare 3% solution in normal saline. Adjust pH to 7·0 with 1M NaOH.
 ix. Petri dishes (90 × 15 mm³): labelled for IgG, IgM and IgA.
  x. Coverslips (22 × 22mm).

Procedure

PREPARATION OF AGED CHROMIC CHLORIDE SOLUTION

a. Adjust the pH of the chromic chloride solution to 5·0 by dropwise addition of 1M NaOH with constant mixing.
b. Check the above solution once a week for three consecutive weeks and readjust the pH to 5·0. Keep at 4 °C.
c. To prepare the working solution, dilute 1/200 (v/v) in isotonic saline.

COATING SRBC WITH PROTEIN A

a. Wash 1 ml SRBC five times in normal saline (containing no PO_4 or protein).
b. To 0·5 ml packed SRBC, add 0·5 ml Protein A solution and 0·5 ml chromic chloride solution.
c. Incubate for 1 h at 30 °C (gently mix after 30 min).
d. Wash once in normal saline (15 ml).
e. Wash twice in BSS (15 ml).
f. Keep on ice after making up with 2·5 ml BSS.

PREPARATION OF AGAR

a. Place 100 mg agar into a conical flask.
b. Add 20 ml BSS and boil until the agar has dissolved. Leave boiling for 10 min.
c. Add 0·3 ml DEAE-dextran.

PREPARATION OF CELLS

Prepare a plasma cell suspension (Section 7.1) containing $0·5–1·0 × 10^6$ cells/ml.

PLAQUE ASSAY

a. Into 3 tubes placed in a water bath at 46 °C mix the following:

  i. Agar, 0·8 ml.
 ii. Antiserum (IgG, IgM or IgA), 25 μl.
iii. SRBC–Protein A, 50 μl.

iv. Isolated plasma cells, 100 µl.
 v. Diluted complement, 25 µl.

 b. Plate out about 100 µl (3 drops) into the Petri dish in three places. Cover with coverslips.
 c. Incubate at 37 °C for 20 h.
 d. Count the number of plaques in each Petri dish (three replicates).
 e. Express the results as plaque-forming cells (PFC)/10^6 as follows:

$$\text{No. PFC/}10^6 = \frac{\text{Mean no. of plaques}}{\text{No. of viable cells/}10^6\text{/ml}} \times 100$$

Comments

 a. Protein A was first isolated from the cell walls of Cowan Strain 1 *Staphylococcus aureus*. It was later found to react with only the Fc portion of a wide variety of IgG molecules but leaves the antigen binding site intact (Forsgren and Sjöquist, 1966). Protein A, supplied by Pharmacia Fine Chemicals, is a highly purified protein isolated from a methycillin-resistant strain of *Staphylococcus aureus*. It binds to the Fc fragment of human IgG of subgroups 1, 2 and 4. It is supplied as a freeze-dried powder which dissolves readily in aqueous solutions.
 b. DEAE-dextran is a polycationic diethylaminoethylether of dextran produced from dextran. Dextran in the agar overlay medium increases plaque formation in a number of assays, with subsequent increase in sensitivity.

B.   Paraprotein secretion by the stored cells

Plasma cells prepared using complement-mediated lysis of the unwanted cells (Section 7.2) can be stored as long as desired in liquid nitrogen. After thawing, the functional activity of the cells can be detected by a plaque assay (*see* Section A for details).

Materials

 i. Eagle's minimal essential medium (MEM).
 ii. Dimethylsulphoxide (DMSO): mix with the cells to a final concentration of 10%.
 iii. Trypan blue, 0·4% (Gibco): dilute 1/4 (v/v) in Eagle's MEM.
 iv. Cycloheximide.

Equipment

Programmable freezing unit (Keltorr): rate of freezing is 1 °C/min to −45 °C and vapour phase −170 °C in liquid nitrogen.

Procedure

STORAGE OF CELLS

   a. Suspend the cells (original bone marrow cells, Percoll-isolated cells and the prepared plasma cells) in Eagle's MEM and add 10% DMSO.
   b. Store in the freezing system as long as desired.

THAWING OF CELLS

   a. Thaw the cells rapidly under hot tapwater or by incubating in a 37 °C water bath.
   b. Wash three times with Eagle's MEM or any physiological solution to remove the DMSO (toxic at normal temperature).
   c. Estimate cell viability using trypan blue exclusion.
   d. Count the total number of cells.
   e. Use half the cells to check the functional activity by using plaque-forming assay as described in Section A.
   f. Incubate the rest of the cells at 37 °C for 45 min with 100 μg/ml cycloheximide to inhibit protein synthesis.
   g. Wash the cells three times before performing plaque assay. Compare the results with the findings on the original marrow and Percoll-isolated cells.

Reproducibility

Paraprotein secretion of the separated plasma cells as tested by protein A plaque assay showed that the purified plasma cells were able to secrete paraprotein, and that the number of plaques was reduced by incubating with cycloheximide, indicating *de novo* protein synthesis rather than passively absorbed immunoglobulin release by damaged cells. *Table* 4.3 shows the result of the plaque-forming cell assay using both fresh cells and cell suspension which had been stored in liquid nitrogen until the day of assay (experiments 2 and 3). After thawing, trypan blue viability of the purified plasma cells in experiment 3 dropped to 50%, even though the sample was stored for a shorter time. Jenner–Giemsa stained cytocentrifuge slides of the cells which had been stored in liquid nitrogen for three days showed that in all samples (original marrow, Percoll-isolated cells and the prepared plasma cells) no myeloid cells survived storage. Some plasma cells, lymphocytes,

Table 4.3. Study of paraprotein secretion by bone marrow cells obtained from patients with myelomatosis

Duration and temperature of storage	Cell Preparation	Type of paraprotein in serum	Plasma cells before storage %	Plasma cells after storage %	Protein A-PFC/10⁶ viable cell			Protein A-PFC/10⁶ viable plasma cells	Viability on the day of the plaque assay
					IgG	IgM	IgA		
Expt. 1 1 day (4 °C)	a. Percoll-isolated cells	IgG		59	1667	0	0	2825	99
	b. Plasma cell preparation	-		90	9333	0	0	10486	90
Expt. 2 21 days (−170 °C)	a. Whole marrow	IgA_K	60	-	0	0	1000	-	95
	b. Percoll-isolated cells	-	70	-	0	0	400	-	80
	c. Plasma cell preparation	-	99	-	0	0	400	-	95
Expt. 3 3 days (−170 °C)	a. Whole marrow	IgG_K	17	65	6952	<20	120	10695	84
	b. Percoll-isolated cells	-	19	34	6614	<20	<20	19453	87
	c. Plasma cell preparation	-	68	58	4418	290	230	7617	50

erythroblasts and monocytes retained their normal appearance. Despite some loss of viability, those plasma cells still viable after freezing and thawing were able to synthesize and secrete paraprotein, since large numbers of plaques were obtained. Using the separated cells (without storage, experiment 1) the number of plaques per 10^6 viable plasma cells increased almost four-fold with purification. However, in experiment 2 after freezing and thawing the PFC response decreased with Percoll fractionation, but did not change with lysis, and in experiment 3 the PFC number decreased slightly when using the isolated cells.

The addition of cycloheximide inhibits the formation of plaques and these results are shown in *Table 4.4*. In all cases the plaques were produced by cells synthesizing the same class of immunoglobulin as that found in the serum of the patient.

Table 4.4. The effect of protein synthesis inhibition on the formation of plaques by the prepared plasma cells

Cell preparation	*Protein A-PFC/10^6 viable cells*			*Protein A-PFC/10^6 viable cells after incubation with cycloheximide*		
	IgG	*IgM*	*IgA*	*IgG*	*IgM*	*IgA*
a. Whole marrow	0	0	1000	0	0	30
b. Percoll-isolated cells	0	0	400	0	0	0
c. Plasma cell population	0	0	400	0	0	50

*All cells were stored for 21 days in liquid nitrogen before testing for protein A-PFC.

Comments

a. The establishment of a culture of the prepared plasma cells using Iscove's modifications of Dulbecco's culture medium with 20% FCS was not very successful. This might be due to the lysis of precursors of the plasma cells by the antibody and complement or perhaps due to lack of co-factors essential for maintaining the neoplastic cells *in vitro*. It is unlikely that it is caused by antibody damage to the plasma cells themselves, since they were still able to secrete paraprotein. One modification of the culture method which may permit longer cultures of plasma cells is the use of a double-chambered culture vessel, with cells cultured on a dialysis membrane separating them from a large culture medium reservoir (Marbrook, 1967). This probably allows diffusion of waste products and nutrients in a beneficial manner: using pokeweed mitogen stimulated peripheral blood lymphocytes, IgG production has been demonstrated over a three week period (McLachlan et al, 1978).

b. Usually myeloma cells can only grow in the presence of feeder cells or condition medium (Nilsson, 1971; Jobin et al, 1974; Hamburger and Salmon, 1977).

It is interesting that Hamburger and Salmon (1977) were able to grow myeloma cells for up to three weeks *in vitro*. The growth was induced by adding human type O erythrocytes or medium conditioned by the adherent spleen cells of mineral oil-primed BALB/c mice.

c. Separation of cell fractions containing 30–90% plasma cells from bone marrow obtained from patients with myelomatosis was also achieved using Ficoll–Hypaque gradient of 1·08 g/ml density (Mavligit et al, 1974).

d. Separation of normal mature bone marrow plasma cells by both cloning techniques and adherence has been described by Mendelow et al (1980) (*see also* Chapter 1, Section 4.12).

Chapter 5

Preparation of Erythroblasts using Erythroid Progenitor Cloning Techniques

(*S. Kaaba*)

1. INTRODUCTION

Stephenson et al (1971) first introduced an *in vitro* clonal assay for erythropoietic progenitors in plasma clots. This development has greatly advanced our understanding of the regulation of erythropoiesis as well as providing a tool for testing factors which may influence erythropoiesis. Iscove et al (1974) replaced the plasma clot with methylcellulose as the support phase (semi-solid cultures) for erythroid progenitor differentiation, which facilitated closer examination of the morphology of the developing cells in the culture system. Colonies of cells or individual cells may be picked out of the culture plates in the viscous methylcellulose by fairly unsophisticated procedures and stained before microscopic examination of the colonies.

With the increasing need to isolate and purify haemopoietic cells and peripheral blood cell precursors, a culture procedure whereby pure cultured erythroblasts may be isolated from culture has been developed. In order to justify subsequent investigations using the cells so prepared, careful morphological examination should be undertaken. The matured erythroblasts, those which have haemoglobinized appreciably in culture, should be of normal size (8–15 μm in diameter), be free of nuclear or cytoplasmic abnormality and abnormal cellular inclusions.

The culture procedure has been described elsewhere (Kaaba et al, 1984) and a more detailed description of the procedure is given in this chapter. It is envisaged that the methods described for obtaining pure

132

erythroblasts would be useful for those who need pure as well as synchronous erythroid cells for their investigations. The cells so prepared may be used for experiments on iron metabolism (iron into haem, ferritin and other molecular species), globin chain synthesis and the study of enzymes involved in haemoglobin synthesis such as δ-amino-levulinic acid.

2. CULTURE MATERIALS

2.1 PREPARATION OF METHYLCELLULOSE

Methylcellulose powder (A4M Premuim) can be obtained from the Dow Chemical Company.

Materials
    i. Methylcellulose: 2·25 g.
   ii. Sterile water: 100 ml.
  iii. Screw-topped glass bottle: 100 ml capacity.
   iv. Autoclave.

Procedure
    a. Weigh out accurately 2·25 g of methylcellulose in a clean 100 ml screw-topped wide-neck glass bottle.
    b. Place cap firmly onto bottle and seal around with autoclave tape.
    c. Autoclave methylcellulose at 15 lb/in^2 at 121 °C for 20–30 min.
    d. Transfer sterile methylcellulose to a clean-air/safety hood and add 100 ml of sterile water. Replace the bottle cap firmly.
    e. Agitate the bottle to begin to disperse the methylcellulose clumps.
    f. Transfer the bottle to a rotary mixer and leave to mix for 24–48 h. If visual clumps of methylcellulose remain after this period, prolong the period of rotation until all the clumps have disappeared.
    g. Aliquot the methylcellulose into 8·4 ml aliquots, in the clean-air hood, into Universal containers. Store in a −20 °C deep freeze.

Comments
    a. It is essential that the sterility of the methylcellulose is maintained in the post-autoclaving period. Therefore, avoid opening the lid of the glass bottle containing the methylcellulose, except in the sterile hood environment.

b. The time period required for the dissolution of the autoclaved methylcellulose can vary. The dissolution time depends on the temperature and rotation cycle.

2.2 PREPARATION OF SOLUBILIZED VITAMIN E

Vitamin E is ordinarily insoluble in aqueous solutions. Commercial preparations of this vitamin can be obtained as highly viscous oils or wax-like solids.

Materials

  i. Vitamin E (d-α-tocopherol, Eastman Organic Chemicals).
 ii. Eagle's Minimal Essential Medium (MEM) (Flow Labs.).
iii. Water bath at 37 °C.

Procedure

a. Weigh out 8 mg of d-α-tocopherol in a sterile universal container (UC).
b. Add 4 ml of Eagle's MEM to the Universal containter (UC).
c. Incubate the UC at 37 °C for 1 h with frequent agitation to disperse the vitamin E.
d. Filter-sterilize the warm solution of vitamin E using a 0·45 μm sterile Millipore filter and aliquot the solution in 200 μl aliquots into sterile ampoules.
e. Store aliquots deep frozen at −20 °C and warm at 37 °C for 30 min shortly before use.

Comments

a. Vitamin E can be particularly troublesome to dissolve in culture medium. It has been found that after 1 h incubation at 37 °C in Eagle's MEM some vitamin E remains as solid in the UC. Longer periods of incubation may prove beneficial when frequent agitation of the UC is employed.
b. Other forms of vitamin E may be used such as the d-α-tocopherol acetate from Sigma. This latter form will go into solution more readily than the wax-like forms of the vitamin. However, it will be necessary to check that the osmolality of the culture medium has not altered significantly as a result of using salts of vitamin E.

2.3 PREPARATION OF IRON-LOADED TRANSFERRIN

All growing cells have a requirement for iron which forms an essential part of all haemoproteins, such as those involved in oxidative metabolism. In developing erythroblasts iron is required in the synthesis of haemoglobin, which eventually becomes densely packed in matured erythrocytes. Each molecule of haemoglobin contains four atoms of iron in the haem nucleus. The utilization of iron by developing erythroblasts for haemoglobin synthesis requires that the iron bonded to transferrin is presented to the erythroid cells. The procedure described here was developed by A. May and is based on that reported by Bates and Wernicke (1971).

Materials

i. Ferric nitrilotriacetate, FeNTA: prepare by dissolving 382 mg nitrilotriacetate (2×10^{-2}M) in 75 ml sterile physiological saline. Add 280 mg of ferric ammonium citrate (10^{-2}M Fe^{3+}) and adjust with pH to 7·3 by adding 1–2 g of solid sodium bicarbonate $NaHCO_3$. Make up the volume to 100 ml with sterile physiological saline.

ii. Human apo transferrin: 200 mg (Behringwerke).

iii. Physiological sodium bicarbonate, $NaHCO_3$, (0·154M): 10–100 ml.

Equipment

i. G_{25} Sephadex column ($2·5 \times 10$ cm, Pharmacia Fine Chemicals): elute to equilibrium with sterile physiological saline, pH 7·3, and adjust with 1M Hepes buffer (Wellcome) at 4 °C (1 ml Hepes in 1 litre sterile physiological saline, pH 7·3).

ii. Colloidion membrane (Sartorius, SM 132 00).

iii. Vacuum dialysis apparatus.

iv. Cuvettes.

v. Spectrophotometer to read at 465 nm wavelength.

vi. Bijou bottle (Sterilin): or any container with top.

Procedure

Prior calculations must be made to determine what amounts of the prepared FeNTA and weight of transferrin should be used to give the desired transferrin saturation. For 30% saturation of transferrin, each µmol transferrin will need 0·66 µmol of ferric iron (Fe^{3+}) as two iron molecules bind to one molecule of transferrin.

PREPARATION OF IRON-LOADED TRANSFERRIN

a. Dissolve 200 mg of pure human apo transferrin in 1·4 ml of 0·154M $NaHCO_3$.

b. Add 0·16 ml FeNTA solution to the transferrin and leave gently rotating at room temperature in a sealed container (Bijou bottle) for 1–2 h.

c. Place the contents of the transferrin–FeNTA mixture onto a Sephadex G_{25} column and elute with Hepes buffered saline.

d. The transferrin peak which appears as a distinct light brown band is collected in a volume of about 10 ml in a Universal container. The low molecular weight salts are eluted with a further 50 ml of buffer.

e. Reduce the volume of the transferrin peak using vacuum dialysis by placing the material into an unused colloidion membrane fitted into the unit at pressures of 25–30 lb/in².

f. Reduce the volume of the transferrin preparation to between 1–1·5 ml and dialyzed against physiological saline (2–3 changes at 4 °C) over a period of 18 hours.

g. Sterilize the transferrin solution by filtration using a 0·45 μm sterile Millipore disposable filter in a clean-air environment.

h. Aliquot transferrin solution into 100 μl aliquots and store deep frozen at −20 °C.

TITRATION OF PREPARED TRANSFERRIN

To determine accurately the saturation of the prepared transferrin, a titration curve must be constructed as follows:

a. Add 0·1 ml transferrin solution to 1·0 ml 0·154M $NaHCO_3$ in a 1·0 ml cuvette and mix well.

b. Read the optical density at 465 nm (OD_{465}).

c. Add 10 μl FeNTA solution. Allow to equilibrate. Read OD.

d. Continue to add 10 μl FeNTA with subsequent reading of the OD until three points past the saturation point (where addition of FeNTA does not lead to significant increase in OD).

e. Plot OD_{465} against μl FeNTA added.

f. Two slopes will be evident, and the point at which the two slopes meet will equal the OD of fully saturated transferrin.

g. Calculate the % saturation of transferrin as follows:

$$\% \text{ Saturation} = \frac{\text{OD start}}{\text{OD fully saturated transferrin}} \times 100 \tag{I}$$

h. Concentration of transferrin:

$$\text{Concentration} = \frac{(\text{OD fully saturated transferrin} \times {}^{*}10 \times 11)}{0·65†} \text{ mg/ml} \tag{II}$$

Reproducibility

In 4 experiments where the amount of transferrin and iron was

---

*In Equation II,11 is the dilution factor and 10 is to convert the figures to mg/ml.
†0·65 is the OD of a 1% solution at OD 465 through 1 cm.

calculated to give 100% saturation of transferrin with iron, it was found by titration that 87–96% saturation of transferrin was produced.

Comments

a. The procedure for producing iron-loaded transferrin at different saturation can be used with a good deal of consistency, provided that the transferrin preparation is pure, and accurate calculations are performed to achieve the correct amounts of FeNTA and transferrin. Control of the pH of all working media is also essential in achieving consistent results, as iron has a greater tendency to be removed from transferrin in acidic environments (Bates and Wernicke, 1971).

b. Bulk preparations of transferrin–iron may be performed and the materials can be stored for an indefinite period at $-20\,°C$.

2.4 CULTURE MEDIA

Depending on the type of cells being cultured an appropriate medium should be selected. Many human and animal malignant cell lines can be grown in fairly unsophisticated culture media supplemented with small amounts of serum (Hutchings and Sato, 1978) and no endogenous growth-enhancing activity. In contrast, haemopoietic cells from human bone marrow have very stringent culture requirements. More nutrient culture media containing greater amounts of serum, growth-enhancing factors such as nucleosides, and specific stimulatory activities (colony-stimulating activity, burst-promoting activity) are required in these cases.

A. Eagle's Minimal Essential Medium (MEM)

Eagle's MEM (Flow Labs.; 10 times working concentration)	10 ml
Sterile distilled water	80 ml
Antibiotic/antimycotic solution (Gibco; 100 times working concentration)	1 ml
Hepes buffer (1M: Gibco)	2 ml
Sodium hydroxide (0·154M; BDH)	5·1 ml

Measure the pH of the above medium at $37\,°C$ and adjust with Hepes buffer or 0·154M NaOH to 7·4. The osmolality should be maintained at between 280–300 mmol/kg of water. Filter through a 0·45 μm sterile Millipore filter into a sterile glass bottle in a clean-air hood. For collecting bone marrow cells add 15 units/ml preservative-free heparin. Store at $-20\,°C$ for period of 1–2 months.

B. Alpha modification of Eagle's MEM

Alpha medium (Flow Labs.; five times working concentration)	2·0 ml
Methylcellulose (A4M; 2·25%)	8·4 ml
NaHCO₃ (Wellcome; 4·4% T027)	1·0 ml
Antibiotic/antimycotic solution (Gibco; 100 times working concentration)	0·2 ml
*Nucleosides (1 mg/ml of the 8 nucleosides listed below; Sigma)	0·2 ml
β-mercaptoethanol (10^{-2}M; BDH)	0·2 ml
Sodium selenite, Na₂SO₃ (10^{-5}M; BDH)	0·1 ml
Vitamin E (Eastman, Section 2.2)	0·1 ml
Transferrin (Behringwerke, Section 2.3)	0·1 ml

Heat-inactivated, freshly filtered (0·45 μm filter, Millipore) pooled human AB serum (33%)

*Nucleosides
Adenosine
Cytosine
Guanosine   Final
Uridine   concentration
Thymidine   in culture,
2¹-deoxyadenosine   10 mg/l.
2¹-deoxycytidine
2¹-deoxyguanosine

The above culture medium may be made up without the addition of serum, aliquoted appropriately (1–2 ml) and stored at −20 °C. All materials used are either supplied sterile, filter-sterilized or sterilized by autoclaving. The pH and osmolality should be checked from time to time.

C. Erythropoietin

Phenyl hydrazine-induced anaemic sheep plasma erythropoitin, Step III (Connaught Laboratories).

a. Resuspend 200 units of Step III erythropoietin (freeze-dried powder) in 10 ml Eagle's MEM at 4 °C.

b. Filter the erythropoietin through a sterile 0·45 μm filter (Millipore) and place in 100 μl aliquots into sterile plastic screw-topped ampoules.

c. Store the erythropoietin aliquots at −70 °C and thaw at room temperature shortly before use.

3. CULTURE METHODS

3.1 FICOLL–HYPAQUE CUSHIONING OF BONE MARROW CELLS

Density gradient centrifugation can be employed to separate peripheral blood and bone marrow cells (Chapters 3 and 4). Böyum (1968) first described the Ficoll method for separation of human nucleated cells from these sources. It has been demonstrated that nucleated cells from the bone marrow may be separated from red cells, matured granulocytes and platelets on a discontinuous Ficoll–Hypaque gradient.

Haemopoietic progenitors concentrated on the Ficoll-Hypaque gradient by the procedure outlined may be cultured and stimulated to differentiate to give colony-forming units–erythroid (CFU-E), burst-forming units–erythroid (BFU-E) and granulocyte–macrophage–colony-forming units (CFU-G/M).

Materials
    i. Ficoll-Hypaque   (Pharmacia   Fine   Chemicals):   density 1·077 g/ml.
    ii. Sterile Universal containers (Sterilin): 20 ml.
    iii. Needles and syringes (sterile).
    iv. Kwills (Hinder-Leslies Ltd): 5 inches long.

Equipment
Clean air/safety hood (Envair).

Procedure
    a. Collect human bone marrow cells into 10 ml Eagle's MEM containing 15 units/ml preservative-free heparin. Break down marrow granules by aspirating through a 25 gauge needle twice.
    b. Centrifuge at 800 g for 10 min in a bench centrifuge and discard the supernatant.
    c. Resuspend in 5 ml of HI-FCS and layer onto 7 ml Ficoll–Hypaque in a sterile Universal container at room temperature.
    d. Centrifuge at 400 g for 30 min.
    e. Bone marrow nucleated cells containing haemopoietic progenitors will be concentrated among the cells banding at the serum/Ficoll interface (white cell layer).
    f. Remove serum (uppermost layer) containing platelets and discard.
    g. Remove interface layer of cells using a sterile Kwill and syringe and place into 5 ml Eagle's MEM containing 30% HI-FCS at 4 °C. Allow to stand for 15 min.
    h. Add a further 5 ml of Eagle's MEM and centrifuge at 800 g for 10 min. Discard the supernatant.

i. Repeat washing procedure by adding 10 ml Eagle's MEM at 4 °C followed by centrifugation. Discard all supernatants.

j. Resuspend cell pellet in 0·3–1·0 ml of Eagle's MEM at 4 °C and determine nucleated cell count using a haemocytometer or Coulter Counter. Prepare cytocentrifuge slides for Jenner–Giemsa staining.

Comments

a. Should a cell count be performed on the original marrow sample and after Ficoll separation, it will be found that the recovery of nucleated cells will depend on the quality of the original marrow sample. A poor marrow aspirate will show considerable haemodilution and consequently a relatively high count of polymorphonuclear cells. These cells are not usually recovered at the interface on Ficoll–Hypaque, but are layered low in the Ficoll gradient or packed at the bottom of the tube with the matured/dense red cells. Thus low recovery will result from a haemodiluted sample.

Bone marrow aspirates are usually diluted by peripheral blood to varying degrees, so that calculations of recovery based on the nucleated cells at the interface on Ficoll and total nucleated cells aspirated will vary considerably.

b. As the cells are being prepared for culture over several days and weeks in some cases, it is imperative that every precaution should be taken to reduce the opportunity for infection of the cells and contamination of the medium:

    i. All containers, medium, serum and instruments which make contact with the cells directly or indirectly should be sterile.

    ii. All the work which involves exposure of the cells or culture medium to the atmosphere should be undertaken in a clean-air hood or safety cabinet.

c. A Percoll (Pharmacia Fine Chemicals) gradient of the appropriate density (1·077 g/ml) may be substituted for Ficoll–Hypaque to separate bone marrow cells (Chapter 4).

3.2   MICROTECHNIQUE FOR ERYTHROID PROGENITOR CULTURE

A restraining factor in the use of erythroid progenitor culture methods, as a means of cell separation and for obtaining pure erythroid cells, is the potential expense of the overall procedure. The procedures involve the use of sterile disposable materials such as syringes, needles, Kwills, culture plates, culture bottles, Universal containers, filters and Bijou bottles. However, the cost of commercially available and standardized erythropoietin is possibly the single most expensive item. For these reasons it is desirable to limit cost wherever possible, and the adoption of a microtechnique in which only 10% of the erythropoietin is required (and marrow cells may be economized) imparts a considerable advantage to the method.

Materials

i. Alpha medium (as detailed in Section 2.4).   0·95 ml
ii. Pooled AB serum (heat-inactivated, HI).   0·55 ml
iii. Erythropoietin (20 units/ml).   20 μl/0·4 ml
iv. Cell suspension (bone marrow). $2–5 \times 10^5$ cells/ml
v. Bijou bottles (Sterilin): capacity 5 ml.
vi. Microtitration plates (Gibco, NUNC): 96 well, flat-bottomed with lids.

Procedure

a. Make up Alpha medium as detailed in Section 2.4, without the addition of pooled human AB serum.

b. Place an aliquot of 0·95 ml into a sterile Bijou bottle using a 1 ml syringe without a needle.

c. Add 0·55 ml HI-human pooled AB serum (pools of 10–15 sera from normal volunteers) to the Alpha medium after filtering the AB serum through a 0·45 μm sterile Millipore filter.

d. Mix thoroughly, and aliquot 0·4 ml quantities into three sterile Bijou bottles.

e. Perform a small erythropoietin dose-response by adding no erythropoietin to the first tube, 5 μl and 20 μl (0·25 units/ml and 1·0 units/ml) to the second and third tube respectively.

f. The appropriate small volume of cell suspension (2–10 μl) may be added to each tube to give 2×10^5 cells/ml. Mix well.

g. Using a 1 ml syringe without a needle, place sterile water into the peripheral wells of a sterile microtitration plate.

h. Dispense 0·1 ml of the complete culture mix (steps a–f above) into each of three wells of the microtitration plate for each erythropoietin dose investigated.

i. Incubate and score colonies and bursts as described in Sections 3.3 and 3.4 below.

Comment

The microtechnique imparts a considerable economy not only of materials but also of operator time, which is conserved since tedious quantitation of colonies is avoided.

3.3 CULTURE PROCEDURE

Haemopoietic progenitor culture procedures invariably involve the stimulated growth of progenitors by humoral substances such as erythropoietin, colony-stimulating activity or burst-promoting activity; the incubation of the cultured cells in an atmosphere of 3–7·5% CO_2 and often reduced O_2 tension; and the quantitation of colonies using defined criteria involving the number of cells in the colony and the configuration of the colony, as well as the degree of haemoglobinization (in the case of erythroid colonies).

Materials and Equipment

i. Alpha medium containing methylcellulose (Sections 2.4 and 3.2).

ii. Microtitration plates (Gibco, NUNC): sterile, 96 well, flat-bottomed, individually wrapped with lids.

iii. Cell suspension (Section 3.1).

iv. Erythropoietin (Section 2.4).

v. Sterile distilled water.

vi. Syringes.

vii. Incubator (fully humidified at 37 °C and equipped to contain 5% CO_2 in air) (Lab-line).

viii. Safety cabinet (Class II, Envair).

ix. Inverted microscope (Leitz Diavert).

Procedure

a. Prepare bone marrow nucleated cells as described in Section 3.1.

b. Prepare culture medium, mix as detailed in Sections 2.4 and 3.2 (culture mix).

c. Add culture mix to sterile microtitration plates (Section 3.2).

d. Incubate plates in humidified 5% CO_2 incubator at 37 °C.

e. Quantitate colony forming units–erythroid (CFU–E) after 7 days in culture as tight clusters of 8 or more cells (*Fig. 5.1a*) showing haemoglobinization (faint pink to dark red colour) at magnification of X 10–100 on an inverted microscope.

Fig. 5.1.
a. Large colony-forming unit–erythroid (CFU-E) in methylcellulose culture from normal human bone marrow cells. Colony shows progressive haemoglobinization towards the centre. Magnification X 78.
b. Burst-forming unit–erythroid (BFU-E) in methylcellulose culture from normal human bone marrow cells. Burst demonstrating classical BFU-E configuration with several centres of haemoglobinization in individual subcolonies. Magnification X 150.

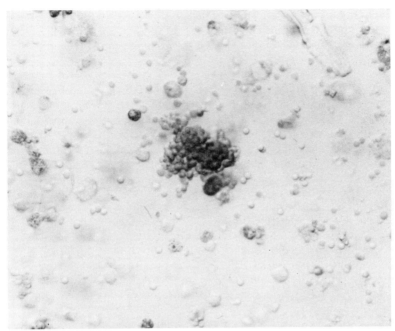

a.

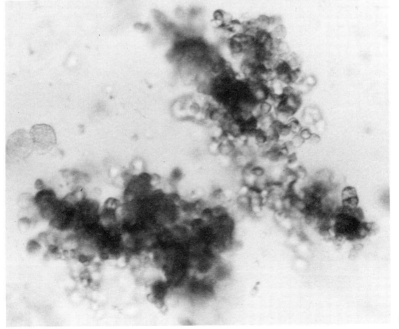

b.

f. Quantitate burst forming units–erythroid (BFU-E) *Fig.* 5.1b as haemoglobinizing cells contained in clusters of 50 or more cells, or 3 or more clusters of 8 or more cells in typical burst configuration.

Comments

    a. Under the culture conditions described above, non-haemoglobinized clusters of cells are often seen. Closer examination of these clusters, as described in Section 4, can be used to establish the myeloid nature of these cells and their probable clonal origin. However, the number of these non-haemoglobinized clusters is often small in the absence of exogenous colony-stimulating activity (CSA).

    b. The configuration of the BFU-E in culture has been described (Ogawa et al, 1977).

It is generally accepted that the BFU-E are the earlier erythroid progenitors which under *in vivo* influence would give rise to the CFU-E (the later erythroid progenitors). By implication, then, the configuration assumed by BFU-E *in vitro* would in essence be a loose association of CFU-E progenitors, the latter being of different cell numbers and shapes, in contact with each other or in discrete clusters in close proximity.

    c. CFU-E and BFU-E numbers in human bone marrow can vary quite considerably. For instance, Ogawa et al (1976) found CFU-E in human bone marrow ranged from 5–280 colonies with a mean of 75 colonies/10^5 nucleated cells. Dainiak et al (1983) found mean CFU-E and BFU-E in healthy individuals' marrows of 97 and 32/10^5 cells respectively. In our own laboratory CFU-E ranged from 20–267/10^5 marrow nucleated cells and BFU-E from 4–60/10^5 cells, with mean values of 82 CFU-E and 19 BFU-E/10^5 cells.

3.4 SCORING ERYTHROID COLONIES

Two distinct erythroid progenitors have been identified in human bone marrow cells, the CFU-E and the BFU-E. Cultures may be performed as described in the preceding sections which allows differentiation of these two types of progenitors. Quantitation of these progenitors involves microscopic identification of clones of erythroblasts which are the proliferation/differentiation products of CFU-E and BFU-E.

Materials

    i. Inverted microscope with graticule (Leitz Diavert).

ii. Digital counter.

Procedure
   a. Examine erythroid cultures (as described in Section 3.3) in microtitration plates using an inverted microscope at magnification of X 10–100.
   b. Place a graticule into one of the eyepieces of the binocular inverted microscope as a guide allowing all of the microtitration wells to be scanned and all the erythroid colonies to be recorded.
   c. Scan each well in a systematic fashion; CFU-E for 7-day cultures and BFU-E for 14-day cultures may be recorded using the criteria described in Section 3.3.

Comments
   a. The criteria defining CFU-E and BFU-E are detailed in the preceding Section 3.3.
   b. The CFU-E form heterogeneous population progenitors with somewhat differing sensitivity to erythropoietin. To quantitate CFU-E, therefore, plateau-stimulatory doses of erythropoietin are required. Poorly understood cell–cell interaction mechanisms may also influence CFU-E differentiation/proliferation, and plateau doses of erythropoietin are likely to vary from one individual preparation to the next.
   c. Without an exogenous source of burst-promoting activity, BPA (Meytes et al, 1979; Aye 1977) burst differentiation will entirely depend on endogenously produced BPA. Burst number (BFU-E) will therefore vary quite considerably from individual to individual.

3.5 HARVESTING CFU-E AND BFU-E FROM CULTURES
The clonal growth of haemopoietic progenitor affords the opportunity to isolate pure cell populations arising as cohorts from individual progenitors. The erythroid progenitors CFU-E and BFU-E, when stimulated to grow under *in vitro* conditions, give rise to clusters of pure erythroblasts which may be isolated for detailed morphological examination or metabolic studies.

Materials
   i. Microtitration plates (Gibco, NUNC): with CFU-E or BFU-E.
   ii. Cytocentrifuge (Shandon Southern).
   iii. Leitz Diavert inverted microscope with stage-mounted micromanipulator (Standard MM manipulation MM3/R) and microtitration stage-mounted plate holder.

   iv. Specially drawn-out Pasteur pipette (with vertical entry, narrow end, 50–100 µm diameter) to be used with microtitration plate.
   v. Silicone rubber tubing: 20–30 cm long, 5 mm diameter.
   vi. Hamilton micrometer screw gauge action syringe: 1 ml.
   vii. Bovine serum albumin (BSA): 2% in phosphate-buffered saline (PBS).
   viii. Microscope slides.
   ix. Graticule.

Procedure
   a. Attach one end of the silicone rubber tubing to the 'wide' end of the Pasteur pipette and the other end to the Hamilton syringe.
   b. Attach the Pasteur pipette in the clamp of the micromanipulator on the stage of the inverted microscope so that the tip (narrow end) is vertically above and centrally over the light beam orifice. Looking through the graticule of the microscope eye-piece, bring the tip of the Pasteur pipette into focus by adjusting the micromanipulator, and then bring it to the centre point of the graticule. Using the vertical adjustment on the micromanipulator, bring the Pasteur pipette to its highest point.
   c. Have the Hamilton syringe resting on a table.
   d. Put a small amount of 2% BSA–PBS in a small container (e.g. Bijou bottle cap). Without altering the position of the Pasteur pipette as set up in step *b*, immerse the tip of the Pasteur pipette into the 2% BSA–PBS. Using controlled movement of the screw piston of the Hamilton syringe, take up about 10–20 µl of BSA–PBS into the tip of the pipette.
   e. Place the microtitration plate onto the stage of the inverted microscope and bring into focus a CFU-E or BFU-E so that it is in the centre of the graticule.
   f. Remove the lid from the microtitration plate and lower the Pasteur pipette tip slowly using the micromanipulator controls.
   g. As the Pasteur pipette tip comes into focus it should be directly over the colony or burst of interest.
   h. Lower the tip of the Pasteur pipette until it makes contact with the colony or burst.
   i. Turn the screw piston of the Hamilton syringe counterclockwise slowly until all the colony or burst has been taken up into the tip of the Pasteur pipette.
   j. Using the micromanipulator controls, bring the Pasteur pipette tip to its highest point.
   k. Replace the lid on the microtitration plate and remove the plate from the microscope stage.

CYTOCENTRIFUGAL PREPARATION OF COLONIES OR BURST

Now the colony or burst has been removed from the culture plate its morphology may be investigated by preparing the cells on a microscope slide. The procedure for cytocentrifugation is outlined in Chapter 2.

a. Place a cytocentrifuge plastic holder (Shandon Southern) on its side close to the inverted microscope.

b. Remove the Pasteur pipette-silicone-rubber-tubing-Hamilton-syringe-apparatus from its attachment point on the micromanipulator.

c. Hold the silicone-rubber-tubing-attached end of the Pasteur pipette in one hand and the Hamilton syringe in the same hand and place the tip of the Pasteur pipette 5–10 mm to the inside surface of the horizontal tube in the cytocentrifuge holder.

d. With the other hand turn the screw piston of the Hamilton syringe slowly clockwise until the material at the tip of the pipette is deposited on the wall of the cytocentrifuge holder.

e. Assemble the cytospin unit, sandwiching the filter with the plastic holder at one end and the microscope slide at the other.

f. Place 300 µl of 2% BSA–PBS (or FCS–PBS) in the vertical 'V'-shaped tube of the cytocentrifuge holder once the unit is fully in place. Balance with another cytocentrifuge holder, filter and microscope slide and centrifuge for 10–15 min at 600 r.p.m.

g. Dry slide immediately after centrifugation, using a hair dryer.

h. Fix the dried slide in 100% methanol for 10 min and stain using Jenner–Giemsa as outlined under Conventional Staining Methods in Chapter 2.

Comments

Figs. 5.2*a* and *b* show typical results which may be obtained with a moderate degree of expertise. As can be seen, the cells in both the CFU-E and the BFU-E show maturational synchrony of clonal origin. Furthermore, the procedure may be used to establish unequivocally the erythroid nature of cells in culture, irrespective of the degree of haemoglobinization shown by the cells in the colony.

Further studies

Where metabolic studies are to be performed on cultured pure erythroblasts, CFU-E or BFU-E, the procedure may be scaled up. Rather than remove a single CFU-E or BFU-E colony, several dozens of each colony type may be removed from the culture plate and placed into a Universal container. The cells may be washed free of methylcellulose and studies involving iron metabolism (iron uptake), ferritin synthesis, δ-aminolevulinic acid (ALA) synthetase activity and

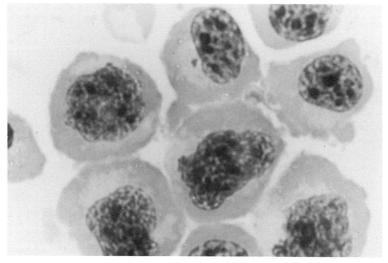

a.

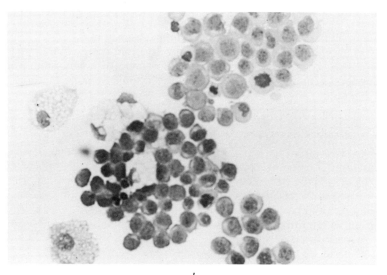

b.

Fig. 5.2.
a. Morphology of erythroid cells in a CFU-E removed from methylcellulose culture in normal human bone marrow cells. Magnification X 600.
b. Morphology of erythroid cells in a BFU-E removed from methylcellulose culture in normal human bone marrow cells. Magnification X 180.

globin chain synthesis may be undertaken on pure erythroblast cells free of contaminating white cells or matured red cells.

It is important that one establishes the number of erythroblasts that will be required for the investigation which is to be undertaken. For instance, a sensitive microtechnique for globin chain synthesis analysis (e.g. α/β chain ratios) will require far fewer cells than a laborious conventional technique for measuring δ-ALA synthetase activity. In this respect it is important to remember that good BFU-E growth will yield clusters of between 1000 and 10 000 cells. CFU-E have cell numbers between 8 and 50 cells but may be up to 20 times more numerous than BFU-E in the culture wells.

4. APPLICATIONS OF THE TECHNIQUE FOR GRANULOCYTE MACROPHAGE PROGENITORS

The other haemopoietic progenitor whose culture requirements is fairly well understood is the CFU-GM (granulocyte/macrophage colony forming units). The CFU-GM progenitors, however, do not give rise to a single cell type in colony but demonstrate the presence of both granulocytes and macrophages. The growth of CFU-GM *in vitro* has been shown to be dependent on the presence of colony-stimulating activity, CSA (Golde and Cline, 1974; Moore, 1974), and it is possible to harvest large numbers of cultured granulocytes and macrophages free of contaminating erythroid cells and matured red cells.

Materials
As described throughout Section 3.

Procedure
  a. Marrow nucleated cells are cultured as previously described in Section 3.
  b. CFU-GM are identified as non-haemoglobinized clusters consisting of 40 or more cells.
  c. The CFU-GM colonies are removed from the culture by the procedure outlined in Section 3.5.
  d. The colonies may be fixed and stained with Jenner–Giemsa. The stained slides are covered with a coverslip using DPX mountant (Chapter 2).

Comments
  a. CFU-GM colonies consisting of immature cells may be stained

with sudan black (Chapter 2) to positively identify granulocyte precursors and immature monocytes.

   b. Myeloperoxidase staining may be used to determine the proportion of neutrophils/eosinophils in the colony (strongly positive) and the presence of monocytes/macrophages (weakly positive). Unusual inclusions in the cultured cells may be investigated using periodic acid–Schiff (PAS) and other stains described in Chapter 2.

   c. Quite clearly it will be beneficial to use a source of CSA in the cultures if one desires a large number of cultured granulocytes or macrophages. CSA may be obtained from a variety of tissues (Golde and Cline, 1974; Moore, 1974; Schlunk and Schleyer, 1980). In the method outlined in Section 3.2, erythropoietin may be left out of the cultures and an appropriate amount of CSA (5-10% in culture medium) added.

5. CULTURED ERYTHROBLASTS IN THE STUDY OF SIDEROBLASTIC ANAEMIA

Abnormal erythropoiesis is well recognized as an outstanding feature of primary acquired sideroblastic anaemia (Bottomley, 1977; Hines and Grasso, 1970). The presence of normal erythrocytes as well as hypochromic microcytic erythrocytes, and normal erythroblasts as well as erythroblasts with iron deposits (sideroblasts), suggests the presence of abnormal as well as normal clones of erythroid progenitors.

Materials
   i. Sideroblastic marrow sample.
   ii. Medium and culture conditions as outlined in Section 3.

Procedure
Cultures may be performed on the marrow nucleated cells. CFU-E and BFU-E may be harvested from the cultures by the procedure outlined in Section 3.5. The colonies may be placed onto microscope slides and stained with Perl's prussion blue reaction (Chapter 2, Section 8.3).

Comments
Up to 20 colonies of CFU-E may be placed on each slide, and 5–7 BFU-E will plate per slide, using the cytocentrifugation procedure

outlined above, without coalescing. After prussion blue staining with Perl's stain (Chapter 2), the cells contained in the colonies and burst may be examined under oil immersion with a light microscope for siderotic iron granules. Erythroid cells containing greater than six granules are regarded as being sideroblasts, and iron granules in the perinuclear area so that one-third or more of the nucleus is surrounded with siderotic granules are designated ringed sideroblasts.

Early findings (Kaaba et al, 1985) suggest that individual clones of CFU-E and BFU-E may contain normal erythroblasts as well as ringed sideroblasts. This may be interpreted as suggesting that, in primary acquired sideroblastic anaemia, erythroid progenitors have a propensity to express abnormal erythropoiesis which may be limited under the culture conditions used thus far.

Fig. 5.3 shows part of a CFU-E colony from a patient with primary acquired sideroblastic anaemia. The pattern of sideroblastic changes seen in this patient after culture was comparable to that seen in the whole marrow before culture.

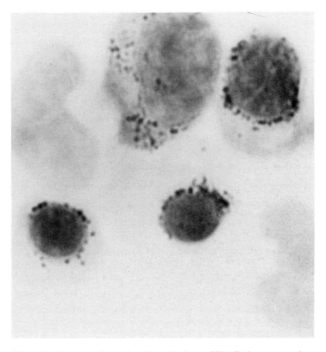

Fig. 5.3. Morphology of erythroid cells in a CFU-E from a patient with sideroblastic anaemia cultured in the methylcellulose system. Note the presence of perinuclear iron deposits (ringed sideroblasts) as well as cytoplasmic iron granules. Stained with Perl's prussion blue reaction. Magnification X 800.

Chapter 6

Miscellaneous Methods

The present chapter includes a variety of methods which can be useful for separating and studying the function of different cell types. Since these procedures do not fall under any of the previous categories it was decided to include them under the above title. The separation principles of these techniques have already been discussed in Chapter 1.

1. LAYERING OF BLOOD LEUCOCYTES BY CENTRIFUGATION ON FICOLL GRADIENTS

Ficoll is a polymer of sucrose with an average molecular weight of 400 000. It can be sterilized by filtration or by autoclaving at 15 lb/in^2.

1.1 SEPARATION OF BLOOD MONONUCLEAR CELLS USING FICOLL

A single-density step method using Ficoll–Triosil of 1·077 g/ml density was developed by Böyum (1968) for the separation of peripheral blood monocytes and lymphocytes from granulocytes and mature red cells. The less dense mononuclear cells are recovered at the plasma/Ficoll interface, while the granulocytes and mature red cells usually sediment to the bottom of the tube. Upon centrifugation the blood cells sediment towards the sample/Ficoll–Triosil interface. At the interface, the erythrocytes tend to aggregate in the Ficoll 400. Since the density of the aggregates is higher than that of the Ficoll–Triosil solution the red cells sediment to the bottom of the tube. In addition, the osmolality of the Ficoll–Triosil solution is slightly high (325 mmol/kg H$_2$O) and this will result in an increase in cell density. The granulocytes are affected more than the lymphocytes.

The granulocytes will therefore attain a density greater than the underlying Ficoll–Triosil and they will sediment through the separation medium to form a layer immediately above the erythrocytes. Lymphocytes, along with other mononuclear cells and platelets, do not have a high enough density to enter the separation medium. They remain as a band at the sample/Ficoll–Triosil interface.

Materials
   i. Preservative-free heparin (Duncan Flockhart Co. Ltd): 15 units/ml blood.
   ii. Ficoll 400 (Pharmacia Fine Chemicals): weigh 9 g into a clean container.
   iii. Triosil (45% (w/v) sodium diatrizoate, Pharmacia Fine Chemicals): measure 20 ml.
   iv. Buffered salt solution (BSS).
   v. Filter (Millipore): 0·45 μm.

Procedure

PREPARATION OF 9% FICOLL SOLUTION
   a. Slowly add 9 g Ficoll to a 100 ml cylinder containing 50–80 ml distilled water.
   b. Leave the mixture on a magnetic stirrer overnight until the Ficoll has dissolved completely.
   c. Make up the volume to 100 ml with distilled water and mix well.
   d. Autoclave the solution if necessary (15 lb/in^2) and store at 4 °C.

PREPARATION OF TRIOSIL SOLUTION
   a. In a clean container, mix 20 ml of Triosil with 25 ml distilled water.
   b. Filter through a 0·45 μm Millipore filter and store at 4 °C in a dark-coloured bottle. Use when required.

PREPARATION OF FICOLL–TRIOSIL SOLUTION
   a. In a clean tube mix 2·4 ml Ficoll with 1 ml Triosil to obtain a solution of 1·077 g/ml density.
   b. Allow the Ficoll–Triosil to warm up to room temperature (18 °C–20 °C) before use. At a lower temperature the density of Ficoll–Triosil increases and this can cause contamination with red cells and granulocytes.

ISOLATION OF MONONUCLEAR CELLS

a. Mix blood with heparin. Prepare a buffy coat and dilute the cells 1:3 (v/v) in BSS.

b. Onto each 3 ml Ficoll–Triosil solution, layer gently 3–4 ml blood or buffy coat suspension using a syringe with attached needle (19 gauge). Avoid mixing the Ficoll–Triosil and blood sample.

c. Centrifuge the tube at 400 g for 30–40 min at room temperature.

d. Draw off the supernatant plasma using a syringe and 19 gauge needle, taking care not to disturb the interface cell layer.

e. Collect the mononuclear cell layer at the interface into a clean tube. It is important to remove all of the interface but a minimum amount of Ficoll–Triosil. Collecting excess Ficoll–Triosil solution causes granulocytic cell contamination.

f. Dilute the cell suspension with a double volume of BSS and centrifuge at 800 g for 7 min.

g. Remove the supernatant and wash the sedimented cells twice in BSS. Suspend the cells in 1 ml BSS.

h. Mix the cells thoroughly and count the total number of nucleated cells. Prepare cytocentrifuge slides and stain with Jenner–Giemsa.

Comments

Separation of normal blood by Ficoll–Triosil allows harvesting of mononuclear cells at the plasma/Ficoll interface, while the granulocytes and mature erythrocytes are sedimented to the bottom of the tube. Using both Ficoll–Triosil and Percoll for the isolation of mononuclear cells from both whole blood and buffy coat, the data indicates (*Table* 6.1) that Ficoll is as effective as Percoll in isolation of mononuclear cells. However, Percoll is the preferred separation medium for the reasons described in Chapter 3, Section 4.1 (Comments).

1.2   LAYERING OF MONONUCLEAR CELLS AND GRANULOCYTES BY DISCONTINUOUS FICOLL GRADIENTS

A rapid separation of blood mononuclear cells and granulocytes (neutrophils) can be achieved by using Ficoll-Hypaque of two different densities. The technique described here can separate a population of white cells into two bands, which form at the interface between the Ficoll layers of different densities during centrifugation. This method is useful when both mononuclear cells and granulocytes are required (Madyastha et al, 1982).

Table 6.1. A comparison of the cellular composition of the mononuclear cell layer prepared using Percoll with that using Ficoll–Triosil, both of 1·077 g/ml density

Experiment number and gradient material	Blood Sample	Monocytes %	Lymphocytes %	Granulocytes %	Number of contaminating red cells per 100 white cells
1					
a. Percoll	Whole blood	7	93	0·4	10
b. Percoll	Buffy coat	6	93	1	10
2					
a. Ficoll–Triosil	Whole blood	4	95	0·8	9
b. Ficoll–Triosil	Buffy coat	8	90	2	7

Materials

    i. Preservative-free heparin (Duncan Flockhart Co. Ltd): 15 units/ml blood (or any suitable anticoagulant).

    ii. Lymphocyte separation medium or Ficoll-Hypaque of 1·077 g/ml density (Pharmacia Fine Chemicals).

    iii. Ficoll 400 (Pharmacia Fine Chemicals): 9·5% (w/v) solution (prepared as in Section 1.1.).

    iv. Hypaque (45% (w/v) sodium diatrizoate, Pharmacia Fine Chemicals): 3 vials (60 ml).

    v. Ficoll-Hypaque of 1·12 g/ml density: mix 100 ml Ficoll solution (9·5%) with the content of 3 vials of Hypaque (2:1, v/v). Store at 4 °C in the dark.

    vi. Buffered salt solution (BSS).

    vii. Polystyrene tube (Sterilin) or siliconized glass tube: 15 ml capacity.

Procedure

PREPARATION OF DISCONTINUOUS GRADIENT

Place 2·5 ml Ficoll-Hypaque solution of 1·12 g/ml density into a polystyrene tube. Onto the surface of this solution, slowly layer 2·5 ml Ficoll-Hypaque solution (using a syringe and needle) of 1·077 g/ml density by allowing the solution to run down the side wall of the tube (two layers should be visible).

LAYERING OF CELLS

    a. Mix blood with heparin and dilute 1:3 (v/v) with BSS. Preferably, a buffy coat may be prepared before dilution with BSS which helps in removing most of the red cells.

    b. Count the total number of white cells and prepare cytocentrifuge slides for Jenner–Giemsa staining.

    c. Carefully, layer 3 ml of the diluted blood onto the discontinuous gradient using a new syringe and needle (use as many gradients as required).

    d. Centrifuge the tube at 600 g for 45 min at room temperature.

    e. Discard the supernatant above the mononuclear cell band (monocytes and lymphocytes) and collect the cell layer. Use the same technique to collect the next layer of cells (neutrophils).

    f. Dilute the recovered cell suspensions (1:3, v/v) with BSS. Centrifuge at 600 g for 5–10 min to sediment the cells.

    g. Wash once with BSS to remove the Ficoll.

    h. Count the total number of white cells from each band and prepare cytocentrifuge slides for morphological examination and differential counting.

Comment

A drop of phenol red dye can be added to the 1·077 g/ml
Ficoll-Hypaque to aid in visualizing the formation of the gradient.

1.3 BANDING OF MONONUCLEAR CELLS AND GRANULO-CYTES BY SINGLE-DENSITY FICOLL GRADIENTS

The method described here can be used to separate blood monocytes
and lymphocytes from the granulocytes and erythrocytes. The red cells
can be detected at the bottom of the tube (A. Al-Sumidaie, Department
of Surgery, Welsh National College of Medicine, Cardiff).

Materials

i. Preservative-free heparin (Duncan Flockhart Co. Ltd):
15 units/ml blood.

ii. Ficoll 400 (Pharmacia Fine Chemicals): prepare 9% (w/v)
solution and autoclave at 15 lb/in^2 for 15 min.

iii. Hypaque, 85% (Pharmacia Fine Chemicals): 40 ml (two
ampoules).

iv. Buffered salt solution (BSS).

v. Polycarbonate tube (MSE Scientific Inst.): capacity 15 ml.

Procedure

PREPARATION OF FICOLL-HYPAQUE

a. Mix 46 parts Ficoll solution with 10 parts Hypaque.

b. Store at 4 °C as 20 ml aliquots.

BANDING OF CELLS

a. Mix blood with heparin. Count the total number of white cells and
prepare Jenner–Giemsa stained slides.

b. In a polycarbonate tube place 3 ml Ficoll-Hypaque solution.

c. Carefully layer 7 ml of whole blood by allowing the blood to run
down the side wall of the tube using a needle and syringe.

d. Centrifuge at 400 g for 30 min in a bench centrifuge.

e. Discard the supernatant and collect the first band of cells
(monocytes and lymphocytes) using a syringe and needle. Discard the
Ficoll-Hypaque above the next layer of cells (granulocytes) and collect
the band of cells into a separate container.

f. Dilute the collected cell suspensions 1:3 (v/v) with BSS and
centrifuge at 400 g for 10 min. Wash once with BSS to remove the
remaining Ficoll-Hypaque.

g. Count the total number of cells recovered from each band and prepare cytocentrifuge slides for Jenner–Giemsa staining to estimate the percentage of each cell type.

Reproducibility

Banding of blood cells by Ficoll-Hypaque separated the mononuclear cells from the granulocytes and from the sedimented red cells. From 50 experiments, the percentage of granulocytes in the final suspensions was greater than 95%. The morphology of the recovered cells was unchanged. The collected mononuclear cells were then fractionated into monocytes and lymphocytes by using a discontinuous density gradient of Percoll as described in Chapter 3, Section 5.1. The red cells were detected at the bottom of the tube. The mean viability of prepared granulocytes was 90%.

Comments

a. Commercial Ficoll–Hypaque (Mono-Poly Resolving media, 1·114 g/ml density) can be purchased from Flow Labs.

b. Studies on the separated cells have been carried out in various disease states. For example the recovered monocytes, after separation of mononuclear cells on a discontinuous density gradient of Percoll, were used to study monocyte migration in patients with breast disease (Al-Sumidaie et al, 1983). The separated granulocytes (neutrophils) were used to examine neutrophil migration in various diseases (Al-Sumidaie, unpublished data).

2.   REMOVAL OF MONOCYTES USING ADHERENCE COLUMNS

2.1   GLASS BEAD ADHERENCE REMOVAL OF MONOCYTES

Adherence of monocytes to glass beads can be used to deplete these cells from blood mononuclear cell suspensions to prepare pure lymphocyte fractions. The method described here is based on that reported by Summers et al (1974).

Materials

i. Preservative-free heparin (Duncan Flockhart Co. Ltd) or any appropriate anticoagulant.

ii. Percoll solution of 1·077 g/ml density (Chapter 3, Section 2).

iii. Concentrated nitric acid.

iv. Glass beads (3 mm) and 60 mesh glass beads (BDH Chemicals Ltd): pool beads and mesh, soak in nitric acid and thoroughly rinse in distilled water. Dry in an oven at 70 °C.

v. Buffered salt solution (BSS): keep at 4 °C.

vi. Autologous plasma: collect about 20–30 ml plasma from 50–100 ml blood. Centrifuge hard to sediment the platelets.

vii. Glass wool.

Procedure

PREPARATION OF GLASS BEAD COLUMN

a. Into the bottom of a 20 ml plastic syringe or siliconized glass column, layer 3 mm glass beads and plug with glass wool above the beads. If using a column, also place a strip of fine nylon gauze over the outlet.

b. Fill the column with 60 mesh glass beads and over that place another layer of 3 mm glass beads. Place in an incubator at 37 °C.

DEPLETION OF MONOCYTES

a. Collect 50–100 ml blood, mix with heparin, and prepare a mononuclear cell layer (MNL) using Percoll of 1·077 g/ml density (Chapter 3, Section 4.1). Prepare cytocentrifuge slides for Jenner–Giemsa and non-specific esterase staining.

b. Wash the MNL with cold BSS and centrifuge at 400 g for 10 min at 4 °C.

c. Resuspend the pelleted cells with 3–5 ml autologous plasma and incubate for at least 10 min at 37 °C.

d. Centrifuge at 400 g for 5–10 min at room temperature.

e. Resuspend the pelleted cells in 3 ml autologous plasma.

f. Layer the cell suspension onto the clamped glass bead column and allow it to pass through under gravity at 37 °C over a period of 30–60 min.

g. Run 20 ml autologous plasma (which has been warmed to 37 °C) into the column. Open the clamp and collect eluted lymphocytes.

h. Add 40 ml of 40% (v/v) plasma in BSS. Collect about 25 ml of the eluent which will also contain lymphocytes.

i. Centrifuge the lymphocytes at 400 g for 10 min and resuspend them in BSS or any physiological medium. Prepare cytocentrifuge slides.

Comments

a. If the monocytes are to be recovered from the column, elute with 40 ml of BSS (Ca^{2+} and Mg^{2+} free) containing 0·2–0·4 g disodium EDTA. The majority of monocytes will be eluted in the first 25 ml.

b. The above method has been used to prepare pure lymphocyte suspensions which were then fractionated onto a continuous density gradient of Percoll to isolate T-lymphocytes (Chapter 3, Section 7.2).

2.2 DEPLETION OF MONOCYTES BY SEPHADEX G-10

A simple, rapid and inexpensive method for isolating blood monocytes and lymphocytes by using Sephadex G-10 columns has been described by Chien and Ashman (1984). Using this technique, both monocytes and lymphocytes can be recovered from the same sample with a good yield and high purity (up to 90% monocytes and 98% lymphocytes).

Materials
   i. Preservative-free heparin (Duncan Flockhart Co. Ltd): 15 units/ml blood.
   ii. Percoll solution or Ficoll with a density of 1·077 g/ml.
   iii. Sephadex G-10 (Sigma).
   iv. Normal saline.
   v. Hank's buffered salt solution (HSS).
   vi. Heat-inactivated foetal calf serum (HI-FCS): prepare HSS containing 15% HI-FCS (15% HI-FCS/HSS).

Procedure

PREPARATION OF MONONUCLEAR CELL LAYER (MNL)
   a. Collect blood, mix with heparin, and prepare MNL using Percoll (Chapter 3) or Ficoll (Section 1).
   b. Count the total cell number and prepare cytocentrifuge slides for staining with Jenner–Giemsa and non-specific esterase.

SEPHADEX G-10 COLUMNS
   a. Suspend Sephadex G-10 in normal saline (2–3 times bed volume) and remove the fine particles and clumps. Autoclave for 30 min.
   b. Plug the opening of a plastic syringe, stoppered with a 3-way stopcock, with glass wool to prevent the Sephadex leaking out of the column.
   c. Pour the Sephadex into the syringe and leave to settle by gravity to the desired volume.
   d. Wash the column with 30–50 ml prewarmed (37 °C) sterile 15% HI-FCS/HSS.

e. Incubate the columns for 15 min at 37 °C before adding the cell mixture.

SEPARATION OF MONOCYTES AND LYMPHOCYTES

   a. Suspend the MNL (up to 100×10^6 cells/ml) in warmed (37 °C) 15% HI-FCS/HSS.
   b. Layer the cells over the column, with 10×10^6 cells/ml packed Sephadex, and elute the excess medium on top of the G-10 until the cells are placed in contact with the beads. Leave for 5 min.
   c. Elute the non-adherent cells at 37 °C with warm 15% HI-FCS/HSS at 2–3 ml/min and collect the eluent (a volume of more than four times the Sephadex bed volume should pass through) into polypropylene tubes. Recover the lymphocytes (up to 98% purity) from the first two fractions (5 ml).
   d. Wash further with 6 times the bed volume with 15% HI-FCS/HSS at room temperature. During the washing procedure, monitor the cell distribution by Coulter Channelizer. Remove the Sephadex from the columns when the size of monocyte and lymphocyte peaks are equal.
   e. Incubate the Sephadex in an ice bath for 30 min in precooled 15% HI-FCS/HSS (in siliconized glass tubes), and agitate gently every 5 min.
   f. Repack the Sephadex into the columns and elute the adherent monocytes with ice-cold 15% HI-FCS/HSS. Collect up to three times the bed volume of eluent which should contain most of the adherent monocytes.

Comment
The functional properties of the prepared monocytes were tested by using them as accessory cells for pokeweed mitogen-stimulated phospholipid synthesis (Chien and Ashman, 1984).

3.   ADHERENCE OF MONOCYTES TO PLASTIC

Since monocytes have the tendency to adhere to plastic (active adherence), this functional activity can be used to isolate the monocytes from mononuclear cell suspensions. In addition, it can be used for the preparation of pure lymphocyte suspensions.

3.1   ADHERENCE TO UNCOATED PLASTIC SURFACES

The method described here is based on that reported by Gadeberg et al (1979).

Materials

    i. Preservative-free heparin (Duncan Flockhart Co. Ltd): 15 units/ml blood.

    ii. Percoll solution of density 1·077 g/ml (prepare as described in Chapter 3) *or* Ficoll-Hypaque (*see also* Section 1).

    iii. Phosphate buffered saline (PBS): keep 30 ml at 37 °C.

    iv. Eagle's minimal essential medium (MEM).

    v. Heat-inactivated foetal calf serum (HI-FCS).

    vi. Eagle's MEM–5% HI-FCS and Eagle's MEM–10% HI-FCS: adjust the pH to 7·4 with sodium bicarbonate.

    vii. EDTA.

Equipment

    i. Petri dishes (35 mm, Falcon Plastic) *or* 16 mm wells of a microtitration plastic plates (Gibco, NUNC).

    ii. Humidified incubator (Lab-Line).

    iii. CO_2 cylinders.

Procedure

ADHERENCE OF MONOCYTES

    a. Collect blood, mix with heparin and prepare mononuclear cell suspension as described in Chapter 3 or Section 1. Prepare cytocentrifuge slides for Jenner–Giemsa and non-specific esterase staining.

    b. Resuspend the mononuclear cells in Eagle's MEM–5% HI-FCS to prepare a suspension containing not more than 20×10^6 cells/ml medium. Place 1 ml cell suspension into the 35 mm Petri dish (or 0·4 ml when using 16 mm dish).

    c. Incubate the cells for 1 h at 37 °C in 5% CO_2 in air in a humidified incubator to allow adherence of monocytes at the bottom of the dish.

    d. Remove the supernatant and wash the dish gently 5 times with the warmed PBS to remove the non-adherent cells, which are mainly lymphocytes. Collect the eluted cells and prepare cytocentrifuge slides.

ELUTION OF MONOCYTES

    a. To elute the adherent monocytes add 2 ml Eagle's MEM–10% HI-FCS containing 0·67% EDTA.

    b. Allow to stand at 4 °C for 10 min.

    c. Wash the dish with Eagle's MEM–10% HI-FCS containing EDTA by flushing the medium over the plastic surface with a Pasteur pipette to elute the adherent cells (monocytes).

d. Wash the monocytes twice with BSS, and prepare cytocentrifuge slides.

e. Estimate the viability of the recovered cells using trypan blue exclusion.

Comment
The adherent monocytes can also be eluted by using a 30 mM lignocaine solution in isotonic PBS (Zanella et al, 1981). Incubate the cells with lignocaine for 30 min at 37 °C and elute by washing with BSS.

3.2 ADHERENCE TO PLASTIC COATED WITH FOETAL CALF SERUM (FCS)

Pre-treatment of the plastic surface with serum is more effective in preventing the passive adherence of monocytes, which is temperature-independent, so the temperature used depends upon the nature of the cells and in this case the adherent cells may not always be recovered. Moreover, coating of surfaces with serum will enhance active adherence, which is dependent on the presence of divalent cations (Ca^{2+} and Mg^{2+}) and temperature (Kumagai et al, 1979).

Materials
Use the same materials mentioned in Section 3.1.

Procedure
PREPARATION OF COATED SURFACE

a. Cover the surface of a plastic dish (35 mm) with 0·5 ml HI-FCS.

b. Keep at 4 °C overnight.

c. Remove the HI-FCS by washing the dishes 3 times with PBS. Add the mononuclear cells (prepared as in Section 3.1).

d. Incubate and remove the non-adherent cells as described in Section 3.1.

e. Elute the adherent cells (monocytes) by first incubating with Eagle's MEM–10% HI-FCS containing 0·67% EDTA at 4 °C for 10 min and then by flushing the medium over the plastic surface with a Pasteur pipette.

f. Determine cell viability by using trypan blue exclusion.

Comments
a. The monocytes can also be eluted without pre-incubation with Eagle's MEM–10% HI-FCS and EDTA but by scraping the surface of

the plastic Petri dish with a rubber policeman (bulb) at 4 °C and then aspirating with a Pasteur pipette. Repeat the process with several washes.

b. The above methods have been used to study the effect of benign and malignant breast diseases, gastro-intestinal tract malignancies and melanoma diseases on monocyte phagocytosis (Al-Sumidaie and Young, 1983).

3.3   PHAGOCYTOSIS BY MONONUCLEAR PHAGOCYTES

The method described here can be used to detect the phagocytic activity of the monocytes (e.g. after adherence) using latex particles. Cells containing more than three latex beads can be considered phagocytotic.

Materials

    i. Latex beads (1×10^{11} beads/ml, Sigma): diameter 0·091 μm.
   ii. Buffered salt solution (BSS).

Procedure

PREPARATION OF LATEX BEADS

To 100 μl latex beads, add 10 ml BSS to prepare 1×10^9 beads/ml suspension.

PHAGOCYTOSIS BY MONOCYTES

    a. Prepare adherent cells as described in the previous sections.
    b. Add 100 μl of latex bead suspension to the Petri dish containing the adherent cells.
    c. Incubate for 1 h at 37 °C in an incubator with 5% CO_2 in air. Mix well every 5 min.
    d. Wash the cells gently with BSS. Prepare cytocentrifuge slide and stain with Jenner–Giemsa.
    e. Count at least 500 cells in random fields. Determine the mean percentage of monocytes that had phagocytosed latex beads.

4.   ISOLATION OF GRANULOCYTIC CELLS

4.1   SEPARATION OF NEUTROPHILS USING DEXTRAN

When anticoagulated blood is layered on top of dextran, the red cells are clumped by dextran and fall down to the bottom of the tube, while the white cells (neutrophils) remain in the upper fractions. The method reported here is based on that reported by Summers et al (1974).

Materials

  i. Dextran 110 (Fisons Pharmaceutical) 6% solution in 0·15M NaCl.
  ii. Percoll solution of 1·077 g/ml density: prepare as reported in Chapter 3, Section 2.1 or Ficoll–Hypaque (Section 1).
  iii. Buffered salt solution (BSS) and 3·5% NaCl.
  iv. Cylinder: capacity 100 ml.

Procedure

SEDIMENTATION OF CELLS

  a. Collect blood, mix with heparin and prepare mononuclear cells using Percoll or Ficoll.
  b. Collect the neutrophil layer of cells just above the red cells at the bottom of the tube.
  c. Wash twice using BSS and resuspend 1:2 (v/v) in BSS. Mix the cells with the dextran solution (1:10, v/v)
  d. Place the above mixture into the cylinder.
  e. Leave to stand at room temperature for 1 h.
  f. Collect the top layer of cells (neutrophils).
  g. Wash the recovered cells three times with BSS.
  h. Prepare cytocentrifuge slides for Jenner–Giemsa staining.
  i. Remove contaminated red cells as described below.

DIFFERENTIAL RED CELL LYSIS

  a. Centrifuge and resuspend the cells in 0·5 ml ice-cold distilled water.
  b. Mix the suspension with a Pasteur pipette for 30 s to allow lysis of red cells but not the leucocytes.
  c. Immediately, add 2 ml ice-cold 3·5% NaCl to restore isotonicity.
  d. Wash the cells twice with BSS to remove the supernatant (containing the haemoglobin and red cell debris).
  e. Prepare cytocentrifuge slides for Jenner–Giemsa staining.
  f. Estimate cell viability by using trypan blue exclusion.

4.2 PURIFICATION OF EOSINOPHILS USING NYLON WOOL COLUMNS

In order to study and characterize blood eosinophils, a pure eosinophil cell suspension is required. Eosinophils constitute 1–6% of the total blood leucocytes, therefore enrichment of these cells may prove difficult. However, Parrillo and Fauci (1978) and Koeffler et al (1980) published a separation technique that can reproducibly give highly purified eosinophil fractions (up to 70% and 98% purity when using normal blood and blood from patients with high eosinophil counts respectively). Their method exploits the high affinity of neutrophils to bind to nylon wool, while eosinophils bind only after a long incubation. The separated eosinophils are found to be highly viable and suffer no changes in their surface marker properties, or their cytotoxic ability, for example in patients with high eosinophil counts (hyper-eosinophilic syndrome).

Materials

  i. Preservative-free heparin (Duncan Flockhart Co. Ltd): 15 units/ml blood.
 ii. Percoll solution or Ficoll of density 1·077 g/ml.
iii. RPMI-1640 medium (Flow Labs).
 iv. Heat-inactivated foetal calf serum (HI-FCS): prepare a solution of RPMI-1640 containing 10% HI-FCS (RPMI–10% HI-FCS).
  v. Dextran T-500 (Pharmacia Fine Chemicals): prepare 3% dextran in normal saline.
 vi. Fenwal-scrubbed nylon wool (Travenol Labs).
vii. Ammonium Chloride (NH_4Cl) in Tris buffer: see Section 7.4.

Procedure

PREPARATION OF NEUTROPHIL-EOSINOPHIL FRACTIONS

a. Collect 60 ml blood (from normal volunteers or from patients), mix with heparin, and prepare mononuclear cells by using Percoll or Ficoll as described in Chapter 3 or Section 1 respectively.

b. Collect the pelleted cells (neutrophils, eosinophils and red cells), and wash three times with RPMI-1640.

c. Mix 5 parts cell suspension with 1 part 3% dextran and allow the erythrocytes to sediment at $1g$ (normal gravity) for 1 h. A sharp interface should be formed between red cells and the leucocytes.

d. Collect the leucocyte-rich layer and wash twice with RPMI-1640.

e. Lyse the remaining red cells with NH_4Cl in Tris buffer as described in Section 7.4. Suspend the unlysed neutrophil-eosinophil mixture in 3–4 ml RPMI–10% HI-FCS.

f. Count the total number of cells and prepare cytocentrifuge slides.

NYLON WOOL COLUMNS

a. Tease about 3 g nylon wool until a thin network is obtained. Pack very gently by pressing the wool into a 35 ml plastic syringe fitted with a 3-way stopcock.

b. Wash the column with 100 ml RPMI–10% HI-FCS. Allow to drain.

c. Place the cell suspension ($100–200 \times 10^6$ cells per 3–4 ml medium) over the nylon wool, and allow to permeate the entire surface of nylon wool by immediately twice eluting and reapplying the eluent into the column.

d. Incubate the column in an upright position at 37 °C for 15 min to allow adherence of neutrophils.

e. Elute the non-adherent eosinophils by adding 50–100 ml warm (37 °C) RPMI–10% HI-FCS.

f. Recover the adherent neutrophils (if required) by placing the column at 4 °C for 30 min. Elute the cells with 100 ml of cold RPMI–10% HI-FCS.

g. Wash the collected cells with RPMI–10% HI-FCS.

h. Count the total cell number and prepare cytocentrifuge slides for Jenner–Giemsa staining.

i. Check cell viability by trypan blue exclusion.

Comments

a. After Jenner–Giemsa staining, identify the eosinophils by the presence in their cytoplasm of coarse granules which are stained an orange-red colour.

b. The absolute number of eosinophils in blood is $0 \cdot 04–0 \cdot 4 \times 10^9$ eosinophils/litre blood.

c. The above method was used to study the cytotoxic ability of eosinophils from patients with the hyper-eosinophilic syndrome against an assortment of target cells utilizing a ^{51}Cr release assay (Parrillo and Fauci, 1978). In addition, this technique was also used by Koeffler et al (1980) to study the distribution of Ia antigens on cells of the eosinophil series.

5.   SEPARATION OF LYMPHOCYTIC CELL POPULATIONS AND BASOPHILS

In this section, methods which can be applied for the separation of lymphocyte populations and basophils are included together since the lymphocytes form the main contaminating cell population in the basophil fraction. Therefore, techniques for isolating lymphocytes can also be used for the negative selection of blood basophils.

5.1　SEPARATION OF B-LYMPHOCYTES USING NYLON WOOL COLUMNS

A.　Elution of B- and T-lymphocytes

The active adherence of B-lymphocytes (with surface immunoglobulin) to nylon wool can be used to isolate these cells from other lymphocyte subpopulations. Using this method, concentrations greater than 80% B-lymphocytes may be obtained (Danilovs et al, 1980).

Materials

　　i. Preservative-free heparin (Duncan Flockhart Co. Ltd): 15 units/ml blood.

　　ii. Percoll solution of 1·077 g/ml density (Chapter 3) *or* Ficoll–Hypaque (*see also* Section 1).

　　iii. RPMI-1640 medium (Flow Labs).

　　iv. Heat-inactivated foetal calf serum (HI-FCS).

　　v. RPMI–5% HI-FCS: prepare and filter through a 0·45 μm Millipore filter into a plastic container (Universal container, Sterilin). Heat to 37 °C for at least 30 min before use (for a 40 ml blood sample 50 ml is required).

　　vi. Fine-mesh nylon-gauze filter (Millipore).

　　vii. Plastic drinking straw (clear); 7 mm in diameter: cut the straw to a 12–14 cm length.

　　viii. Fenwal-scrubbed nylon wool (Travenol Labs): 3 denier, 3·81 cm type 200.

　　ix. Spencer-Wells forceps.

Procedure

PREPARATION OF CELLS

　　a. Collect 40 ml blood, mix with heparin and prepare mononuclear cells using Percoll (*see also* Chapter 3, Section 4.1) or Ficoll–Hypaque (Section 1). Deplete monocytes (if required) as described in Sections 2 and 3.

　　b. Prepare cytocentrifuge slides for Jenner–Giemsa staining and direct fluorescence staining to determine the percentage of B-lymphocytes.

PREPARATION OF NYLON WOOL COLUMN

　　a. Tease a small amount (0·1 g) nylon wool until a thin network is obtained. Pack very gently by pressing a small amount of the nylon wool into the column using a glass rod or a Kwill, then pack the rest of the wool by tapping the straw against the table. Fill about 6 cm length into the straw about 4 cm from the end. Use a new column for each 40 ml of blood.

  b. Wash the colum through with about 15–20 ml RPMI. Allow to drain.

  c. Fold back one end of each straw just below the level of the wool and clip off with Spencer-Wells forceps.

  d. Add RPMI–5% HI-FCS to each straw to just above the nylon wool and place in an upright position at 37 °C for 30 min before use.

ISOLATION OF B-LYMPHOCYTES

  a. Resuspend the mononuclear cells in warmed (37 °C) RPMI–5% HI-FCS (approximately 0·6 ml/straw). Remove any aggregates by passing the cells through a fine-mesh nylon gauze filter or by allowing them to settle.

  b. Restart the column and drain off RPMI–5% HI-FCS. Replace the clip.

  c. Pipette the cells onto the nylon wool and cover with RPMI–5% HI-FCS. Allow the cells to move all the way into the wool.

  d. Incubate in an upright position at 37 °C for 30 min.

  e. Remove the clip, place the straw vertically and elute the non-adherent cells (T-cells and some platelets) by collecting 15 ml (5 ml with straw upright, 5 ml with straw upside down and 5 ml with the straw upright again) of warmed RPMI–5% HI-FCS from each straw. Allow to drain.

  f. Elute the adherent cells (B-lymphocytes and few platelets) by adding 1·5 ml RPMI–5% HI-FCS to the column and squeezing vigorously at the level of the nylon wool while the medium is passing through. Repeat the elution procedure twice and collect B-lymphocytes in a clean (sterile) container.

  g. Wash the recovered cells twice with RPMI–5% HI-FCS.

  h. Prepare cytocentrifuge slides to determine the percentage of lymphocytes.

  i. Estimate the percentages of T- and B-lymphocytes using E-rosetting and immunofluorescence staining respectively (Chapter 2).

Comments

  a. Packed washed straws can be filled with RPMI and frozen for later use.

  b. B- and T-cells recovered from the column may be further fractionated onto a continuous density gradient of Percoll as described in Chapter 3.

c. Packing the column with a thick layer of nylon wool may cause trapping of T-lymphocytes and therefore higher contamination.

d. B-lymphocytes prepared by the above method have been used for HLA tissue typing (Blood Transfusion Centre, Cardiff, UK).

B.   Removal of platelets from T-lymphocytes

Since thrombin can induce platelet aggregation this can be used to remove the platelets from the cell suspension. The method described here should be used with caution, since it may affect the results of some studies (such as HLA system studies).

Materials
  i. Thrombin, 100 units/ml (from human plasma, Sigma).
  ii. RPMI-1640 (Flow Labs).

Procedure
  a. Add one drop of thrombin to the cells suspended in a small volume of RPMI.
  b. Rotate the tube by hand to cause clumping of the platelets.
  c. Allow the clumps to settle and pipette out the cells.

Comment

A milder method for the removal of platelets is described in Chapter 3, Section 4.1 (*Comments*).

5.2   PURIFICATION OF NATURAL KILLER CELLS BY NEGATIVE SELECTION

One of the important defence mechanisms of the human body is natural killer (NK) activity, which is directed, for example, against malignant cells (Hanna and Burton, 1981) and viral infections (Trinchier and Santoli, 1978; Santoli et al, 1978). Morphological analyses and structural studies of various lymphoid cell populations suggest that a subpopulation of lymphocytes known as 'large granular lymphocytes' (LGL) is usually responsible for mediating a great majority of human NK cytoxicity (Timonen and Saksela, 1980; Timonen et al, 1981; Ortaldo et al, 1981; Abo and Balch, 1981; and Luini et al, 1981).

Purification of blood LGL (which results in a great enrichment of NK cells) using a discontinuous Percoll gradient, followed by removal of contaminating T-lymphocytes by E-rosetting, has been described by

Timonen et al (1982). NK cell purity of 60–80% was obtained in the low-density fractions of the gradient. Further enrichment of NK cells (up to 90% purity) was then achieved after removing the T-cells from the enriched fractions. The purified cells were found useful in further studies, such as in the assessment of the interferon production capacity of human NK cells *in vivo* (Timonen et al, 1980) and in cultures (Timonen et al, 1982).

Materials

   i. Preservative-free heparin (Duncan Flockhart Co. Ltd): 15 units/ml blood.

   ii. Percoll (Pharmacia Fine Chemicals).

   iii. Percoll Solution or Ficoll of density 1·077 g/ml.

   iv. Phosphate-buffered saline (PBS), 10 times working concentration.

   v. RPMI-1640 medium (Flow Labs.).

   vi. Heat-inactivated foetal calf serum (HI-FCS).

   vii. Culture medium (10% HI-FCS/RPMI): prepare 10% HI-FCS/RPMI solution containing 0·29 mg/ml glutamine and antibiotics (100 IU/ml penicillin and 100 μg/ml streptomycin). Adjust the tonicity to 285 mmol/kg H_2O by adding distilled water to lower the osmolality and with PBS (10 × conc.) to increase it.

   viii. Sheep red blood cells: *see* Chapter 2, Section 9.1.

   ix. Nylon wool: *see* Section 5.1.

   x. Falcon 2095 centrifuge tubes (Falcon Plastic): 15 ml capacity.

Procedure

DEPLETION OF MONOCYTES AND LYMPHOCYTES

   a. Collect blood, mix with heparin, and prepare a mononuclear cell layer (MNL) as described in Chapter 3, or Chapter 6, Section 1.1. Resuspend the MNL in culture medium.

   b. Deplete the adherent monocytes by using plastic dishes as described in Section 3.

   c. Remove the adherent B-lymphocytes from the remaining MNL by using nylon wool columns (Section 5.1).

   d. Prepare cytocentrifuge slides for detecting monocytes. Identify B-lymphocytes by direct immunofluorescence (Chapter 2).

DISCONTINUOUS PERCOLL GRADIENT

Prepare Percoll solutions immediately before use.

   a. Make iso-osmotic Percoll by using 8% (v/v) PBS (10 × conc.) in purchased Percoll. Adjust the osmolality to 285 mmol/kg H_2O by adding 0·1% (v/v) PBS (10 × conc.) or 1% (v/v) Percoll to increase or lower the osmolality respectively.

  b. Prepare Percoll solutions with seven different densities by adding culture medium as shown in Table 6.2. Adjust the tonicity of the medium using PBS (10 × conc.) to increase the osmolality and distilled water to lower it.

Table 6.2. Preparation of Percoll solutions of different densities for the separation of natural killer cells

Percoll solution number	Iso-osmotic Percoll (μl)	Culture medium (μl)	Density (g/ml)
1	2550	3450	1·053
2	2700	3300	1·060
3	2850	3150	1·063
4	3000	3000	1·068
5	3150	2850	1·073
6	3300	2700	1·077
7	4000	2000	1·080

  c. To form the discontinuous density gradient, place 1·5 ml of Percoll solution 7 into a Falcon tube, and onto the surface of this solution carefully layer 1·5 ml solution 6, using a syringe and needle, by allowing the solution to run on the side wall of the tube just above the surface of the first layer.

  d. Using the same technique, layer 2·5 ml of solutions 5, 4, 3, 2, and 1. Seven separate layers should be visible.

  e. Gently layer the non-adherent MNL (50–80 × 10^6 cells/ml culture medium) on top of the gradient.

  f. Centrifuge the cells at 550 g for 30 min at room temperature.

  g. Into a sterile tube, collect the first cell band at the top of the gradient using a syringe and needle. Discard the following layer of medium and recover the second cell band (contains up to 80% NK cells) into another tube. Remove the solution above the third cell layer and collect the cells (contains up to 60% NK cells). Use the same technique to recover the remaining 4 cell bands.

  h. Sediment the cells in each fraction by diluting the suspending Percoll solution with at least 10-fold of culture medium and centrifuge at 400 g for 10 min.

  i. Wash the pelleted cells twice with culture medium.

  j. Count the total cell number and prepare cytocentrifuge slides for Jenner–Giemsa staining (see Comment a.).

SECOND-STEP ENRICHMENT OF NK CELLS

a. Pool the cells collected from fractions 2 and 3. Count the total cell number.

b. Deplete the contaminating T-lymphocytes by rosetting with sheep red blood cells (Chapter 2). Sediment the rosetted T-cells from the non-rosetted NK cells by centrifugation on a Percoll or Ficoll cushion (1·077 g/ml density) at 550 g for 30 min. Collect the interface layer of cells (contains up to 90% NK cells).

Comments

a. To stain the cells, fix the air-dried slides in methanol for 10 min and air-dry again. Stain in 10% aqueous Giemsa of pH 7·2, for 25 min. Rinse with phosphate-buffered water (7·2 pH) and dry the slides with a hair dryer. Identify the LGL by the relatively high cytoplasmic/nuclear ratio, cytoplasmic azurophilic granules, and the kidney-shaped and eccentric nuclei. LGL comprise only 3–6% of the blood white cell population (Timonen et al, 1982).

b. The density of each fraction in the gradient can be determined by using density marker beads (Chapter 3).

c. Purification of LGL by negative selection has been described by Froelich et al (1983). In their method, the non-adherent MNL (obtained after adherence to nylon wool) were incubated with Leu-1 monoclonal antibody. The Leu-1 positive cells are then mixed with antibody-coated bovine erythrocytes to form rosettes. The pelleted rosetted cells were then centrifuged on Ficoll cushion and the interface cell layer were found to contain more than 90% LGL (NK cells) as detected using monoclonal antibodies.

d. Measurement of cytotoxic activity of LGL can be performed by the use of a 4-hour ^{51}Cr release assay against K562 as reported by Timonen et al (1981) and Herberman et al (1981).

5.3 ISOLATION OF T-LYMPHOCYTE SUBPOPULATIONS

Separation methods incorporating the use of differentially expressed cell surface markers (positive selection) constitute the most sensitive techniques for the purification of cell populations and subpopulations. A positive selection of T-lymphocyte subpopulations can be achieved by using monoclonal antibodies against their cell surface markers. Highly enriched T-cell suspensions are incubated with monoclonal antibody, then placed into anti-mouse-antibody-coated Petri dishes. Adherent cells (positive) and nonadherent cells (negative) for the specific monoclonal antibody are recovered after incubation.

The method described here is based on that published by Becton Dickinson and on that reported by Engleman et al (1981) and Gatenby et al (1981).

Materials

    i. Preservative-free heparin (Duncan Flockhart Co. Ltd): 15 units/ml blood.
    ii. Sheep red blood cells (SRBC) preserved in Alsevier's solution.
    iii. Anti-Leu-2a monoclonal antibody (Becton Dickinson): specific for T_G (suppressor) lymphocytes; or anti-Leu-3a monoclonal antibody (Becton Dickinson): specific for T_M (helper) lymphocytes.
    iv. Goat-anti-mouse immunoglobulin G (IgG; Pharmacia Fine Chemicals): affinity purified.
    v. Heat-inactivated foetal calf serum (HI-FCS).
    vi. Phosphate-buffered saline (PBS) Dulbecco 'A' with Ca^{2+} and Mg^{2+} (Oxoid tablets): dissolve each tablet in 100 ml distilled water.
    vii. 5% HI-FCS/PBS.
    viii. 1% HI-FCS/PBS.
    ix. 0·05M Tris buffer, pH 9·5.
    x. Plastic Petri dishes (sterile): 15 × 100 mm.

Procedure

PURIFICATION OF T-CELLS

    a. Collect blood, mix with heparin and prepare mononuclear cells by using 1·077 g/ml Percoll (Chapter 3, Section 4.1) or Ficoll (*see also* Section 1). Count the total nucleated cell number, and prepare cytocentrifuge slides for Jenner–Giemsa staining.
    b. To prepare pure lymphocyte suspensions, deplete the monocytes by adherence (Sections 2 and 3) or by carbonyl iron phagocytosis (Chapter 3, Section 4.2).
    c. Prepare T-lymphocyte suspensions by E-rosetting (Chapter 2, Section 9.1) and separate the rosetted cells from the non-rosetted cells by pelleting the former through 1·077 g/ml Percoll or Ficoll. Remove SRBC by lysis as described in Sections 4.1 and 7.4. Pure T-lymphocyte fractions can also be prepared by using nylon-wool columns (Section 5.1).

COATING OF ANTI-MOUSE ANTIBODY

    a. Dilute goat-anti-mouse IgG with 0·05M Tris buffer to give a concentration of 10 μg/ml.

b. Add 10 ml diluted antibody to each Petri dish and incubate at room temperature for 40 min.

c. Wash three times with PBS and once with 1% HI-FCS/PBS.

PREPARATION OF ANTIBODY-TREATED LYMPHOCYTES

a. Dilute the monoclonal antibody to 10 µg/ml in PBS.

b. Mix cell pellet (2–3×10^7 cells) with 20 µg (2 ml) of diluted monoclonal antibody.

c. Incubate at room temperature for 20 min.

d. Centrifuge at 400 g for 5 min. Wash the pelleted cells twice with 5% HI-FCS/PBS.

PURIFICATION OF LYMPHOCYTE SUBPOPULATIONS

a. Resuspend the cells (<2–3×10^7) in 3 ml of 5% HI-FCS/PBS and place onto one coated Petri dish.

b. Incubate at 2–8 °C for 2 h.

c. Collect the supernatant (containing the non-adherent cells) by decanting.

d. Wash the Petri dish gently with 6 ml of 1% HI-FCS/PBS and decant. Repeat gentle washing 4 times, pooling washes. Collect cells (negative cells).

e. Add 15–20 ml of 1% HI-FCS/PBS to the Petri dish and pipette vigorously to remove adherent cells (positive cells).

f. Check the Petri dish for cells using an inverted microscope (if required).

g. Repeat washing to remove the remaining adherent cells.

h. Detect the prepared cells by using immunofluorescence staining (Section 5.5).

Comments

a. T_M-cells and T_G-cells have receptors for the Fc portion of IgM and IgG molecules respectively. T_M-cells constitute about 55% of blood T-lymphocytes. T_G-cells accounted for 10–15% of T-lymphocytes. T_M-cells and T_G-cells can be detected by rosette formation with ox red cells coated with rabbit IgM and IgG anti-ox red cell antibodies (Platsoucas and Catsimpoolas, 1980b).

b. The purified T-lymphocyte subpopulations can also be identified by FACS analysis.

5.4 ISOLATION OF T-SUPPRESSOR LYMPHOCYTES BY PANNING TECHNIQUES

The use of cell surface markers for classification of subsets of cells has further explained the role of different cell populations of the immune system in various responses and their involvement in the pathological disorders. Purification of lymphocyte subsets has been established by exploiting the differences in their surface markers.

Tsoi et al (1982) published a separation method which employs the use of monoclonal antibodies and immunoglobulin (Ig)-coated dishes (panning) for purifying cell subsets from peripheral blood. For separating T- and B-cells (with more than 90% and 80% purity respectively), the dishes were coated with $F(ab)_2$ fragments of anti-human Ig (direct panning). To select T-cell subsets, the cells were first incubated with monoclonal antibodies specific to cell surface antigens and then separated in dishes coated with anti-mouse Ig (indirect panning).

Materials

 i. Preservative-free heparin (Duncan Flockhart Co. Ltd): 15 units/ml blood.
 ii. Percoll solution or Ficoll of density 1·077 g/ml.
 iii. Phosphate-buffered saline free of Ca^{2+} and Mg^{2+} (PBS) (Gibco).
 iv. RPMI (Flow Labs.).
 v. Heat-inactivated foetal calf serum (HI-FCS): prepare 1% HI-FCS/PBS and 5% HI-FCS/PBS solutions.
 vi. Bovine serum albumin (BSA): prepare 1% BSA/PBS and 5% BSA/PBS solutions.
 vii. Pooled human serum (PHS): prepare RPMI/50% PHS.
 viii. Mouse serum (MS): prepare RPMI/10% MS.
 ix. Poly-L-lysine (Sigma): for each dish, use 15 ml poly-L-lysine at a concentration of 100 μg/ml PBS.
 x. Tris buffer, 0·05M, pH 9·5.
 xi. $F(ab)_2$ goat-anti-human immunoglobulin (Ig) (Tago): for each dish, dissolve 160 μg in 15 ml of 0·05M Tris buffer.
 xii. Goat-anti-mouse immunoglobulin G(IgG), affinity purified (Tago): for each dish, dissolve 75 μg in 15 ml 0·05M Tris buffer.
 xiii. Monoclonal antibodies to human T-lymphocytes (Ortho Pharmaceutical Co.): the instructions for using these antibodies are usually supplied by the manufacturer. Use *either* OKT4 monoclonal antibody: specific for T_M (helper/inducer); *or* OKT8 monoclonal antibody: specific for T_G (suppressor/cytotoxic).
 xiv. Plastic Petri dishes, polystyrene (25 × 100 mm).

Procedure

PREPARATION OF MONONUCLEAR CELL LAYER (MNL)

a. Collect blood, mix with heparin, and prepare MNL as described in Chapter 3 using Percoll and in Section 1 for Ficoll.

b. Resuspend the MNL in 3 ml of 5% HI-FCS/PBS to a concentration of 10×10^6 cells/ml. Prepare cytocentrifuge slides for Jenner–Giemsa and non-specific esterase staining.

c. Keep a small volume of the cell suspension for the detection of T- and non-T-cells.

COATING OF THE PLASTIC DISHES

a. To each plastic dish, add 15 ml of poly-L-lysine solution (to improve the adsorption of anti-human Ig) and leave for 1 h at room temperature.

b. Wash the dishes three times with PBS.

c. Add 15 ml F(ab)$_2$ goat-anti-human Ig antibody solution per dish and keep overnight at 4 °C.

d. Wash the dishes 3 times with PBS.

e. Add 15 ml of 5% BSA/PBS to each dish and leave for 1 h at room temperature to cover any free poly-L-lysine on the plastic surface.

f. Wash the dishes 3 times with PBS and once with 1% HI-FCS/ PBS.

ENRICHMENT OF T- AND B-LYMPHOCYTES

Use either the whole MNL or remove the monocytes, for example by adherence.

a. Place 3 ml cell suspension (containing 3×10^7 cells) into each coated dish and leave for 70 min at room temperature. Shake the cells gently once during the incubation.

b. Incline each dish gently and collect the non-adherent cells (mostly T-lymphocytes) by collecting all the supernatant from the side of the dish.

c. Carefully wash each dish five times with 8 ml 1% HI-FCS/PBS per dish and collect the cells from the washings in a separate container or pool with the enriched T-cell fraction from step *b.*

d. To recover the adherent cells (mostly B-lymphocytes, and monocytes if present), add 25 ml RPMI/50% PHS per dish and incubate overnight (or for 12 h) at 37 °C in an incubator with 5% CO_2 in air.

e. Collect the adherent cells using gentle hydrostatic pressure with the aid of a plastic capillary pipette (Falcon Plastic).

f. Count the total cell number in each fraction and check cell viability by trypan blue exclusion. Prepare cytocentrifuge slides for differential staining.

g. Determine the percentages of T- and B-lymphocytes by E-rosetting (Chapter 2) and by immunofluorescence staining (Section 5.5).

FRACTIONATION OF T-CELL SUBSETS

Use the non-adherent cells from the above section and the cells recovered from the washings (i.e. enriched T-cell fraction).

a. To coat the plastic dishes, add 15 ml affinity purified goat-anti-mouse IgG antibody solution to each dish and continue the coating as described above.

b. Dilute the monoclonal antibody, specific for distinct T-cell antigen, 1:500–1:1000, in 1% BSA/PBS. Add 500 μl for each 3×10^7 cells.

c. Place the cells at $4\,^\circ$C for 30 min to allow antibody–antigen reaction to occur.

d. Wash the cells twice and resuspend in 5% HI-FCS/PBS (10×10^6 cells/ml).

e. Add the cells to the coated dishes and incubate at $4\,^\circ$C for 70 min. Mix the cells once during incubation.

f. Collect the non-adherent cells by gently inclining the dish and then collecting the supernatant medium from the side of the dish.

g. In a separate container pool the cells from subsequent washings. These cells may also be discarded.

h. To recover the adherent cells, that is cells that adhere through interaction between the specific monoclonal antibody on their surface and the goat-anti-mouse Ig on the plate, add 25 ml RPMI/10% MS per plate.

i. Incubate overnight or for 12 h at $37\,^\circ$C in an incubator with 5% CO_2 in air.

j. Collect the detached cells with a Pasteur pipette. Count the total cell number and prepare cytocentrifuge slides for differential staining.

k. Estimate cell viability by trypan blue exclusion.

l. Detect B-lymphocytes by direct immunofluorescence. Identify T-cells and their subsets (T_M, T_G) by indirect immunofluorescence (Section 5.5).

Comments

a. The eluted cells may suffer stripping or capping of their surface markers or antigens which may be resynthesised after 6 days' incubation. To avoid stripping or capping, the adherent cells may be detached after incubation with serum in the cold (Tsoi et al, 1982).

b. The above method was used to study suppressor activity of a myelofibrosis patient who was treated by bone marrow transplantation (Tsoi et al, 1982).

5.5 INDIRECT IMMUNOFLUORESCENCE STAINING

Viable cells with membrane marker determinants present in the suspension can react with unlabelled antibodies (specific to the markers) added to the suspension in the presence of sodium azide, which helps to prevent capping and shedding of the membrane receptors. The cells are then washed carefully and reincubated with a labelled antibody (e.g. fluoresceinated antibody) directed against the protein-antibody complexes. These bindings are then made visible by irradiation with light of a suitable wavelength under a fluorescence microscope, or analysed by Fluorescence Activated Cell Sorter (FACS). The indirect fluorescence staining method is more sensitive than the direct fluorescence staining described in Chapter 2.

Materials

  i. Phosphate buffered saline (PBS) Dulbecco 'A' (Section 5.3).
 ii. Bovine serum albumin (BSA).
iii. Washing medium: prepare PBS solution containing 1% BSA and 0·02% sodium azide.
 iv. Monoclonal antibodies: use the appropriate antibody for each cell type (e.g. OKT4 and OKT8 monoclonal antibodies are used to detect T-helper and T-suppressor cells respectively).
  v. Fluoresceinated goat-anti-mouse IgG antibody (Tago).

Procedure

  a. Wash the cells twice with washing medium.
  b. Place 50 µl cell suspension (containing 0·5–1 × 10⁶ cells) into plastic tubes according to the number of antisera to be used. Include controls for staining with washing medium (control 1) and with fluoresceinated antibody (control 2).
  c. Add 0·1 ml of appropriate monoclonal antibody and incubate for 30 min at 4 °C (on ice). Agitate cell mixture once or twice during incubation.
  d. Wash the cells twice (3 min at 400 g) with the washing medium. Discard the supernatant.
  e. To the cell pellet, add 0·1 ml of fluoresceinated goat-anti-mouse IgG antibody and incubate for 30 min at 4 °C.
  f. Wash the cells twice as above and resuspend with 0·1 or 0·5 ml washing medium. Keep the cells on ice while preparing slides.
  g. Place one small drop of cell suspension on a slide, cover with a coverslip and press gently. Seal with nail varnish and examine immediately using a fluorescence microscope. Estimate the number of positively stained cells by counting at least 200 cells.
  h. Check the control slides for negatively stained cells.

Comments

    a. If the cells cannot be analysed within 30 min, add 10 µl of 8% formalin (approximately 2% final concentration).

    b. For the use of Leitz fluorescence microscope, *see* Chapter 2, Section 9.3. The viable cells are stained in a patched pattern, while the dead cells in the suspension are homogeneously stained with labelled antibody. In a few instances, viable cells can show a weak ring-staining which is an artifact.

    c. To detect B-lymphocytes by direct fluorescence staining, add 0·1 ml of fluoresceinated $F(ab)_2$ goat-anti-mouse IgG (Tago) to the cell pellet and incubate for 30 min at 4 °C. Proceed as described above (step *f.* onwards). To enumerate T-lymphocytes, use indirect fluorescence staining and anti-T-lymphocyte monoclonal antibody (Pan T, Becton Dickinson).

    d. B-lymphocytes can also be detected by their ability to form structures known as rosettes with mouse red blood cells (M-rosettes) when both are mixed together under optimum conditions. Using peripheral blood, at least half (5–10%) of the B-lymphocytes can form M-rosettes.

    The principles of this technique are similar to the E-rosette test for T-lymphocytes except for using freshly drawn mouse red cells from a laboratory mouse (e.g. CBA strain). To prepare the red cells, add 1 ml of mouse blood to 1 ml of 32 g/l trisodium citrate and 9 ml saline. Use the cells within 3 days (Stathopoulos and Elliott, 1974; Catovsky et al, 1976; Cherchi and Catovsky, 1980). Proceed with the test as described for E-rosetting technique in Chapter 2.

    e. An improved E-rosette assay can also be utilized for detecting T-lymphocytes (Weiner et al, 1973). Prepare a 2% sheep red cell suspension (0·2 ml packed sheep red cells + 10 ml BSS). Wash three times in BSS and add 15 IU/ml neuraminidase (Sigma, Type VI). Incubate the cells at 37 °C for 30 min. Wash three times and prepare 2% (v/v) neuraminidase-treated red cell suspension. The treated cells can then be kept for at least seven days (at 4 °C). Proceed with rosetting technique as reported in Chapter 2.

5.6   NEGATIVE SELECTION OF BASOPHILS USING DENSITY GRADIENT CENTRIFUGATION AND PANNING

In order to study the basophil role in, for example, allergic phenomena and immediate hypersensitivity in man, a method which can separate these cells without altering their biological properties is required.

    Basophils usually constitute 1% or less of the total blood leucocyte population, therefore enrichment of these cells may be found difficult. Positive selection, for example, adherence of basophils to glass beads, has been described by Pruzansky and Patterson (1981). However, in this technique the cell membrane usually binds to the glass beads. This interaction may lead to changes in structure of the membrane and, along with that, to an altered function. Therefore, in certain experimental work which involves basophils, separation methods which exploit density differences between basophils and other cell populations present in the suspension is recommended. This technique also allows simultaneous isolation of other cell types present in the mixture. A further suitable approach for separating basophils is that which depends on the positive selection of the unwanted cells, leaving the basophils intact. In the following sections methods which apply one or both of these principles for the sparation of blood basophils are described.

A.   One-step fractionation of basophils, mononuclear cells and neutrophils

A concurrent enrichment of blood basophils, mononuclear cells and granulocytes can be achieved by using a discontinuous Percoll gradient which consists of Percoll solutions of three different densities. After centrifugation of the leucocyte-rich layer, three cell bands which form at the interfaces between Percoll layers can be collected. This procedure was first published by Kauffman et al (1983).

Materials

i. EDTA (Na$_2$): to 30 ml blood, add 0·48 ml 10% EDTA as an anticoagulant.

ii. Dextran T-500 (Pharmacia Fine Chemicals): to 100 ml 0·15M NaCl, add 3 g glucose and 6 g dextran.

iii. Percoll (Pharmacia Fine Chemicals).

iv. NaCl, 1·2M.

v. Eagle's minimal essential medium (MEM).

vi. Polypropylene tubes (Falcon Plastic 2017): 17 × 100 mm.

Procedure

REMOVAL OF RED CELLS

a. Collect blood in EDTA solution. At least 20 ml blood should be collected to recover a sufficient number of basophils for degranulation test.

b. Mix 5 parts blood with 1 part 6% dextran in 3% glucose and 0·15M NaCl. Incubate at 37 °C for 30–40 min to allow sedimentation of red cells. A sharp interface should be formed between red cells and leucocyte-rich plasma.

c. Collect the plasma layer containing the white cells and centrifuge for 10 min at 150 g and 4 °C.

d. Resuspend the pelleted cells in 1 ml autologous plasma.

DISCONTINUOUS PERCOLL GRADIENT

a. To prepare iso-osmotic Percoll, mix 9 parts purchased Percoll with 1 part 1·2M NaCl and store at −20 °C. Adjust the pH to 7·4 by adding 1M HCl.

b. Prepare Percoll solutions of densities 1·100, 1·082 and 1·072 g/ml by adding 0·12M NaCl. Use the method described in Chapter 2, Section 2.1.

c. Using a syringe and needle, place 2 ml Percoll solution of density 1·100 g/ml into a polypropylene tube. Onto the surface of the above Percoll layer, gently layer 2 ml Percoll solution of density 1·082 g/ml by allowing the solution to run on the side wall of the tube just above the surface of the first layer. Using the same technique, place the third layer of Percoll (1·072 g/ml) on the top of the previous solutions (three layers should be visible).

d. Carefully, layer the leucocyte-rich suspension (1 ml) on top of the discontinuous gradient and centrifuge in a swing-out rotor at 400 g for 20 min at 4 °C. Accelerate the centrifuge gently.

e. Stop the centrifuge gradually to avoid disrupting the gradient. Discard the supernatant plasma and collect the first cell band (contains mononuclear cells and few basophils) at the top of the upper Percoll solution of 1·072 g/ml density, by using a syringe and needle. Remove the next Percoll solution and collect the second band of cells which consists of more than 15% basophils and mononuclear cells (use this fraction for further enrichment of the basophils by using panning technique, *see below*). Apply the same procedure to recover the next interface cell band formed between 1·082 and 1·100 g/ml Percoll solutions (contains up to 98% neutrophils). The cell layer at the bottom of the tube contains platelets, neutrophils and eosinophils.

f. Wash the collected cell fractions once with 10 ml MEM at 4 °C.

g. Count the total cell number and prepare cytocentrifuge slides for differential staining. For counting the basophils, use the method described in Section C.

h. Check cell viability by trypan blue exclusion.

Comments

a. Test the functional activity of the purified basophils by degranulation test (Kauffman et al, 1983).

b. The above method was used to study the role of basophils, mononuclear cells, eosinophils and neutrophils in bronchial asthma (Kauffman et al, 1983).

B. Two-step separation of basophils

The technique described in this section can be used to enrich blood basophils more than 50-fold. This can be achieved by firstly using a discontinuous Percoll gradient and secondly, further enrichment of basophils can then be obtained by removing the contaminating mononuclear cells by adherence to coated plastic dishes. The method was originally described by Landry and Findlay (1983).

Materials

i. EDTA(Na$_2$): to 30–35 ml whole blood, add 0·48 ml 10% EDTA(Na$_2$) as an anticoagulant.

ii. Phosphate-buffered saline (PBS) Dulbecco 'A' (Oxoid tablets) (Section 5.3).

iii. Dextran T-500 (Pharmacia Fine Chemicals): add 6 g dextran and 3 g glucose to 100 ml 0·15M NaCl.

iv. Pipes buffer (Piperazin-N,N-bis(2-ethanesulfonic acid)) 10 times working concentration (10 × conc.); prepare a solution containing the following:

Pipes	250 mM
NaCl	1180 mM
KCl	50 mM
NaOH	430 mM
EDTA (Na$_2$)	100 mM

v. Percoll (Pharmacia Fine Chemicals).

vi. Human serum albumin (HSA): prepare 0·03% HSA/Pipes, working concentration (1 × conc.).

vii. Heat-inactivated foetal calf serum (HI-FCS): prepare 2% HI-FCS/PBS.

viii. Goat-anti-mouse IgG (Tago): dilute 100 µg (0·1 ml) antibody in 10 ml PBS/dish.

ix. Monoclonal antibodies (Becton Dickinson): Anti-Leu 1 (pan T) monoclonal antibody: specific for T-lymphocytes; *and* Anti-HLA-DR monoclonal antibody: specific for B-lymphocytes, monocytes, macrophages, and activated T-lymphocytes.

x. Plastic Petri dishes (Fisher 8–757–12).

Procedure

PREPARATION OF LEUCOCYTE-RICH LAYER

a. Collect blood in EDTA solution (to prevent platelets clumping) and then mix 5 parts blood with 1 part of 6% dextran and 3% glucose in 0·15M NaCl.

b. Incubate at 37 °C for 30–40 min (or allow to stand for 90 min at room temperature) to allow sedimentation of erythrocytes.

c. Collect the leucocytes above the red cell layer and centrifuge for 10 min at 150 g at 4 °C.

d. Remove the supernatant plasma and resuspend the sedimented cells in 1 ml of the remaining autologous plasma.

DISCONTINUOUS PERCOLL GRADIENT

a. Prepare iso-osmotic Percoll solution by mixing 9 parts Percoll and 1 part Pipes buffer (10 × conc.).

b. Make 55% and 65% iso-osmotic Percoll in Pipes buffer (1 × conc.).

c. Layer 10 ml 55% Percoll solution onto the top of 10 ml 65% Percoll solution using a syringe and needle. Allow the Percoll solution to run on the side wall of the tube (two layers should be visible).

BANDING OF BASOPHILS

a. Gently, add the leucocyte-rich layer onto the top of the discontinuous gradient using a syringe and needle. Centrifuge the tube at 400 g for 20 min at room temperature in a swing-out rotor.

b. After centrifugation three cell bands should be formed. Discard the supernatant suspending medium above the first layer and collect the cells (mostly large mononuclear cells and basophils). Repeat the same technique to recover the next cell band (contains up to 15-fold enriched basophils) formed between 55% and 65% Percoll solutions. The cells at the bottom of the tube consist of neutrophils, eosinophils, and erythrocytes.

c. Wash each cell fraction twice with at least 30 ml of 0·03% HSA/Pipes and centrifuge at 250 g for 10 min at 4 °C.

d. Resuspend the cells with 0·03% HSA/Pipes. Count the total cell number and prepare cytocentrifuge slides.

e. For more accurate basophil counting, stain the cells with alcian blue as described in Section C (*below*).

f. Check cell viability by trypan blue exclusion.

ENRICHMENT OF BASOPHILS BY PANNING

Percoll-purified basophils obtained as described above may be further enriched to more than 29-fold by using panning and monoclonal antibodies to remove the contaminating mononuclear cells.

Procedure

COATING OF PLASTIC DISCHES

   a. Add 10 ml of diluted goat-anti-mouse IgG antibody to each dish and keep overnight or for 12 h at 4 °C.
   b. Remove excess antibody and wash the dishes three times with 10 ml PBS. To store the coated dishes, add 2% HI-FCS/PBS, wrap in Parafilm, and store at −20 °C. Before using, thaw at room temperature and discard the HI-FCS/PBS.

ENRICHMENT OF BASOPHILS

Use the cells collected from the band formed between 55% and 65% Percoll.
   a. Resuspend the cells (1–5×10^5 cells) in 0·1 ml 0·03% HSA/Pipes.
   b. Add the monoclonal antibodies to a final concentration of about $1 \, \mu g/10^6$ cells and keep for 1 h at 4 °C.
   c. Wash the cells twice with 0·03% BSA/Pipes, centrifuge at $240 \, g$ for 5 min at 4 °C.
   d. Resuspend the cells in 3 ml of cold 2% HI-FCS/PBS and layer the suspension onto the coated dishes.
   e. Keep for 60 min at 4 °C. Resuspend the cells by shaking the dish after 30 min.
   f. Remove the non-adherent cells by pipetting off the supernatant. Wash the dishes three times with 2% HI-FCS/PBS and pool the cells recovered from the washing.
   g. Centrifuge at $240 \, g$ for 10 min at 4 °C.
   h. Resuspend the cells in 0·03% BSA/Pipes.
   i. Count the total number of cells and prepare cytocentrifuge slides. For more precise counting of the basophils, stain with alcian blue (Section C).
   j. Determine the functional activity of the basophils by histamine release after incubation with antigens (Kauffman et al, 1983; Landry and Findlay, 1983).

C.   Basophil counting

The lower percentage of basophils in blood (less than 1%) makes the determination of the differential counting and the total cell number a time-consuming process and requires the examination of at least 1000 leucocytes to obtain a reliable differential count. Therefore, a method which stains only the basophils will be more convenient for this purpose. The technique described by Gilbert and Ornstein (1975) succeeded in staining only the heparin-containing granules of the basophils and this allows direct counting of these cells.

Materials

i. EDTA(Na$_2$): prepare 0·1% EDTA(Na$_2$) solution in 0·9% NaCl.

ii. Colouring solution: prepare a solution of deionized distilled water containing 0·76% cetyl pyridinium chloride, 0·7% lanthanum chloride 6H$_2$O, 0·09% NaCl, 0·21% Tween 20 and 0·143% alcian blue 8GN (colour index No. 74240). Filter through a 1 μm filter.

iii. 1M HCl.

Procedure

a. Dilute 0·1 ml blood in 0·4 ml EDTA solution.

b. Add 0·45 ml colouring solution and mix gently for 1 min.

c. Add 0·05 ml 1M HCl to reduce the pH and increase staining contrast and mix gently. At this stage the cells have been diluted 1:10.

d. Count the total basophil number using a Fuchs-Rosenthal haemocytometer. Count the total ruled areas of two chambers to obtain reasonable precision.

e. Calculate the total number of basophils as follows:

let N = basophil number in an area of 18 mm^2 of diluted blood.

$\dfrac{N}{18}$ = basophils in an area of 1 mm^2 of diluted blood.

$\dfrac{N}{18} \times 5$ (depth) = basophils in a volume of 1 mm^3 of diluted blood.

$\dfrac{N}{18} \times 5 \times 10$ (dilution) = basophils in an area of 1 mm^3 of whole blood.

or N $\times$ 2·77 $\times$ 10^6 = basophils/litre blood.

Comment

There are normally 0·03–0·15 $\times$ 10^9 basophils/litre blood.

6. CARBONYL IRON DEPLETION OF BONE MARROW MONOCYTES

In this section a method is described to illustrate the phagocytic activity of bone marrow monocytes and the extent to which these cells can be depleted from bone marrow cell suspensions (F. Ali and A. May, unpublished observations).

Materials

i. Carbonyl iron particles (Goodfellow Metals): sterilize and store as described in Chapter 3, Section 4.2.
ii. Heat-inactivated foetal calf serum (HI-FCS).
iii. Eagle's minimal essential medium (MEM).
iv. Patient's own (autologous) plasma: for providing Ca^{2+} and Mg^{2+} necessary for active phagocytosis (Chapter 3, Section 4.2).
v. Percoll solution of $1 \cdot 077$ g/ml density: prepare as described in Chapter 3, Section 2.2.
vi. Rotary mixer.

Procedure

a. Isolate bone marrow buffy coat cells suspended in Eagle's MEM. Prepare cytocentrifuge slides for Jenner–Giemsa and non-specific esterase staining.

b. Resuspend the cells (not more than 6×10^6 bone marrow cells) in 1 ml Eagle's MEM-autologous plasma ($2 \cdot 3$ ml Eagle's MEM + $1 \cdot 3$ ml plasma).

c. Incubate the cells with carbonyl iron suspension as described in Chapter 3, Section 4.2. A control tube may be included without carbonyl iron suspension.

d. Carefully layer the cells (test and control) onto Percoll cushions, centrifuge ($400 g$ for 20 min) and collect the band of cells at the interface from each tube as described in Chapter 3, Section 4.

e. Wash the cells twice with Eagle's MEM, or any cell suspending medium.

f. Count the total number of cells collected at the interface and prepare cytocentrifuge slides of both the interface and the pellet for Jenner–Giemsa and non-specific esterase staining.

Reproducibility

Carbonyl iron depletion of monocytes from two normal bone marrow samples produced a significant loss of monocytes at the interface layer when compared with controls ($8 \cdot 5\%$ and 4% monocytes without carbonyl iron, 5% and $1 \cdot 7\%$ monocytes with carbonyl iron, respectively). The total number of the remaining cells at the interface was 10×10^6 and 12×10^6 without carbonyl iron, whereas there were $4 \cdot 6 \times 10^6$ and $5 \cdot 9 \times 10^6$ after incubation with carbonyl iron.

Comments

a. Since bone marrow cells, in particular the monocytes, tend to aggregate when present in high concentrations, it is preferable to process not more than 6×10^6 bone marrow cells per tube.

b. Incubating the bone marrow cells at 37 °C in an incubator with 5% CO_2 in air may improve the phagocytosis by monocytes of carbonyl iron particles.

c. EDTA anticoagulant should be avoided because it chelates Ca^{2+} and Mg^{2+} necessary for the carbonyl iron phagocytosis by monocytes.

d. A magnetic stirrer may also be used to pull the carbonyl iron-loaded cells away from the cell suspension.

7. PHAGOCYTOSIS AND ROSETTE FORMATION BY BLOOD AND MARROW CELLS

The following methods can be used to achieve active phagocytosis of protein A-coated sheep red blood cells (SpA-SRBC) by peripheral blood monocytes or bone marrow myeloid and monocytic cells. No phagocytosis occurs with non-coated sheep red blood cells under the same conditions. In addition, a high proportion of marrow cells are able to form a strong and stable rosettes with SpA-SRBC, whereas no rosettes will form with SRBC alone. Since SpA-SRBC are actively phagocytosed by blood monocytes this would be a useful vehicle for the introduction of haemoglobin into monocytes for the study of haemoglobin catabolism. The method described here was developed jointly with A. May.

7.1 PROTEIN A-COATING OF SHEEP RED BLOOD CELLS (SpA-SRBC)

The method described here is based on those of Sandrin et al (1978) and Parish and McKenzie (1978). To achieve binding of the ligand (Protein A) to sheep red cells, aged chromic chloride solution (Godling, 1976) is usually used.

Materials

i. Sheep red blood cells (SRBC) preserved in Alsevier's solution (not more than 10 days old).

ii. Chromic chloride ($CrCl_36H_2O$): weigh 1 gram.

iii. NaCl: 0·9% (w/v) (isotonic saline).

iv. Protein A (Pharmacia Fine Chemicals) (Chapter 4, Section 7.3, *Comments*): dissolve 5 mg freeze-dried Protein A in 2.5 ml isotonic

saline to prepare 2 mg/ml solution, and store at −20 °C as 1 ml
aliquots.
  v. Phosphate buffer saline (PBS).
 vi. Heat-inactivated foetal calf serum (HI-FCS).
vii. PBS–10% HI-FCS.

Procedure

PREPARATION OF AGED CRCL₃ SOLUTION (STOCK)
  a. Dissolve 1 g CrCl₃ in 100 ml isotonic saline.
  b. Adjust the pH to 6·0 by dropwise addition of 1M NaOH with
constant mixing.
  c. Check the above solution once a week for three consecutive
weeks and readjust the pH to 6·0.
  d. Store the aged stock solution at room temperature. To prepare a
working solution dilute 1/10 (v/v) in isotonic saline.

PREPARATION OF 10% SRBC
  a. Wash 1 ml SRBC suspension four times with isotonic saline.
  b. Dilute the sedimented cells with isotonic saline to obtain a 10%
suspension.

COATING OF SRBC WITH PROTEIN A (SPA-SRBC)
  a. Mix 800 μl of 2 mg/ml Protein A solution with 1 ml 10% SRBC
suspension.
  b. Add dropwise, with constant vortex mixing, 0·2 ml CrCl₃.
  c. Leave the cells for 5 min at room temperature to allow the
reaction to proceed.
  d. Terminate the reaction by adding 7 ml PBS (phosphate anions
prevent the CrCl₃ coupling to proteins).
  e. Centrifuge the tube at 400 g for 5 min.
  f. Wash the sedimented cells once with 5 ml PBS and resuspend in
PBS–10% HI-FCS to prepare a 2% SpA-SRBC suspension.
  g. Store the SpA-SRBC at 4 °C for a week at the most, to be used
when required.

7.2 PHAGOCYTOSIS AND ROSETTING OF SHEEP
ERYTHROCYTES BY BLOOD CELLS

The method described here can be used to achieve rosetting of blood
cells or phagocytosis of protein A-coated sheep red blood cells
(SpA-SRBC) by monocytes.

The procedure is based on that reported by Parish and McKenzie (1978) using chromic chloride ($CrCl_3$).

Materials

i. Preservative-free heparin (Duncan Flockhart Co. Ltd): 15 units/ml blood.
ii. Phosphate buffered saline (PBS).
iii. Eagle's minimal essential medium (MEM).
iv. Heat-inactivated foetal calf serum (HI-FCS).
v. Percoll or Ficoll of 1·077 g/ml density: prepare as described in Chapter 3, Section 2 or Chapter 6, Section 1.

Procedure

a. Collect blood in heparin, and prepare a buffy coat suspended in Eagle's MEM.

b. Separate the mononuclear cells using Percoll or Ficoll.

c. Count the total number of cells and dilute the cell suspension with Eagle's MEM to give a concentration of 3×10^6 cells/ml. Prepare cytocentrifuge slides for staining with Jenner–Giemsa.

d. Into one of two tubes, add 0·5 ml cell suspension, 0·5 ml SpA-SRBC together with 0·25 ml HI-FCS. Add to the other tube 0·3 ml cell suspension, 0·3 ml SpA-SRBC and 0·3 ml HI-FCS. For phagocytosis, add cells and SpA-SRBC in a ratio of 1:100 (i.e. 2×10^8 SpA-SRBC to 2×10^6 mononuclear cells).

e. Resuspend the cells and examine for rosetting using a haemocytometer and coverslip.

f. Carefully, layer the rosetted cells on the top of the Percoll cushion, centrifuge (400 g for 20 min at room temperature) and collect the cells at the Eagle's MEM/Percoll interface.

g. Wash twice with Eagle's MEM and count the total number of cells. Prepare cytocentrifuge slides for Jenner–Giemsa staining.

h. Keep a small volume of the cell suspension to estimate the percentage of E-rosetting (Chapter 2, Section 9.1).

Comments

a. In one rosetting experiment, the blood cells were incubated with SpA-SRBC and then the rosetted cells were sedimented to the bottom of the tube on a Percoll cushion. E-rosetting of the cells collected at the interface showed an enrichment of T-lymphocytes. The percentage increased from 78% in the original blood mononuclear cells to 90% in the cell suspension collected after incubation with SpA-SRBC and separation by Percoll. SpA-SRBC will rosette cells with surface IgG by reacting with the Fc portion of this molecule (Forsgren and Sjöquist, 1966; Sjöquist et al, 1967), and Ghetie et al (1974) showed that cell lines secreting IgG formed many more rosettes with SpA-SRBC than those which did not. B-lymphocytes involved in the production of IgG probably account for the lymphocytes which form rosettes and the lymphocytes at the interface will be enriched in T- and null lymphocytes (Romagnani et al, 1980).

   b. Phagocytosis of SpA-SRBC by blood monocytes was also achieved after incubating the mononuclear cells with SpA-SRBC. Efficient phagocytosis can also be achieved using Protein A-coated rabbit red cells under the same conditions. Phagocytosis of SpA-rabbit erythrocytes has been used to study the accumulation and release of isoferritins during incubation *in vitro* of blood mononuclear cells (Worwood et al, 1984).

7.3   INCUBATION OF BONE MARROW CELLS WITH PROTEIN A-COATED SHEEP ERYTHROCYTES

The method described below will produce both phagocytosis of protein A-coated sheep red blood cells (SpA-SRBC) and rosetting of some bone marrow cells (*see also* Comment *a*, Section 7.2). However, it should be noted that the following method has not been pursued for further studies.

Materials

   i.   SpA-SRBC: prepare as described above (Section 7.1).
   ii. Heat-inactivated foetal calf serum (HI-FCS).
   iii. Phosphate buffered saline (PBS) with 10% HI-FCS (PBS–10% HI-FCS).
   iv. Toluidine blue: 0·1% in PBS.

Procedure

   a. Prepare bone marrow cell suspension to give a concentration of 10×10^6 cells/ml PBS–10% HI-FCS.
   b. In a clean tube placed on ice, mix 0·5 ml of the bone marrow cell suspension and 0·5 ml 2% SpA-SRBC together with 0·25 ml HI-FCS.
   c. Incubate for 1 h at 37 °C (this relatively long incubation enhances phagocytosis).
   d. Centrifuge at 250 g for 5 min and resuspend the cells using a Pasteur pipette.
   e. Mix one drop of each cell suspension with toluidine blue. After 1

min, place one drop onto a clean haemocytometer, cover with a clean coverslip and examine under the microscope for rosettes.

f. Prepare cytocentrifuge slides for staining with Jenner–Giemsa.

g. Layer the cell suspension on a Percoll cushion, centrifuge and collect interface band of cells as described in Chapter 4, Section 2.

h. Remove attached SRBC by lysis as described below.

Comments

a. In one experiment carried out using the procedure described in Section 7.3, examination of a toluidine blue stained wet preparation of bone marrow cells incubated with SpA-SRBC showed that typical rosettes were formed. The late erythroid cells were quite easy to recognize and non-rosetted late erythroblasts were also seen. Both weak (a few SpA-SRBC/cell) and strong (layers of SpA-SRBC) rosettes were formed which were not disrupted either by warming to room temperature or by mixing with a Pasteur pipette. The control mixture with SRBC alone had no rosettes, so that those formed by SpA-SRBC were quite specific. The percentage of each cell type rosetted was counted from a cytocentrifuge slide stained with Jenner–Giemsa and the results are presented in *Table* 6.3. They show that although all the cell types formed rosettes, the myeloid cells, monocytes and large lymphocytes formed them most readily. Only a few erythroblasts and small lymphocytes were rosetted. The SpA-SRBC were seen to be phagocytosed by the myeloid and monocytic cells, whereas this did not occur in the control with non-coated SRBC.

Table 6.3. Protein A-SRBC rosettes of normal human bone marrow cells, estimated from a cytocentrifuge preparation stained with Jenner–Giemsa

Cell Type	% Rosetted Cells
Myeloid	86
Erythroid	4
Monocytes	94
Large lymphocytes	76
Small lymphocytes	18

b. Ficoll-Triosil (Section 1) separation of the rosetted cells resulted in the sedimentation of over half the nucleated cells normally present in the interface as shown in *Table* 6.4. Monocytes containing ingested SpA-SRBC and lymphocytes were found both at the interface and in the pellet. Therefore, the most promising effect seems to be in bringing down some mononuclear cells into the pellet.

Table 6.4. Separation of Protein A-SRBC rosettes of normal bone marrow cells on Ficoll–Triosil at a density of 1·077 g/ml

Samples	Cells/ml × 10^6	Myeloid %	Erythroid %	Monocytes & Lymphocytes %
1. Cells before Ficoll Separation				
a. Control	—	72	19	9
b. Test	—	71	18	11
2. Cells after Ficoll Separation				
I. Interface layer				
a. Control	3·7	46	30	24
b. Test	1·7	31	16	53
II. Sedimented cells				
a. Control	—	74	18	8
b. Test	—	65	26	10

Table 6.5. Time course for SpA-SRBC rosetting of bone marrow cells incubated at 4°C, room temperature and 37°C. Interface layer of cells obtained after separation on Ficoll–Triosil at a starting density of 1·077 g/ml

Temperature used	Interface layer	Time of incubation in minutes								
		10 min			30 min			60 min		
		Myeloid %	Erythroid %	Monocytes & Lymphocytes %	Myeloid %	Erythroid %	Monocytes & Lymphocytes %	Myeloid %	Erythroid %	Monocytes & Lymphocytes %
4°C	Control	77	16	7	69	13	18	71	15	14
	Test	50	14	36	60	16	24	45	12	44
Room temp.	Control	78	11	11	81	12	8	74	18	8
	Test	62	19	20	–	–	–	76	13	11
37°C	Control	79	11	11	75	6	20	86	6	8
	Test	58	19	23	68	9	24	73	4	24

c. Many bone marrow cells were still able to form rosettes with the SpA-SRBC after the first rosetting of bone marrow cells. Therefore, a time course (10, 30 and 60 min) of SpA-SRBC rosetting of bone marrow cells was carried out at 4 °C, room temperature and 37 °C, using the above procedure. This was performed to determine the optimum conditions necessary for maximum removal of the myeloid, monocytic and lymphocytic cells for the enrichment of erythroblasts. The higher temperature used enhanced phagocytosis of the SpA-SRBC. *Table* 6.5 shows that rosetting at 4 °C for 60 min produced a considerable enrichment of monocytic and lymphocytic cells in the interface from the test sample and that there was loss of some myeloid cells.

7.4   REMOVAL OF SHEEP RED BLOOD CELLS BY LYSIS

After rosetting of cells the attached and free sheep red blood cells can be removed from the suspension by lysis using a method based on that described by Boyle (1968).

Materials
  i. Stock solutions:
     A. 0·16M NH_4Cl; dissolve 8·3 g NH_4Cl in 1 litre distilled water.
     B. 0·17M Tris, pH 7·65; dissolve 20·6 g Tris in 1 litre distilled water and adjust the pH to 7·65 with HCl.
  ii. Working solutions: mix 9 parts of solution A with 1 part solution B.
  iii. Phosphate buffered saline (PBS).

Procedure
  a. Mix 1 ml Tris-buffered NH_4Cl working solution with 1 ml cell suspension.
  b. Keep the tube at room temperature for 10 min.
  c. Add 10 ml ice-cooled PBS to stop the reaction.
  d. Centrifuge at 400 *g* for 5 min at room temperature.
  e. Wash the sedimented cells twice and resuspend with PBS.
  f. Prepare cytocentrifuge slides and stain with Jenner–Giemsa for examination of the removal of sheep red blood cells.

References

ABO T. and BALCH C. M. (1981) A differentiation antigen on human NK and K cells identified by a monoclonal antibody (HNK-1). *J. Immunol.* **127**, 1024–1029.

AIUTI F., CEROTTINI J.-C., COOMBS R. R. A. et al (1974) Special technical report: identification, enumeration and isolation of B and T lymphocytes from human peripheral blood. *Scand. J. Immunol.* **3**, 521–532.

ALBERTSSON P.-Å. (1971) *Partition of Cell Particles and Macromolecules.* New York, Wiley-Intersciences.

ALI F. M. K., MAY A., McLAREN G. D. and JACOBS A. (1982) A two-step procedure for obtaining normal peripheral blood T lymphocytes using continuous equilibrium density gradient centrifugation on Percoll. *J. Immunol. Methods* **49**, 185–191.

ALI F. M. K., MAY A., JONES B. M. and JACOBS A. (1983) Enrichment of erythroblasts from human bone marrow using complement-mediated lysis: measurement of ferritin. *Br. J. Haematol* **53**, 227–235.

ALI F. M. K., WEETMAN A. P. and MAY A. (1985) Separation of malignant plasma cells from the bone marrow of patients with myelomatosis. *Br. J. Haematol.* **59** (3), 419–423.

AL-SUMIDAIE A. M., JONES D. L. and YOUNG H. L. (1984) Characterization of the under-agarose method for quantifying migration of highly purified human monocytes. *J. Immunol. Methods* **75**, 129–140.

AL-SUMIDAIE A. and YOUNG L. (1983) Migration and production by highly purified human mononuclear phagocytes. *Br. J. Surg.* **70**, 695.

ARNDT-JOVIN D. J. and JOVIN T. M. (1978) Automated cell sorting with flow systems. *Ann. Rev. Biophys. Bioeng.* **7**, 527–558.

AXELRAD A. A., McLEOD D. A., SHREEVE H. M. and HEATH D. A. (1974) Properties of cells that produce erythrocytic colonies *in vitro. In: Haemopoiesis in Culture* (Ed. Robinson, W.) Washington, US Government Printing Office, pp. 226–234.

AYE M. T. (1977) Erythroid colony formation in cultures of human marrow: effect of leukocyte conditioned medium. *J. Cell Physiol.* **91**, 69–77.

BAINE R. M. and BENSON J. M. (1981) Cultured erythroid cells as a model for Hb regulation: ability of cultured cells to synthesize Hb Lepore and HbA_2 and to maintain balanced globin synthesis. *Blood* **57**, 873–878.

BATES G. W. and WERNICKE J. (1971) The kinetics and mechanism of iron (III) exchange between chelates and transferrin. *J. Biol. Chem.* **246**, 3679–3685.

BERGER C. L. and EDELSON R. L. (1979) Comparison of lymphocyte function after isolation by Ficoll–Hypaque flotation or elutriation. *J. Invest. Dermatol.* **73** (3), 231–235.

BERGMAN D. G., BLAKESLEE J. R. and WOLEF D. A. (1977) Separation of cells containing R-type virus-like particles from a Simian Virus 40-induced hamster tumour cell line. *J. Natl Cancer Inst.* **58**, 295–299.

BERRIDGE M. V. and OKECH N. (1979) Surface antigens of murine hemopoietic stem cells. I. Cross Reactivity of antisera against differentiated hemopoietic cells with bone marrow stem cells. *Exp. Hematol.* **7**, 452–468.

BEUTLER E., WEST C. and BLUME K. G. (1976) The removal of leukocytes and platelets from whole blood. *J. Lab. Clin. Med.* **88**, 328–333.

BEVAN A., BURNS G. F., GRAY L. and CAWLEY J. C. (1980) Cytochemistry of human T-cell subpopulations. *Scand. J. Immunol.* **11**, 223–233.

BEVERLEY P. C. L., LINCH D. and DELIA D. (1980) Isolation of human haematopoietic progenitor cells using monoclonal antibodies. *Nature* **287**, 332–333.

BIANCO C. and NUSSENZWEIG V. (1971) Theta-bearing and complement-receptor lymphocytes are distinct populations of cells. *Science* **173**, 154–156.

BIANCO C., PATRICK R. and NUSSENZWEIG V. (1970) A population of lymphocytes bearing a membrane receptor for antigen-antibody-complement complexes. 1. Separation and characterization. *J. Exp. Med.* **132**, 702–720.

BIRD A. G. and BRITTON S. (1979) A live human B-cell activator operating in isolation of other cellular influences. *Scand. J. Immunol.* **9** (6), 507–510.

BOLTZ R. C. Jr., TODD P., STREIBEL M. J. and LOUIE M. K. (1973) Preparative electrophoresis of living mammalian cells in a stationary Ficoll gradient. *Prep. Biochem.* **3**, 383–401.

BOTTOMLEY S. S. (1977) Porphyrin and iron metabolism in sideroblastic anaemia. *Semin. Hematol.* **14** (2), 169–185.

BOTTOMLEY S. S. (1980) Sideroblastic Anaemia *In: Iron in Biochemistry and Medicine II*, (Eds. Jacobs A. and Worwood M.). New York, Academic Press, p. 363.

BOYLE W. (1968) An extension of the ^{51}Cr-release assay for the estimation of mouse cytotoxins. *Transplantation* **6**, 761–764.

BÖYUM A. (1968) Isolation of mononuclear cells and granulocytes from human blood. Isolation of mononuclear cells by one centrifugation, and of granulocytes by combining centrifugation and sedimentation at 1 g. *Scand. J. Clin. Lab. Invest.* **21** (supp. 97), 77–89.

BRADLEY T. R. and METCALF D. (1966) The growth of mouse bone marrow cells *in vitro. Aust. J. Exp. Biol. Med. Sci.* **44**, 287–299.

BROWN J. E. and THEIL E. C. (1978) Red cells, ferritin, and iron storage during amphibian development. *J. Biol. Chem.* **253**, 2673–2678.

BRUBAKER L. H. and EVANS W. H. (1969) Separation of granulocytes, monocytes, lymphocytes, erythrocytes and platelets from human blood and relative tagging with diisopropylfluorophosphate (DFP). *J. Lab. Clin. Med.* **73**, 1036–1041.

BURGHOUTS J., PLAS A. M., WESSELS J. et al (1978) Method for enrichment of proliferating myeloid cells from normal and leukemic human bone marrow. *Blood* **51**, 9–20.

CANN H. M. and HERZENBERG L. A. (1963) *In vitro* studies of mammalian somatic cell variation. II. Isoimmune cytotoxicity with a cultured mouse lymphoma and selection of resistant variants. *J. Exp. Med.* **117**, 267–284.

CANTOR L. N., MORRIS A. J., MARKS P. A. and RIFKIND R. A. (1972) Purification of erythropoietin-responsive cells by immune hemolysis. *Proc. Natl Acad. Sci. USA* **69**, 1337–1341.

CANTOR H., SIMPSON E., SATO V. L. et al (1975) Characterization of subpopulations of T-lymphocytes. I. Separation and functional studies of peripheral T-cells binding different amounts of fluorescent anti-Thy 1,2(theta) antibody using a fluorescence-activated cell sorter (FACS). *Cell. Immunol.* **15**, 180–196.

CASALI P. and PERUSSIA B. M. (1977) C_3-reacted Sepharose: a preparative method for separating T and B lymphocytes. *Clin. Exp. Immunol.* **27**, 38–42.

CATOVSKY D., CHERCHI M., OKOS A et al (1976) Mouse red-cell rosettes in B-lymphoproliferative disorders. *Br. J. Haematol.* **33**, 173–177.

CATSIMPOOLAS N. (1977) *Methods of Cell Separation*, Vol. 1. New York, Plenum Press.

CATSIMPOOLAS N. (1980) *Methods of Cell Separation*, Vol. 3. New York, Plenum Press.

CATSIMPOOLAS N., GRIFFITH A. L. and SKRABUT E. M. (1978) An alternate method for the preparative velocity sedimentation of cells at unit gravity. *Anal. Biochem.* **87**, 243–248.

CHALEVELAKIS G., CLEGG J. B. and WEATHERALL D. J. (1976) Globin synthesis in normal human bone marrow. *Br. J. Haematol.* **34**, 535–557.

CHERCHI M. and CATOVSKY D. (1980) Mouse RBC rosettes in chronic lymphocytic leukaemia: different expression in blood and tissues. *Clin. Exp. Immunol.* **39**, 411–415.

CHESS L. and SCHLOSSMAN S. F. (1976) Anti-immunoglobin columns and the separation of T, B and null cells. *In: In vitro Methods in Cell Mediated and Tumor Immunity* (Eds. Bloom B. R. and David J. R.) New York, Academic Press, pp. 255–261.

CHESS L. and SCHLOSSMAN S. F. (1977) Human lymphocyte subpopulations. *Adv. Immunol*, **25**, 213–241.

CHESS L., MACDERMOTT R. P. and SCHLOSSMAN S. F. (1974) Immunologic functions of isolated human lymphocyte subpopulations. I. Quantitative isolation of human T and B cells and response to mitogens. *J. Immunol.* **113**, 1113–1121.

CHIAO J. W. and GOOD R. A. (1976) Studies of the presence of membrane receptors for complement, IgG and the sheep erythrocyte rosetting capacity on the same human lymphocytes. *Eur. J. Immunol.* **6**, 157–162.

CHIAO J. W., PANTIC V. S. and GOOD R. A. (1974) Human peripheral lymphocytes bearing both B-cell complement receptors and T-characteristics for sheep erythrocytes detected by a mixed rosette method. *Clin. Exp. Immunol.* **18**, 483–490.

CHIAO J. W., PANTIC V. S. and GOOD R. A. (1975) Human lymphocytes bearing both receptors for complement components and SRBC. *Clin. Immunol. Immunopathol.* **4**, 545–556.

CHIEN M. M. and ASHMAN R. F. (1984) Rapid separation of human monocytes and lymphocytes by Sephadex G-10. *J. Immunol. Methods* **71**, 25–36.

CLAESSON M. H., RODGER M. B., JOHNSON G. R. et al (1977) Colony formation by human T lymphocytes in agar medium. *Clin. Exp. Immunol.* **28**, 526–534.

CLEGG J. B. and NAUGHTON M. A. (1965) An improved method for the characterization of human haemoglobin mutants: identification of $\alpha_2\beta_2^{95GLU}$ haemoglobin N (Baltimore), *Nature* **207**, 945–947.

CONTRERAS T. J., JEMIONEK J. F., STEVENSON H. C. et al (1980) An improved technique for the negative selection of large numbers of human lymphocytes and monocytes by counterflow centrifugation-elutriation. *Cell. Immunol.* **54**, 215–229.

CORASH L. M., PIOMELLI S., CHEN H. C. et al (1974) Separation of erythrocytes according to age on a simplified density gradient. *J. Lab. Clin. Med.* **84**, 147–151.

CORASH L., TAN H. and GRALNICK H. R. (1977) Heterogeneity of human whole blood platelet subpopulations. I. Relationship between buoyant density, cell volume and ultrastructure. *Blood* **49**, 71–87.

DACIE J. V., LEWIS S. M. (1975a) Blood-cell cytochemistry and supplementary techniques, 5. *In: Practical Haematology* (Eds. Dacie J. V. and Lewis S. M.), Singapore, Toppan, pp. 12–13.

DACIE J. V. and LEWIS S. M. (1975b) Preparation and staining methods for blood and bone marrow films. 3 *In: Practical Haemotology* (Eds. Dacie J. V. and Lewis S. M.). Singapore, Toppan, pp. 79–82.

DACIE J. V. and LEWIS S. M. (1975c) Blood-cell cytochemistry and supplementary techniques, 5 *In: Practical Haematology* (Eds. Dacie J. V. and Lewis S. M.). Singapore, Toppan, pp. 120–121.

DACIE J. V. and LEWIS S. M. (1975d) Blood-cell cytochemistry and supplementary techniques, 5 *In: Practical Haematology* (Eds. Dacie J. V. and Lewis S. M.). Singapore, Toppan, pp. 124–126.

DACIE J. V. and LEWIS S. M. (1975e) Blood-cell cytochemistry and supplementary techniques, **5** In: Practical Haemotology (Eds. Dacie J. V. and Lewis S. M.). Singapore, Toppan, pp. 126–127.

DACIE J. V. and LEWIS S. M. (1975f) Blood-cell cytochemistry and supplementary techniques, **5** In: Practical Haematology (Eds. Dacie, J. V. and Lewis, S. M.). Singapore, Toppan, pp. 136–139.

DACIE J. V. and LEWIS S. M. (1984) Blood-cell cytochemistry and supplementary techniques, **6** In: Practical Haematology (Eds. Dacie J. V. and Lewis S. M.). Edinburgh, Churchill Livingstone, pp. 84–90.

DAINIAK N., KULKARNI V., HOWARD D. et al (1983) Mechanism of abnormal erythropoiesis in malignancy. Cancer **51**, 1101–1106.

DANILOVS J. A., AYOUB G. and TERASAKI P. I. (1980) B lymphocyte isolation by thrombin-nylon wool. In: Histocompatibility Testing (Ed. Terasaki P. I.). Los Angeles UCLA, Tissue Typing Laboratory, pp. 287–288.

de SIMONE C., DONNELI G., MELI D. et al (1982) Human eosinophils and parasitic diseases. II. Characterization of two cell fractions isolated at different densities. Clin. Exp. Immunol. **48** (1), 249–255.

DICKLER H. B., ADKINSON N. F. and TERRY W. D. (1974) Evidence for individual human peripheral blood lymphocytes bearing both B and T cell markers. Nature **247**, 213–215.

DIERICH M. P., PELLEGRINO M. A., FERRONE S. and REISFELD R. A. (1974) Evaluation of C_3 receptors on lymphoid cells with different complement sources. J. Immunol. **112**, 1766–1773.

EDELMAN G. M. and RUTISHAUSER U. (1974) Specific fractionation and manipulation of cells with chemically derivatized fibres and surfaces. In: Methods in Enzymology (Eds. Jakoby, W. and Wilchek, M.), Vol. **34**, pp. 195–225.

EDLEMAN G. M., RUTISHAUSER U. and MILLETTE C. F. (1971) Cell fractionation and arrangement on fibres, beads and surfaces. Proc. Natl. Acad. Sci. **68** (2), 2153–2157.

ELDER G. H. (1980) Haem synthesis and breakdown. In: Iron in Biochemistry and Medicine II (Eds. Jacobs A. and Worwood M.). London, Academic Press, pp. 258–259.

ENGLEMAN E. G., BENIKE C. J., GRUMET F. C. and EVANS R. L. (1981) Activation of human T lymphocyte subsets: helper and suppressor/cytotoxic T cells recognize and respond to distinct histocompatibility antigens. J. Immunol. **127** (5), 2124–2129.

EPSTEIN L. B., KRETH H. W. and HERZENBERG L. A. (1974) Fluorescence-activated cell sorting of human T and B lymphocytes. II. Identification of the cell type responsible for interferon production and cell proliferation in response to mitogens. Cell. Immunol. **12**, 407–421.

ERSLEV A. J. and WEISS L. (1977) Structure and function of the bone marrow. In: Haematology (Eds. Williams W. J., Beutler E., Erlsev A. J. and Rundles R. W.). New York, McGraw-Hill, pp. 58–60.

FALKOFF R. M., PETERS M. and FAUCI A. S. (1982) T-cell enrichment and depletion of human peripheral blood mononuclear cell preparations. Unexpected findings in the study of the functional activities of the separated populations. J. Immunol. Methods **50**, 39–49.

FAUSER A. A. and MESSNER H. A. (1978) Granuloerythropoietic colonies in human bone marrow, peripheral blood and cord blood. Blood **52**, 1243–1248.

FAUSER A. A. and MESSNER H. A. (1979) Identification of megakaryocytes, macrophages and eosinophils in colonies of human bone marrow containing neutrophilic granulocytes and erythroblasts. Blood **53**, 1023–1027.

FERRARINI M., MORETTA L., ABRILE R. and DURANTE M. L. (1975) Receptors for IgG molecules on human lymphocytes forming spontaneous rosettes with sheep red cells. Eur. J. Immunol. **5**, 70–72.

FEUCHT H. E., HADAM M. R., FRANK F. and RIETHMULLER G. (1980) Efficient separation of human T-lymphocytes from venous blood using PVP-coated colloidal silica particles (Percoll). *J. Immunol. Methods* **38**, 43–51.

FONG S. (1983) Solid phase fractionation of lymphoid cells on ligand-coated plastic plates. *In: Cell Separation Methods and Selected Applications*, Vol. 2 (Eds. Pretlow T. G. and Pretlow T. P.) New York, Academic Press, pp. 203–219.

FONG S., FOX R. I., ROSE J. E. et al (1981) Solid-phase selection of human T lymphocyte subpopulations using monoclonal antibodies. *J. Immunol. Methods* **46**, 153–163.

FOON K. A., SCHROFF R. W. and GALE R. P. (1982) Surface markers on leukemia and lymphoma cells: recent advances. *Blood* **60**, 1–19.

FORSGREN A. and SJÖQUIST J. (1966) 'Protein A' from *S. aureus*, 1. Pseudo-immune reaction with human gamma-globulin. *J. Immunol.* **97** (6), 822–827.

FROELICH C. J., SIBBITT W. L. and BANKHURST A. D. (1983) Enrichment of natural killer cells by negative selection: comparison to Percoll gradient separation method. *J. Immunol. Methods* **64**, 327–333.

GADEBERG O. V., RHODES J. M. and LARSEN S. O. (1979) Isolation of human peripheral blood monocytes: a comparative methodological study. *J. Immunol. Methods* **31**, 1–10.

GAHMBERG C. G., JOKINEN M. and ANDERSSON L. C. (1978) Expression of the major sialoglycoprotein (glycophorin) on erythroid cells in human bone marrow. *Blood* **52**, 379–387.

GARTNER I. (1980) Separation of human eosinophils in density gradients of polyvinyl-pyrrolidone-coated silica gel (Percoll). *Immunology* **40**, 133–136.

GATENBY P. A., KOTZIN B. L. and ENGLEMAN E. G. (1981) Induction of immunoglobulin-secreting cells in the human autologous mixed leukocyte reaction. Regulation by helper and suppressor lymphocyte subsets defined with monoclonal antibodies. *J. Immunol.* **127**, 2130–2135.

GHETIE V., NILSSON K. and SJÖQUIST J. (1974) Detection and quantitation of IgG on the surface of human lymphoid cells by rosette formation with Protein A-coated sheep red blood cells. *Eur. J. Immunol.* **4**, 500–505.

GHETIE V., MOTA G. and SJÖQUIST J. (1978) Separation of cells by affinity chromatography on SpA-Sepharose 6MB. *J. Immunol. Methods* **21**, 133–141.

GIDDINGS J. C., PIOVELLA F., RICETTI M. et al (1980) Characterization of procoagulant activity produced by cultures of human monocytes and lymphocytes separated in colloidal silica-polyvinylpyrrolidone gradients. *Clin. Lab. Haematol.* **2** (2), 121–128.

GILBERT H. S. and ORNSTEIN L. (1975) Basophil counting with a new staining method using alcian blue. *Blood* **46**, 279–286.

GMELIG-MEYLING F. and WALDMANN T. A. (1980) Separation of human blood monocytes and lymphocytes on a continuous Percoll gradient. *J. Immunol. Methods* **33**, 1–9.

GMELIG-MEYLING F. H., KOOY-BLOK L. and BALLIEUX R. E. (1974) Complement-dependent cytolysis of human B lymphocytes with anti-light chain antisera. *Eur. J. Immunol.* **4**, 332–337.

GMELIG-MEYLING F., Van Der HAM M. and BALLIEUX R. E. (1976) Binding of IgM by human T lymphocytes. *Scand. J. Immunol.* **5**, 487–495.

GODLING J. W. (1976) The chromic chloride method of coupling antigens to erythro-cytes: definition of some important parameters. *J. Immunol. Methods* **10**, 61–66.

GOLDE D. W. and CLINE M. J. (1974) Regulation of granulopoiesis. *N. Engl. J. Med.* **291**, 1388–1395.

GOOD R. A. (1972) Recent studies on the immunodeficiencies of man. *Am. J. Pathol.* **69**, 489–490.

GOUD T. J. L. and van FURTH R. (1975) Proliferative characteristics of monoblasts grown *in vitro*. *J. Exp. Med.* **142**, 1200–1217.

GREAVES M. F. and BROWN G. (1974) Purification of human T and B lymphocytes. *J. Immunol.* **112**, 420–423.

GREGORY C. J. and EAVES A. C. (1977) Human marrow cells capable of erythropoietic differentiation *in vitro:* definition of three erythroid colony responses. *Blood* **49**, 855–864.

GRIFFITH A. L., CATSIMPOOLAS N. and WORTIS H. H. (1975) Electrophoretic separation of cells in a density gradient. *Life Sci.* **16**, 1693–1702.

GRIFFITH O. M. (1978) Separation of T and B cells from human peripheral blood by centrifugal elutriation. *Anal. Biochem.* **87**, 97–107.

GRONOWICZ E., COUTINHO A. and MELCHERS F. (1976) A plaque assay for all cells secreting Ig of a given type or class. *Eur. J. Immunol.* **6**, 588–590.

GROSSI C. E., WEBB S. R., ZICCA A. et al (1978) Morphological and histochemical analysis of two human T-cell subpopulations bearing receptor for IgM or IgG. *J. Exp. Med.* **147**, 1405–1417.

GUPTA S. and GOOD R. A. (1978) Human T cell subsets in health and disease. *In: Human Lymphocyte Differentiation: Its Application to Human Cancer.* (Eds. Serrou C. B. and Rosenfeld C.). Amsterdam, Elsevier Biomedical Press, pp. 367–375.

GUPTA S. and GOOD R. A. (1980) Markers of human lymphocyte subpopulations in primary immunodeficiency and lymphoproliferative disorders. *Sem. Hematol.* **17** (1), 1–29.

GUPTA S. and GRIECO M. H. (1975) Rosette formation with mouse erythrocytes, probable marker for human B lymphocytes. *Int. Arch. Allergy Appl. Immunol.* **49**, 734–742.

GUPTA S., ROSS G., GOOD R. A. and SIEGAL F. P. (1976) Surface markers on human eosinophils. *Blood* **48**, 755–763.

GUPTA S., FERNANDES G., NAIR M. and GOOD R. A. (1978) Spontaneous and antibody-dependent cell mediated cytotoxicity by human T cell subpopulations. *Proc. Natl Acad. Sci. USA* **75**, 5137–5141.

GUTIERREZ C., BERNABE R. R., VEGA J. and KREISLER M. (1979) Purification of human T and B cells by a discontinuous density gradient of Percoll. *J. Immunol. Methods* **29**, 57–63.

HALL R. and MALIA R. (1984) Haemopoiesis. *In: Medical Laboratory Haematology.* (Eds. Hall R. and Malia R.). London, Butterworths, pp. 1–16.

HAMBURGER A. and SALMON S. E. (1977) Primary bioassay of human myeloma stem cells. *J. Clin. Invest.* **60**, 846–854.

HANNA N. and BURTON R. C. (1981) Definitive evidence that natural killer (NK) cells inhibit experimental tumor metastasis *in vivo. J. Immunol.* **127**, 1754–1758.

HANNIG K. (1972) Free-flow electrophoresis. *In: Methods of Microbiology* (Eds. Norris J. R. and Ribbons D. W.) Vol 5B, New York, Academic Press, pp. 513–548.

HARRISON P. M., CLEGG G. A. and MAY K. (1980) Ferritin structure and function. *In: Iron in Biochemistry and Medicine II* (Eds. Jacobs A. and Worwood M.). London, Academic Press, p. 152.

HASKILL S. (1981) Unit gravity sedimentation of tumor-associated macrophages. *In: Manual Macrophage Methodology* (Eds. Herscowitz H. B., Holden H. T., Bellanti J. A. et al). New York, Marcel Dekker, pp. 81–91.

HELINEK T. G., DEVLIN T. M. and CH'IH J. J. (1982) Initial inhibition and recovery of protein synthesis in cycloheximide-treated hepatocyes. *Biochem. Pharmacol.* **31** (2), 1219–1225.

HERBERMAN R. B., ORTALDO J. R. and TIMONEN T. (1981) Assay of augmentation of natural killer cell activity and antibody-dependent cell-mediated cytotoxicity by interferon. *Methods Enzymol.* **79**, 477–484.

HINES J. D. and GRASSO J. A. (1970) The sideroblastic anaemia. *Semin. Hematol.* **7** (1), 86–106.

HJORTH R., JONSSON A.-K. and VRETBLAD P. (1981) A rapid method for purification of human granulocytes using Percoll. A comparison with dextran sedimentation. *J. Immunol. Methods* **43**, 95–101.

HODGETTS J. (1984) A study of human erythroid bone marrow cells and their iron metabolism. MSc Thesis, University of Wales College of Medicine.

HODGETTS J., PETERS S. W., HOY T. G. and JACOBS A. (1986a) The ferritin content of normoblasts and megaloblasts from human bone marrow. *Clin. Sci.* **70**, 47–51.

HODGETTS J., HOY T. G. and JACOBS A. (1986b) Iron uptake and ferritin synthesis in human erythroblasts. *Clin. Sci.* **70**, 53–57.

HORWITZ D. A. and GARRETT M. A. (1977) Distinctive functional properties of human blood L lymphocytes: a comparison with T lymphocytes, B lymphocytes, and monocytes. *J. Immunol.* **118**, 1712–1721.

HUDSON L. and HAY F. C. (1980) *Practical Immunology*, 2nd Ed., Oxford, Blackwell Scientific Publications.

HUNT T. (1976) Control of globin synthesis. *Br. Med. Bull.* **32** (3), 257–261.

HUTCHINGS S. E. and SATO G. H. (1978) Growth and maintenance of Hela cells in serum-free medium supplemented with hormones. *Proc. Natl Acad. Sci. USA* **75**, 901–904.

ISCOVE N. N., SIEBER F. and WINTERHALTER K. H. (1974) Erythroid colony formation in cultures of mouse and human bone marrow: analysis of the requirement for erythropoietin by gel filtration and affinity chromatography on agarose-concanavalin-A. *J. Cell. Physiol.* **83**, 309–320.

JERRELLS T. R., DEAN J. H., RICHARDSON G. L. and HERBERMAN R. B. (1980) Depletion of monocytes from human peripheral blood mononuclear leukocytes: comparison of the Sephadex G-10 column method with other commonly used techniques. *J. Immunol. Methods* **32**, 11–29.

JOBIN M. E., FAHEY J. L. and PRICE Z. (1974) Long-term establishment of a human plasmacyte cell line derived from a patient with IgD multiple myeloma. *J. Exp. Med.* **140**, 494–507.

JOHNSON G. R. and METCALF D. (1977) Pure and mixed erythroid colony formation *in vitro* stimulated by spleen conditioned medium with no detectable erythropoietin. *Proc. Natl Acad. Sci.* **74**, 3879–3882.

JONDAL M., HOLM G. and WIGZELL H. (1972) Surface markers on human T and B lymphocytes. 1. A large population of lymphocytes forming non-immune rosettes with sheep red blood cells. *J. Exp. Med.* **136**, 207–215.

JONES B. M. (1982) Human isoferritins: detection, quantitation and significance. PhD thesis. University of Wales College of Medicine, Cardiff.

JONES B. M. and WORWOOD M. (1978) An immunoradiometric assay for the acidic ferritin of human heart: application of human tissues, cells and serum. *Clin. Chim. Acta* **85**, 81–88.

JOVIN T., CHRAMBACH A. and NAUGHTON M. A. (1964) An apparatus for preparative temperature-regulated polyacrylamide gel electrophoresis. *Anal. Biochem.* **9**, 351–369.

JULIUS M. H., MASUDA T. and HERZENBERG L. A. (1972) Demonstration that antigen-binding cells are precursors of antibody-producing cells after purification with a fluorescence-activated cell sorter. *Proc. Natl Acad. Sci.* **69**, 1934–1938.

KAABA S., SCHREUDER W. O., TING W. C. and JACOBS A. (1984) Inhibition of erythroid colony growth *in vitro* by serum from patients with disseminated bronchial cancer. *Exp. Hematol.* **12**, 641–644.

KAABA S., JACOBS A. and BARNES K. (1985) Sideroblastic colonies in erythroid cultures grown from normal human bone marrow. *J. Clin. Pathol.* **38**, 68–72.

KAPLAN M. E. and CLARK C. (1974) An improved rosetting assay for detection of human T lymphocytes. *J. Immunol. Methods* **5**, 131–135.

KAPLAN M. E., WOODSON M. and CLARK C. (1976) Detection of human T lymphocytes by rosette formation with AET-treated sheep red cells. *In: In Vitro Methods in Cell-Mediated and Tumor Immunity* (Eds. Bloom B. R. and David J. R.). New York, Academic Press, pp. 83–88.

KAPLOW L. S. and EISENBERG M. (1975) Leukocyte differentiation and enumeration by cytochemical-cytographic analysis. *In: First International Symposium On Pulse-Cytophotometry* (Eds. Haanen C. A. M., Hillen H. F. P. and Wessels J. M. C.). European Press, Medikon, Belgium, pp. 262–274.

KAPLOW L. S., DAUBER H. and LERNER E. (1976) Assessment of monocyte esterase activity by flow cytophotometry. *J. Histochem. Cytochem.* **24**, 363–372.

KARCIOGLU G. L. and HARDISON J. E. (1978) Iron-containing plasma cells. *Arch. Intern. Med.* **138**, 97–100.

KATZ D. H. and BENACERRAF B. (1972) The regulatory influence of activated T cells on B cell responses to antigen. *Adv. Immunol.* **15**, 1–94.

KAUFFMAN H. F., LEVERING P. R. and de VRIES K. (1983) A single centrifugation step method for the simultaneous separation of different leukocytes with special reference to basophilic leukocytes. *J. Immunol. Methods* **57**, 1–7.

KAY H. D., BONNARD G. D., WEST W. H. and HERBERMAN R. B. (1977) A functional comparison of human Fc-receptor-bearing lymphocytes active in natural cytotoxicity and antibody-dependent cellular cytotoxicity. *J. Immunol.* **118**, 2058–2066.

KAY N. E., ACKERMAN S. K. and DOUGLAS S. D. (1979) Anatomy of the immune system. *Semin. Hematol.* **16**, 252–282.

KEDAR E., de LANDAZURI M. O. M. and BONAVIDA B. (1974) Cellular immunoadsorbents: a simplified technique for separation of lymphoid cell populations. *J. Immunol.* **112**, 1231–1243.

KENNETH J. P. (1981) Adherence to plastic or glass surfaces. *In: Manual of Macrophage Methodology* (Eds. Herscowtiz H. B., Holden H. T., Bellanti J. A. et al). New York, Marcel Dekker.

KIRCHNER H., CHUSED T. M., HERBERMAN R. B. et al (1974) Evidence of suppressor cell activity in spleens of mice bearing primary tumors induced by moloney sarcoma virus. *J. Exp. Med.* **139**, 1473–1487.

KOEFFLER H. P., LEVINE A. M., SPARKES M. and SPARKES R. S. (1980) Chronic myelocytic leukemia: eosinophils involved in the malignant clone. *Blood* **55**, 1063–1065.

KÖHLER G. and MILSTEIN C. (1975) Continuous cultures of fused cells secreting antibody of predefined specificity. *Nature* **256**, 495–497.

KOLLER C. A., KING G. W., HURTUBISE P. E. et al (1973) Characterization of glass-adherent human mononuclear cells. *J. Immunol.* **111**, 1610–1612.

KONIJN A. M., HERSHKO C. and IZAK G. (1979) Ferritin synthesis and iron uptake in developing erythroid cells. *Am. J. Hematol.* **6**, 373–379.

KRETH H. W. and HERZENBERG L. A. (1974) Fluorescence-activated cell sorting of human T and B lymphocytes. I. Direct evidence that lymphocytes with a high density of membrane-bound immunoglobulin are precursors of plasmacytes. *Cell. Immunol.* **12**, 396–406.

KUMAGAI K., ITOH K., HINUMA S. and TADA M. (1979) Pretreatment of plastic Petri dishes with fetal calf serum. A simple method for macrophage isolation. *J. Immunol. Methods* **29**, 17–25.

KUPER S. W. A., BIGNALL J. R. and LUCKCOCK E. D. (1961) A quantitative method for studying tumour cells in blood. *Lancet* **I**, 852–853.

KURNICK J. T., ÖSTBERG L., STEGAGNO M. and KIMURA A. K. (1979) A rapid method for the separation of functional lymphoid cell populations of human and animal origin on PVP-silica (Percoll) density gradients. *Scand. J. Immunol.* **10**, 563–573.

KURTZ S. R., CARCIERO R. and VALERI C. R. (1979) Factors that influence the process of [51]chromium labelling of human granulocytes isolated from blood by counterflow centrifugation. *Transfusion* **19** (4), 398–403.

LAJTHA L. G. (1975) Haemopoietic stem cells. *Br. J. Haematol.* **29**, 529–535.

LANDRETH K. S., KINCADE P. W., LEE G. et al (1982) Enrichment of human marrow lymphocytes with monoclonal antibodies to murine antigens. *Proc. Natl Acad. Sci. USA* **79**, 2370–2374.

LANDRY F. J. and FINDLAY S. R. (1983) Purification of basophils by negative selection. *J. Immunol. Methods* **63**, 329–336.

LARSSON E. L., ANDERSSON J. and COUTINHO A. (1978) Functional consequences of sheep red blood cell rosetting for human T cells; gain of reactivity to mitogenic factors. *Eur. J. Immunol.* **8**, 693–696.

LEDBETTER J. A., ROUSE R. V., MICKLEM H. S. and HERZENBERG L. A. (1980) T cell subsets defined by expression of Ly-1,2,3 and Thy-1 antigens. *J. Exp. Med.* **152**, 280–295.

LEE T., MALONE B., WASSERMAN S. I. et al (1982) Activities of enzymes that metabolize platelet-activating factor (*l*-alkyl-2-acetyl-sn-glycero-3-phosphocholine) in neutrophils and eosinophils from humans and the effect of a calcium ionophore. *Biochem. Biophys. Res. Commun.* **105**, 1303–1308.

LEVIS W. R. and ROBBINS J. H. (1972) Methods for obtaining purified lymphocytes, glass-adherent mononuclear cells and a population containing both cell types from human peripheral blood. *Blood* **40**, 77–89.

LINCH D. C., BOYLE D. and BEVERLEY P. C. L. (1982) T-cell and monocyte requirements for erythropoiesis. *Acta Haematol.* (Basel) **67**, 34–38.

LING N. R., BISHOPS S. and JEFFERIS R. (1977) Use of antibody-coated red cells for the sensitive detection of antigen and in rosette tests for cells bearing surface immunoglobulins. *J. Immunol. Methods* **15**, 279–289.

LIPTON J. M., LINK N. A., BREARD J. et al (1980a) Monocytes do not inhibit peripheral blood erythroid burst forming unit colony formation. *J. Clin. Invest.* **65**, 219–223.

LIPTON J. M., REINHERZ E. L., KUDISCH M. et al (1980b) Mature bone marrow erythroid burst-forming units do not require T cells for induction of erythropoietin-dependent differentiation. *J. Exp. Med.* **152**, 350–360.

LOURENCO G., EMBURY S., SCHRIER S. L. and KEDES L. H. (1978) Decreased ribosomal RNA content and *in vitro* RNA synthesis in purified bone marrow erythroblasts of patients with idiopathic ineffective erythropoiesis and diGuglielmo disease. *Am. J. Hematol.* **5**, 169–182.

LUINI W., BORASCHI D., ALBERTI S. et al (1981) Morphological characterization of a cell population responsible for natural killer activity. *Immunology* **43**, 663–668.

LY I. A. and MISHELL R. I. (1974) Separation of mouse spleen cells by passage through columns of Sephadex G-10. *J. Immunol. Methods* **5**, 239–247.

MADYASTHA P., MADYASTHA K. R., WADE T. and LEVINE D. (1982) An improved method for rapid layering of Ficoll–Hypaque double density gradients suitable for granulocyte separation. *J. Immunol. Methods* **48**, 281–286.

MAHMOUD A. A. F., KELLERMEYER R. W. and WARREN K. S. (1974) Monospecific antigranulocyte sera against human neutrophils, eosinophils, basophils and myeloblasts. *Lancet* **2** (7890), 1163–1166.

MANGAN K. F. and DESFORGES J. F. (1980) The role of T lymphocytes and monocytes in the regulation of human erythropoietic peripheral blood burst forming units. *Exp. Hematol.* **8** (6), 717–727.

MARBROOK J. (1967) Primary immune response in cultures of spleen cells. *Lancet* **2**, 1279–1281.

MATEYKO G. M. and KOPAC M. J. (1963) Cytophysical studies on living normal and neoplastic cells. *Ann. N.Y. Acad Sci.* **105**, 185–218.

MAVLIGIT G. M., GUTTERMAN J. U., HERSH E. M. and ALEXANIAN R. (1974) Cell-mediated immunity to plasma cell myeloma: specific inhibition by a serum factor adhering to effector lymphocytes. *Proc. Soc. Exp. Biol. Med.* **147**, 537–540.

MAY A., DE SOUZA P., BARNES K., KAABA S. and JACOBS A. (1982) Erythroblast iron metabolism in sideroblastic marrow. *Br. J. Haematol.* **52**, 611–621.

MAZUR A. and CARLETON A. (1963) Relation of ferritin iron to heme synthesis in marrow reticulocytes. *J. Biol. Chem.* **238**, 1817–1824.

McDONALD G. A., DODDS T. C. and CRUICKSHANK B. (1978) *Atlas of Haematology*. Edinburgh, Churchill Livingstone.

MALACHLAN S. M., REESMITH B., PETERSEN V. B. et al (1978) A system for studying thyroid stimulating antibody production *in vitro*. *J. Clin. Lab. Immunol.* **1**, 45–50.

McLEOD D. L., SHREEVE M. M. and AXELRAD A. A. (1976) Induction of megakaryocyte colonies with platelet formation *in vitro*. *Nature* **261**, 492–494.

MEISTRICH M. L. (1983) Experimental factors involved in separation by centrifugal elutriation. *In: Separation Methods and Selected Applications* (Eds. Pretlow T. G. and Pretlow T. P.), Vol. 2, New York, Academic Press, pp. 33–61.

MELAMED M. R., ADAMS L. A., TRAGANOS F. and KAMENTSKY L. A. (1973) Initial observations on instrumental differential blood leukocyte counts during chemotherapy of patients with leukemia. *Eur. J. Cancer* **9**, 181–184.

MELAMED M. R., ADAMS L. R., TRAGANOS F. et al (1972) Acridine orange metachromasia for characterization of leukocytes in leukemia, lymphoma and other neoplasms. *Cancer* **29**, 1361–1368.

MENDELOW B., GROBICKI D., KATZ J. and METZ J. (1980) Separation of normal mature bone marrow plasma cells. *Br. J. Haematol.* **45**, 251–262.

METCALF D. (1981) The clonal culture *in vitro* of human leukemic cells. *In: Methods In Hematology: The Leukemic Cells* (Ed. Catovsky D.), Churchill Livingstone, Edinburgh, pp. 220–251.

MEYSKENS F. L., HOLMES D. K. and GERNER E. W. (1978) Separation of normal human bone marrow granulocytes by centrifugal elutriation. *Exp. Hematol.* **6** (3), 50.

MEYSKENS F. L., KIEFER C. A., HOLMES D. K. and GERNER E. W. (1979) Separation of normal human bone marrow cells by counterflow centrifugal elutriation. 1. Morphological analysis and subfractionation of neutrophilic granulocytes. *Exp. Hematol.* **7**, 401–410.

MEYTES D., MA A., ORTEGA J. A. et al (1979) Human erythroid burst-promoting activity produced by phytohaemagglutinin-stimulated radio-resistant peripheral blood mononuclear cells. *Blood* **54**, 1050–1057.

MICKLEM H. S. (1979) B lymphocytes, T lymphocytes and lymphopoiesis. *Clin. Haematol.* **8**, 395–419.

MILLER J. F. A. P. and MITCHELL G. F. (1969) Thymus and antigen-reactive cells. *Transplant. Rev.* **1**, 3–42.

MILLER R. G. and PHILLIPS R. A. (1969) Separation of cells by velocity sedimentation. *J. Cell Physiol.* **73**, 191–201.

MISHELL B. B. and SHIIGI S. M. (1980) *Selected methods in cellular immunology*. San Francisco, W. H. Freeman.

MÖLLER E. and MÖLLER G. (1962) Quantitative studies of the sensitivity of normal and neoplastic mouse cells to the cytotoxic action of isoantibodies. *J. Exp. Med.* **115**, 527–553.

MOORE M. A. S. (1974) *In vitro* studies in the myeloid leukaemias *In: Advances In Acute Leukaemia* (Eds. Cleton F. J., Crowther D. and Malpas J. S.). North Holland, American Elsevier.

MORETTA L., FERRARINI M., DURANTE M. L. and MINGARI M. C. (1975) Expression of a receptor for IgM by human T cells *in vitro*. *Eur J. Immunol.* **5**, 565–569.

MORETTA L., FERRARINI M., MINGARI M. C. et al (1976) Subpopulations of human T cells identified by receptors for immunoglobulins and mitogen responsiveness. *J. Immunol.* **117**, 2171–2174.

MORETTA L., WEBB S. R., GROSSI C. E. et al (1977) Functional analysis of two human T-cell subpopulations: helper and suppression of B-cell responses by T-cells bearing receptors for IgM or IgG. *J. Exp. Med.* **146**, 184–200.

NATHAN C. F., ASOFSKY R. and TERRY W. D. (1977) Characterization of the nonphagocytic adherent cell from the peripheral cavity of normal and BCG-treated mice. *J. Immunol.* **118**, 1612–1621.

NILSSON, K. (1971) Characteristics of established myeloma and lymphoblastoid cell line derived from an E myeloma patient: a comparative study. *Int. J. Cancer* **7**, 380–396.

NORDLING S., ANDERSSON L. C. and HÄYRY P. (1972) Separation of T and B lymphocytes by preparative cell electrophoresis. *Eur. J. Immunol.* **2**, 405–410.

NORRIS D. A., MORRIS R. M., SANDERSON R. J. and KOHLER P. F. (1979) Isolation of functional subsets of human peripheral blood monocytes. *J. Immunol.* **123** (1), 166–172.

NOVATO-SILVA E., NOGUEIRA-MACHADO J. A. and GAZZINELLI G. (1980). *Schistosoma mansoni*: comparison of the killing effect of granulocytes and complement with or without antibody on fresh and cultured schistosomula *in vitro*. *Am. J. Trop. Med. Hyg.* **29**, 1263–1267.

NUNEZ M. T., GLASS J., FISCHER S. et al (1977) Transferrin receptors in developing murine erythroid cells. *Br. J. Haematol.* **36**, 519–526.

NUNEZ M. T., COLE E. S. and GLASS J. (1980) Cytosol intermediates in the transport of iron. *Blood* **55**, 1051–1055.

ODA M. and PUCK T. T. (1961) The interaction of mammalian cells with antibodies. *J. Exp. Med.* **113**, 599–610.

OEHLER J. R., HERBERMAN R. B., CAMPBELL D. A. Jr. and DJEU J. Y. (1977) Inhibition of rat mixed lymphocyte cultures by suppressor macrophages. *Cell. Immunol.* **29**, 238–250.

OGAWA M., PARMLEY R. T., BANK H. L. and SPICER S. S. (1976) Human marrow erythropoiesis in culture: I. Characterization of methylcellulose colony assay. *Blood* **48**, 407–417.

OGAWA M., MAcEACHERN M. D. and AVILA L. (1977) Human marrow erythropoiesis in culture: II. Heterogeneity in the morphology, time course of colony formation, and sedimentation velocity of the colony-forming cells. *Am. J. Hematol.* **3**, 29–36.

OLOFSSON T., GÄRTNER I. and OLSSON I. (1980) Separation of human bone marrow cells in density gradients of polyvinylpyrrolidone-coated silica gel (Percoll). *Scand. J. Haematol.* **24**, 254–262.

ORTALDO J. R., SHARROW S. O., TIMONEN T. and HERBERMAN R. B. (1981) Determination of surface antigens on highly purified human NK cells by flow cytometry with monoclonal antibodies. *J. Immunol.* **127**, 2401–2409.

PARISH C. R. and HAYWARD J. A. (1974) The lymphocyte's surface. III. Function of Fc receptor, C^3 receptors and surface Ig-bearing lymphocytes; identification of a radio-resistent B cell. *Proc. R. Soc. Lond. (Biol.)* **187**, 379–395.

PARISH C. R. and McKENZIE I. F. C. (1978) A sensitive rosetting method for detecting subpopulations of lymphocytes which react with alloantisera. *J. Immunol. Methods.* **20**, 173–183.

PARRILLO J. E. and FAUCI A. S. (1978) Human eosinophils: purification and cytotoxic capability of eosinophils from patients with the hypereosinophilic syndrome. *Blood* **51**, 457–473.

PEETERS H. (1979) *Separation of cells and subcellular elements*. Oxford, Pergamon.

PELLEGRINO M. A., FERRONE S. and THEOFILOPOULOS A. N. (1976) Isolation of human T and B lymphocytes by rosette formation with 2-aminoethyli-sothiouronium bromide (AET)-treated sheep red cells and with monkey red cells. *J. Immunol. Methods* **11**, 273–279.

PERLMANN P., PERLMANN H. and WIGZELL H. (1972) Lymphocyte mediated cytotoxicity *in vitro*. Induction and inhibition by humoral antibody and nature of effector cells. *Transplant. Rev.* **13**, 91–114.

PERTOFT H. and LAURENT T. C. (1968) The use of gradients of colloidal silica for the separation of cells and subcellular particles *In: Modern Separation Methods of Macromolecules and Particles* (Ed. Gerritsen T.) Vol. 2. Wiley Interscience. New York, John Wiley, pp. 71–90.

PERTOFT H. and LAURENT T. C. (1977) Isopycnic separation of cells and cell organelles by centrifugation in modified colloidal silica gradients. *In: Methods of Cell Separation* (Ed. Catsimpoolas N.) Vol. 1. New York, Plenum Press, pp. 25–65.

PERTOFT H., BACK O and KIESSLING K. L. (1969) Separation of various blood cells in colloidal silica-polyvinylpyrrolidone gradients. *Exp. Cell Res.* **50**, 355–368.

PERTOFT H., RUBIN K, KJELLEN L. et al (1977) The viability of cells grown or centrifuged in a new density gradient medium, Percoll (TM). *Exp. Cell. Res.* **110**, 449–457.

PERTOFT H., LAURENT T. C., LÅÅS T. and KAGEDÅL L. (1978) Density gradients prepared from colloidal silica particles coated by polyvinylpyrrolidone (Percoll). *Anal. Biochem.* **88**, 271–282.

PERTOFT H., HIRTENSTEIN M. and KÅGEDAL L. (1979) Cell separations in a new density medium, Percoll®. Cell Populations. *In: Methodological Surveys. (B) Biochemistry*, (Ed. Reid E.). Vol. 9. Chichester, Ellis Horwood, pp. 67–80.

PERTOFT H., JOHNSSON A., WÄRMEGÅRD B. and SELJELID R. (1980) Separation of human monocytes on density gradients of Percoll. *J. Immunol. Methods* **33**, 221–229.

PETERS R. (1982) Globin chain synthesis in sideroblastic anaemia. MSc Thesis, University of Wales College of Medicine, Cardiff.

PETERS R. E., MAY A. and JACOBS A. (1983a) Globin chain synthesis ratios in sideroblastic anaemia. *Br. J. Haematol.* **53**, 201–209.

PETERS S. W., JACOBS A. and FITZSIMONS E. (1983b) Erythrocyte ferritin in normal subjects and patients with abnormal iron metabolism. *Br. J. Haematol.* **53**, 211–216.

PETERSON E. A. and EVANS W. H. (1967) Separation of bone marrow cells by sedimentation at unit gravity. *Nature* **214**, 824–825.

PHILLIPS J. H. and BABCOCK G. F. (1983) NKP-15: a monoclonal antibody reactive against purified human natural killer cells and granulocytes. *Immunology Letters* **6**, 143–149.

PHILLIPS S. G., KABAT E. A. and MILLER O. J. (1980) Nylon-fibre affinity selection of red blood cells and tissue culture cells on the basis of cell surface determinants. *Exp. Cell. Res.* **127**, 361–371.

PLATSOUCAS C. D. (1983) Separation of cells by preparative density gradient electrophoresis. *In: Cell Separation Methods and Selected Applications* (Eds. Pretlow T. G. and Pretlow T. P.). New York, Academic Press, pp. 145–182.

PLATSOUCAS C. D. and CATSIMPOOLAS N. (1980a) Biological methods for the separation of lymphoid cells. *In: Methods of Cell Separation* (Ed. Catsimpoolas, N.) Vol. 3. New York, Plenum Press, pp. 160–165.

PLATSOUCAS C. D. and CATSIMPOOLAS N. (1980b) Biological methods for the separation of lymphoid cells. *In: Methods of Cell Separation* (Ed. Catsimpoolas, N.) Vol. 3. New York, Plenum Press, p. 167.

PLATSOUCAS C. and CATSIMPOOLAS N. (1980c) Biological methods for the separation of lymphoid cells. *In: Methods of Cell Separation* (Ed. Catsimpoolas, N.) Vol. 3. New York, Plenum Press, pp. 160–173.

PLATSOUCAS C. D. and CATSIMPOOLAS N. (1980d) Biological methods for the separation of lymphoid cells. *In: Methods of Cell Separation* (Ed. Catsimpoolas, N.) Vol. 3. New York, Plenum Press, p. 174.

PLATSOUCAS C. D., GRIFFITH A. L. and CATSIMPOOLAS N. (1976) Density gradient electrophoresis of mouse spleen lymphocytes: separation of T and B cell fractions. *J. Immunol. Methods* **13**, 145–152.

PLATSOUCAS C. D., GOOD R. A. and GUPTA S. (1979) Separation of human T lymphocyte subpopulations (T_μ, T_γ) by density gradient electrophoresis. *Proc. Natl Acad. Sci. USA* **76**, 1972–1976.

PLATSOUCAS C. D., GOOD R. A. and GUPTA S. (1980) Separation of human lymphocyte subpopulations by density gradient electrophoresis. I. Different mobilities of T (T_μ, T_α) and B lymphocytes from human tonsils. *Cell. Immunol.* **51**, 238–249.

PLATSOUCAS C. D., BECK J. D., KAPOOR N. et al (1981) Separation of human bone marrow cell populations by density gradient electrophoresis: differential mobilities of myeloid (CFU-C), monocytoid, and lymphoid cells. *Cell. Immunol.* **59**, 345–354.

PRETLOW T. G. (1971) Estimation of experimental conditions that permit cell separations by velocity sedimentation on isokinetic gradients of Ficoll in tissue culture medium. *Annal. Biochem.* **41**, 248–255.

PRETLOW T. G. and PRETLOW P. P. (1982) *Cell Separation Methods And Selected Applications*, Vol. 1, New York, Academic Press.

PRETLOW T. G. and PRETLOW P. P. (1983) *Cell Separation Methods And Selected Applications*, Vol. 2, New York, Academic Press.

PRICE G. B., STEWART S. and KROGSRUD R. L. (1979) Characterization of stem cells and progenitors of hemopoiesis by cell sorting. *Blood Cells* **5**, 161–174.

PRUZANSKY J. J. and PATTERSON R. (1981) Enrichment of human basophils. *J. Immunol. Methods* **44**, 183–190.

QUEISSER U., QUEISSER W. and SPIER T. Z. B. (1971) Polyploidization of megakaryocytes in normal humans, in patients with idiopathic thrombocytopenia and with pernicious anaemia. *Br. J. Haematol* **20**, 489–501.

REARDEN A. and MASOUREDIS S. P. (1977) Blood group D antigen content of nucleated red cell precursors. *Blood* **50**, 981–986.

REID C. D. L., BAPTISTA L. C., DEACON R. and CHANARIN I. (1981) Megaloblastic change is a feature of colonies derived from an early erythroid progenitor (BFU-E) stimulated by monocytes in culture. *Br. J. Haematol.* **49**, 551–561.

RENNIE C., THOMPSON S., PARKER A. C. and MADDY A. (1979). Human erythrocyte fractionation in 'Percoll' density gradients. *Clin. Chim. Acta* **98**, 119–125.

RINEHART J. J., ZANJANI E. D., NOMDEDEU B. et al (1978) Cell–cell interaction in erythropoiesis: role of human monocytes. *J. Clin. Invest.* **62**, 979–986.

ROBINSON J., SIEFF C., DELIA D. et al (1981) Expression of cell-surface HLA-DR, HLA-ABC and glycophorin during erythroid differentiation. *Nature* **289**, 68–71.

ROMAGNANI S., ALMERIGOGNA F., GIUDIZI G. M. and RICCI M. (1980) Rosette formation with protein A-coated erythrocytes: a method for detection of both IgG-bearing cells and another subset of human peripheral blood B lymphocytes. *J. Immunol. Methods* **33**, 11–21.

ROMSLO I. (1980) Intracellular Transport of Iron. *In: Iron in Biochemistry and Medicine II* (Eds. Jacobs A. and Worwood M.). London, Academic Press, p. 325.

ROSS G. D. and POLLEY M. J. (1975) Specifity of human lymphocyte receptors. *J. Exp. Med.* **141**, 1163–1180.

ROTHBARTH P. H., HENDRIKS-STURKENBOOM I. and PIOEM J. S. (1976) Identificiation of monocytes in suspensions of mononuclear cells. *Blood* **48**, 139–147.

ROZENSZAJN L. A., SHOHAM D. and KALECHMAN I. (1975) Clonal proliferation of PHA-stimulated human lymphocytes in soft agar culture. *Immunology* **29**, 1041–1055.

RUTHERFORD T. R. and HARRISON P. R. (1979) Globin synthesis and erythroid differentiation in a Friend cell variant deficient in heme synthesis. *Proc. Natl Acad. Sci USA.* **76**, 5660–5664.

RUTISHAUSER U. S. and EDELMAN G. M. (1977) Fractionation and manipulation of cells with chemically modified fibers and surfaces. *In: Methods of Cell Separation*, (Ed. Catsimpoolas N.) Vol. 1. New York, Plenum Press, p. 203.

SANDERSON R. J., PALMER N. F. and BIRD K. E. (1975) Separation of red cells into age groups by counterflow centrifugation. *Biophys. J.* **15**, (321a), abstr. F-AM-K10.

SANDERSON R. J., SHEPPERDSON F. T., VATTER A. E. and TALMAGE D. W. (1977) Isolation and enumeration of peripheral blood monocytes. *J. Immunol.* **118**, 1409–1414.

SANDRIN M. S., POTTER T. A., MORGAN G. M. and McKENZIE I. F. (1978) Detection of mouse alloantibodies by rosetting with protein A-coated sheep red blood cells. *Transplantation* **26**, 126-130.

SANTOLI D., TRINCHIERI G. and LIEF F. S. (1978) Cell-mediated cytotoxicity against virus-infected target cells in human. *J. Immunol.* **121**, 526–531.

SCHLOSSMAN S. F. and HUDSON L. (1973) Specific purification of lymphocyte populations on a digestible immunoabsorbent. *J. Immunol.* **110**, 313–315.

SCHLUNK T. and SCHLEYER M. (1980) The influence of culture conditions on the production of colony-stimulating activity by human placenta. *Exp. Hematol.* **8**, 179–184.

SEGAL A. W., FORTUNATO A. and HERD T. (1980) A rapid single centrifugation step method for the separation of erythrocytes, granulocytes and mononuclear cells on continuous density gradient of Percoll. *J. Immunol. Methods* **32**, 209–214.

SHEPP M., TOFF H., YAMADA H. and GABUZDA T. G. (1972) Heterogeneous metabolism of marrow ferritins during erythroid cell maturation. *Br. J. Haematol.* **22**, 377–382.

SHER R. and GLOVER A. (1976) Isolation of human eosinophils and their lymphocyte-like rosetting properties. *Immunology* **31**, 377–341.

SHOHAM D., DAVID E. B. and ROZENSZAJN L. A. (1974) Cytochemical and morphological identification of macrophages and eosinophils in tissue cultures of normal human bone marrow. *Blood* **44**, 221–233.

SHORTMAN K., WILLIAMS N., JACKSON H. et al (1971) The separation of different cell classes from lymphoid organs. IV. The separation of lymphocytes from phagocytes on glass bead columns, and its effect on subpopulations of lymphocytes and antibody forming cells. *J. Cell. Biol.* **48**, 566–579.

SHORTMAN K., WILLIAMS N. and ADAMS P. (1972) The separation of different cell classes from lymphoid organs. V. Simple procedures for the removal of cell debris, damaged cells and erythroid cells from lymphoid cell suspension. *J. Immunol. Methods* **1**, 273–287.

SHORTMAN K., von BOEHMER H., LIPP J. and HOPPER K. (1975) Subpopulations of T-lymphocytes: physical separation, functional specialization and differentiation pathways of subsets of thymocytes and thymus-dependent peripheral lymphocytes. *Transplant. Rev.* **25**, 163–210.

SHORTMAN K., FIDLER J. M., SCHLEGEL R. A. et al (1976) Subpopulations of B lymphocytes: physical separation of functionally distinct stages of B-cell differentiation. *Contemp. Top. Immunobiol.* **5**, 1–45.

SJÖQUIST J., FORSGREN A., GUSTAFSON G. T. and STALENHEIM G. (1967) Biological importance of the Fc-region of gamma globulins. *Cold Spring Harbor Symp. Quant. Biol.* **32**, 577–581.

SPEYER B. E. and FIELDING J. (1979) Ferritin as a cytosol iron transport intermediate in human reticulocytes. *Br. J. Haematol.* **42**, 255–267.

SPOONER R. J., PERCY R. A. and RUMLEY AG. (1979) The effect of erythrocyte ageing on some vitamin and mineral dependent enzymes. *Clin. Biochem.* **12**, 289–290.

STATHOPOULOS G. and ELLIOTT E. V. (1974) Formation of mouse or sheep red-blood-cell rosettes by lymphocytes from normal and leukaemic individuals. *Lancet* **2**, 600–601.

STEINKAMP J. A. (1977) Multiparameter analysis and sorting of mammalian cells. *In: Methods of Cell Separation* (Ed. Catsimpoolas N.) Vol. **1**, New York, Plenum Press, pp. 251–306.

STEPHENSON J. R., AXELRAD A. A., McLEOD D. L. and SHREEVE M. M. (1971). Induction of colonies of hemoglobin-synthesizing cells by erythropoietin *in vitro*. *Proc. Natl. Acad. Sci.* **68** (2), 1542–1546.

STOBO J. D. (1982) Cellular interaction in the expression and regulation of immunity. *In: Basic & Clinical Immunology* (Eds. Stites D. P., Stobo J. D., Fudenberg H. H. and Wells J. V.) 4th ed. Los Altos, California, Lange, p. 89.

SUMMERS H., WORWOOD M. and JACOBS A. (1974) Ferritin in normal erythrocytes, lymphocytes, polymorphs and monocytes. *Br. J. Haematol.* **28**, 19–26.

SWEET H. (1985) The effect of pre-term delivery on the fetal to adult erythropoietic switchover. MSc Thesis, University of Wales College of Medicine, Cardiff.

TAI P.-C. and SPRY C. J. F. (1977) Purification of normal human eosinophils using the different binding capacities of blood leukocytes for complexed rabbit IgG. *Clin. Exp. Immunol.* **28**, 256–260.

TAI P.-C. and SPRY C. J. F. (1980) Enzymes altering the binding capacity of human blood eosinophils for IgG antibody-coated erythrocytes (EA). *Clin. Exp. Immunol.* **40**, 206–219.

TAKAHASHI T., OLD L. J., McINTIRE K. R. and BOYSE E. A. (1971) Immunoglobulin and other surface antigens of cells of the immune system. *J. Exp. Med.* **134**, 815–832.

TARGAN S. and JONDAL M. (1978) Monolayer immune complex (MIC) fractionation of Fc receptor bearing human spontaneous killer cell. *J. Immunol. Methods* **22**, 123–129.

THOMPSON R. B. (1979) The leukocytes: granulopoiesis. The granulocytes and monocytes. *In: A Short Textbook of Haematology* (Ed. Thomson R. B.). London, Pitman Medical, pp. 25–44.

THORSBY E. (1967) Cell specific and common antigens on human granulocytes and lymphocytes demonstrated with cytotoxic hetero-antibodies. *Vox Sang.* **13**, 194–206.

TIMONEN T. and SAKSELA E. (1980) Isolation of human NK cells by density gradient centrifugation. *J. Immunol. Methods* **36**, 285–291.

TIMONEN T., SAKSELA E., VIRTANEN I. and CANTELL K. (1980) Natural killer cells are responsible for the interferon production induced in human lymphocytes by tumor cell contact. *Eur. J. Immunol.* **10**, 422–427.

TIMONEN T., ORTALDO J. R. and HERBERMAN R. B. (1981) Characteristics of human large granular lymphocytes and relationship to natural killer and K cells. *J. Exp. Med.* **153**, 569–582.

TIMONEN T., REYNOLDS C. W., ORTALDO J. R. and HERBERMAN R. B. (1982) Isolation of human and rat natural killer cells. *J. Immunol. Methods* **51**, 269–277.

TRENTIN J. J. (1971) Determination of bone marrow stem cell differentiation by stromal hemopoietic inductive microenvironments (HIM). *Am. J. Pathol.* **65**, 621–628.

TRINCHIER G. and SANTOLI D. (1978) Anti-viral activity induced by culturing lymphocytes with tumour-derived or virus-transformed cells. Enhancement of human natural killer cell activity by interferon and antagonistic inhibition of susceptibility of target cells to lysis. *J. Exp. Med.* **147**, 1314–1333.

TSOI M.-S., APRILE J., DOBBS S. et al (1982) Enrichment (and depletion) of human suppressor cells with monoclonal antibodies and immunoglobulin-coated plates. *J. Immunol. Methods* **53**, 293–305.

TSOUKAS C. D., CARSON D. A., FONG S. et al (1980) Cellular requirements for pokeweed mitogen-induced autoantibody production in rheumatoid arthritis. *J. Immunol.* **125**, 1125–1129.

ULMER A. J. and FLAD H. D. (1979) Discontinuous density gradient separation of human mononuclear leucocytes using Percoll as gradient medium. *J. Immunol. Methods* **30**, 1–10.

VALENTINE W. N., OSKI F. A., PAGLIA D. E. et al (1967) Hereditary hemolytic anemia with hexokinase deficiency: role of hexokinase in erythrocyte aging. *N. Engl. J. Med.* **276**, 1–11.

WALTER H. (1974) Fractionation of mammalian blood cells by partition in two-polymer aqueous phases. *In: Methods In Enzymology* (Eds. Fleischer and Parker). New York, Academic Press, 637–647.

WALTER H. (1982) Separation and subfractionation of blood cell populations based on their surface properties by partitioning in two-polymer aqueous phase systems. *In: Cell Separation Methods and Selected Applications*, Vol. 1, (Eds. Pretlow T. G. and Pretlow T. P.). New York, Academic Press.

WALTER H. and NAGAYA H. (1975) Separation of human rosette and non-rosette-forming lymphoid cells by countercurrent distribution in an aqueous two-phase system. *Cell. Immunol.* **19**, 158–161.

WALTER H., KROB E. J., GARZA R. and ASCHER G. S. (1969a) Partition and countercurrent distribution of erythrocytes and leukocytes from different species. *Exp. Cell. Res.* **55**, 57–64.

WALTER H., KROB E. J. and ASCHER G. S. (1969b) Separation of lymphocytes and polymorphonuclear leukocytes by countercurrent distribution in aqueous two-polymer phase systems. *Exp. Cell Res.* **55**, 279–283.

WEBB S. R. and COOPER M. D. (1973) T cells can bind antigen via cytophilic IgM antibody, made by B cells. *J. Immunol.* **111**, 275–277.

WEETMAN A. P., McGREGOR A. M. and HALL R. (1983) Methimazole inhibits thyroid autoantibody production by an action on accessary cells. *Clin. Immunol. Immunopathol.* **28**, 39–45.

WEINER M. S., BIANCO C. and NUSSENZWEIG V. (1973) Enhanced binding of neuraminidase-treated sheep erythrocytes to human T lymphocytes. *Blood* **42**, 939–946.

WEINER R. S. and SHAH V. O. (1980) Purification of human monocytes: isolation and collection of large number of peripheral blood monocytes. *J. Immunol. Methods* **36**, 89–97.

WEISS L. (1981) Haemopoiesis in mammalian bone marrow. *In: Microenvironments in Haemopoietic and Lymphoid Differentiation* (Eds. Porter R. and Whelan J.). London, Pitman Press, pp. 5–21.

WIGZELL H. (1976a) Enrichment or depletion of surface-immunoglobulin-coated cells using anti-immunoglobulin antibodies and glass or plastic bead columns. *In: In Vitro Methods in Cell-Mediated and Tumor Immunity* (Eds. Bloom B. R. and David J. R.). New York, Academic Press, pp. 245–253.

WIGZELL H. (1976b) Specific affinity fractionation of lymphocytes using glass or plastic bead columns. *Scand. J. Immunol.* **5** (5), 23–29.

WINTROBE M. M., LEE G. R., BOGGS D. R. et al (1974) The normal hemopoietic system: Part II. *In: Clinical Hematology* (Eds. Wintrobe M. M., Lee G. R., Boggs D. R. et al). Philadelphia, Lea & Febiger.

WOLFF D. A. (1975) The separation of cells and subcellular particles by colloidal-silica density centrifugation. *In: Methods in Cell Biology* (Ed. Prescott D. M.) Vol. **10**, New York, Academic Press, pp. 85–104.

WORWOOD M., HOURAHANE D. and JONES B. M. (1984) Accumulation and release of isoferritins during incubation *in vitro* of human peripheral blood mononuclear cells. *Br. J. Haematol.* **56**, 31–43.

YAM L. T., LI C. Y. and CROSBY W. H. (1971) Cytochemical identification of monocytes and granulocytes. *Am. J. Clin. Pathol.* **55**, 283–290.

ZANELLA A., MANTOVANI A., MARIANI M. et al (1981) A modified 'low pH' lignocaine method to isolate human monocytes: a comparison with other separation procedures. *J. Immunol. Methods* **41**, 279–288.

Appendices

A. CONVERSION OF CENTRIFUGAL FORCE TO REVOLUTIONS PER MINUTE

The relative centrifugal force (RCF) g, used throughout this text, can be converted to revolutions per minute (r.p.m) by measuring the radius of the centrifuge as follows:

Draw a straight line through the radius scale (I) and the centrifugal force scale (II). The intercept on scale (III) gives the revolutions per minute.

RFC can be evaluated directly from the nomogram illustrated in *Fig.* A-1. In addition, it can also be calculated from the formula:

$$RFC\ (g) = 0.0000284 \times R \times (rpm)^2$$

where R = radius in inches from the centre of the centrifuge shaft to the middle of the centrifuge tube.

Metric system:

$$RCF\ (g) = 0.0000112 \times R \times (rpm)^2$$

where R = radius in centimetres.

Comments

The relative centrifugal force (g) varies with the position in the centrifuge tube, and also with the type of rotor used.

B. UNITS OF WEIGHT AND MEASUREMENT

1. *Weight* [unit: gram (g)]

kg	kilogram	$(=10^3 g)$
mg	milligram	$(=10^{-3} g)$
µg or γ	microgram	$(=10^{-6} g)$
ng or µmg	nanogram	$(=10^{-9} g)$
pg or µµg	picogram	$(=10^{-12} g)$

212

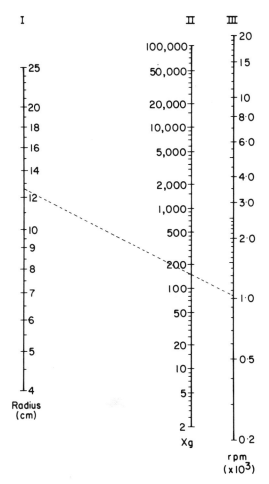

Fig. A.1. Nomogram for the computation of relative centrifugal force (by courtesy of Hudson & Hay, 1980) *Practical Immunology*, Oxford, Blackwell Scientific Publications.

2. *Length* [unit: metre (m)]

dm	decimetre	$(=10^{-1}m)$
cm	centimetre	$(=10^{-2}m)$
mm	millimetre	$(=10^{-3}m)$
μm or μ micrometre		$(=10^{-6}m)$
nm or mμ nanometre		$(=10^{-9}m)$

3. *Volume* [unit: litre (l) = dl^3]

dl	decilitre	$(=10^{-1}l)$
ml	millilitre	$(=10^{-3}l)$

μl	microlitre	$(=10^{-6}l)$
nl	nanolitre	$(=10^{-9}l)$
pl	picolitre	$(=10^{-12}l)$
fl$(=\mu l^3)$	femtolitre	$(=10^{-15}l)$

4. *Amount of substance* [unit: mole (mol)]

| mmol | millimole | $(=10^{-3}mol)$ |
| μmol | micromole | $(=10^{-6}mol)$ |

Molarity (M) is an expression of molar concentration; it is equivalent to mol/l.

C. CLEANING AND STERILIZATION OF LABORATORY GLASSWARE

The procedure for autoclaving described below may be used for:

   a. Glassware.
   b. Autoclavable metalware such as scissors, metal sieves and dissecting instruments.
   c. Autoclavable filter units such as supplied by Millipore.
   d. Distilled water (for sterilization).
   e. Autoclavable pipette tips (plastic, for Gilson's and other automatic pipettes).
   f. Autoclavable culture ingredients such as methylcellulose.

Materials
   i. Decon 90 (Decon Laboratories Ltd.).
   ii. Distilled water.

Equipment
   i. Autoclave.
   ii. Aluminium foil paper.
   iii. Autoclaving bags.
   iv. Autoclave tape (indicates that the correct temperature has been obtained).

Procedure
All laboratory glassware which is to be used for tissue culture purposes should be thoroughly cleaned in a detergent such as Decon 90 and rinsed several times in distilled water. It is preferred that glassware should be oven-dried immediately after washing and prepared for autoclaving.

PREPARATION OF ITEMS

Tighten all glass bottles with appropriate tops (then loosen a turn), with 2 drops of water being introduced into the bottle before sealing. Glass beakers and V-necked flasks should be sealed over with aluminium foil paper. Place the materials mentioned at (d) and (f) above in loosely sealed glass bottles. Place the items mentioned at (b) (c) and (e) above into autoclave bags of appropriate size and seal with autoclave tape. It is recommended that these materials should be double wrapped, with the items to be autoclaved contained in an inner sealed bag. Attach to each item a strip of autoclave tape (placed on the item or on the autoclave bag containing the item).

AUTOCLAVING PROCEDURE

a. Place all material to be autoclaved safely into autoclave and secure the lid of the autoclave.

b. Switch on the machine and autoclave at $15\,lb/in^2$ at $121\,°C$ for 20–30 min.

c. Allow the autoclave to depressurize before opening.

d. Open autoclave and allow the items to cool for 30 min. If autoclave bags containing some items are damp after 30 min, carefully remove from autoclave and allow to dry in air.

e. Store autoclaved items and open only in clean-air laminar flow hood or safety cabinet.

D. SILICONIZATION OF GLASSWARE

The production of a silicon surface on glassware helps in preventing cell adherence (especially of monocytes) to the surface of the glass tube or Pasteur pipette.

Materials

i. Dimethyldichlorosilane solution, about 2% in 1,1,1 trichloroethane (Repelcote, BDH): to give water-repellent properties to glassware (*Corrosive: do not inhale*).

ii. Distilled water.

iii. Two cylinders: each of 100 ml capacity.

Procedure

Wear rubber gloves and use a fume cupboard provided with an exhaust fan.

  a. Place about 90 ml Repelcote solution in one cylinder. Fill the other cylinder with distilled water.
  b. Immerse the glassware (Pasteur pipettes etc.,) in the Repelcote solution for 1 min.
  c. Using forceps remove the glassware from the first cylinder and place in the distilled water for 1 min.
  d. Dry with cotton wool and then place in an oven at 100 °C for at least 10 min or overnight in an incubator at 37 °C. Autoclave the glassware if sterile work is to be performed.

E. HEAT-INACTIVATION OF COMPLEMENT

In some techniques it is necessary to inactivate the complement present in fresh plasma or serum of human or non-human origin. This can be achieved by incubating the serum or plasma for 30 min in a water bath at 56 °C. Complement system is rendered inactive after storage of the plasma or serum for a long period.

F. MEASUREMENT OF THE OSMOLALITY OF VARIOUS SOLUTIONS

The osmolality mentioned throughout the text was measured by freezing point depression using an Osmometer, Model 3L (Advanced Instruments).

G. MEASUREMENT OF pH OF VARIOUS SOLUTIONS

This was carried out using a Pye Unicam pH meter (Model 290 MK2) for room temperature measurements and a Radiometer (Copenhagen ABL2: Acid-Base Laboratory) for measurement at 37 °C.

Manufacturers and Distributors

Acid-Base Laboratory: *see* Radiometer A/S.

Advanced Instruments: from MSE Scientific Instruments (*see below*).

Aldrich Chemical Co, The Old Brickyard, New Road, Gillingham, Dorset SP8 4JL.

American Hospital Supply (AHS, Harleco Co), Station Road, Didcot, Oxfordshire OX11 7NP.

ATAGO: from ChemLabs Instruments Ltd, Mornmister House, 129 Upminster Road, Hornchurch, Essex RM11 3XJ.

BDH Chemicals Ltd, Baird Road, Enfield, Middlesex EN1 1SH.

Beckman Instruments Inc, Progress Road, Sands Industrial Estate, High Wycombe, Bucks HP12 4JL.

Becton Dickinson, Laboratory Impex Ltd, Lion Road, Twickenham, Middlesex.

Behringwerke, Hoechst House, Salisbury Road, Houndslow, Middlesex TW4 6JH.

Connaught Laboratories, 73 Maygrove Road, West Hampstead, London.

Dakopatts (DAKO): Mercia-Brocades Ltd, Brocades House, Pyrford Road, West Byfleet, Weybridge, Surrey KT14 6RA.

Decon Laboratories Ltd, Portslade, Brighton BN4 1EQ.

Difco Laboratories Ltd, PO Box 14B, Central Avenue, West Molesey, Surrey.

Dow Chemicals Company, Colorcon Ltd, Orpington Trading Estate, Sevenoaks Way, Orpington, Kent BR5 3SR.

Duncan Flockhart Co Ltd, 700 Oldfield Lane North, Greenfield, Middlesex UB6 0MD.

Envair, York Avenue, Broadway Industrial Estate, Hallingdon, Rossendale, Lancashire.

Eastman Organic Chemicals, Kodak Ltd, Kirby, Liverpool.

Falcon Plastic (Division of Becton Dickinson), Between Towns Road, Cowley, Oxford OX4 3LY.

Fisher: from A. R. Horwell, 2 Grangeway, Kilburn High Road, London NW6 2BP.

Fisons Scientific Equipment, Bishop Meadow Road, Loughborough LE11 0RG.
Flow Laboratories Ltd, Victoria Park, Heatherhouse Road, Irvine, Ayrshire, Scotland.
Gallenkamp A. & Co, PO Box 290, Technico House, Christopher Street, London EC2P 2ER.
Gibco Europe Ltd, 3 Washington Road, Sandyford Industrial Estate, Paisley PA3 4EP, Renfrewshire, Scotland.
Goodfellow Metals, Science Park, Milton Road, Cambridge.
Hinder-Leslies Ltd, Higham Hill Road, London E17 6EJ.
Keltorr b.v., Hoornseweg, 10–1823 DH-ALKMAAR, Netherlands.
Lab-line, PO Box 55, Uxbridge, Middlesex UB8 1LA.
Leitz Ltd, 48 Park Street, Luton, Bedfordshire LU1 3HP.
Millipore Corporation Ltd, Abbey Road, Park Royal, London NW10 7SP.
MSE Scientific Instruments, Manor Royal, Crawley, West Sussex.
Ortho Pharmaceuticals, Saunderton, High Wycombe, Buckinghamshire.
Oxoid Ltd, Wade Road, Basingstoke, Hampshire RG24 0PW.
Pharmacia Fine Chemicals Ltd, Midsummer Boulevard, Milton Keynes MK9 3HP.
Radiometer A/S (Acid-Base Laboratory), Emdrupvej 72-DK-2400, Copenhagen, Denmark.
Sarstedt Ltd, 68 Boston Road, Beaumont Leys, Leicester LE4 1AW.
Sartorius: V. A. Howe, 88 Peterborough Road, London SW6.
Shandon Southern Ltd, 93–96 Chadwich Road, Astmoor Industrial Estate, Runcorn, Cheshire.
Sigma London Chem. Co. Ltd, Fancy Road, Poole, Dorset BH17 7NH.
Sterilin Ltd, 43 Broad Street, Teddington, Middlesex TW11 8QZ.
TAGO: from Tissue Culture Services (see below).
Tissue Culture Services, 10 Henry Road, Slough SL1 2QL.
Travenol Laboratories, Caxton Way, Thetford, Norfolk IP24 38E.
Wellcome Reagents Ltd, 303 Hither Green Lane, London SE13 6TL.

INDEX